DUKE UNIVERSITY PUBLICATIONS

PHYSICIAN TO THE WORLD

Bust of Gorgas by Bryant Baker, Alabama State Capitol

WILLIAM CRAWFORD GORGAS

OCTOBER 3, 1854—JULY 4, 1920

HIS VISION AND HIS INITIATIVE TRANSLATED THE KNOWN
SCIENTIFIC FACTS CONCERNING YELLOW FEVER INTO PRAC-
TICAL ACCOMPLISHMENT, THEREBY MAKING POSSIBLE THE
CONTROL OF THIS SCOURGE OF THE TROPICS AND THE
BUILDING OF THE PANAMA CANAL.

PHYSICIAN TO THE WORLD

The Life
of
General William C. Gorgas

BY

JOHN M. GIBSON

DURHAM, NORTH CAROLINA
Duke University Press
1950

PRINTED IN THE UNITED STATES OF AMERICA
BY THE SEEMAN PRINTERY, INC., DURHAM, N. C.

To

the late Miss Mary Gorgas
and the other members of the Gorgas family
WHO WERE SO VERY HELPFUL IN PROVIDING
MATERIAL AND INFORMATION ON THEIR
DISTINGUISHED AND BELOVED KINSMAN

THIS BOOK WAS PUBLISHED WITH THE
ASSISTANCE OF THE INCOME FROM THE
P. HUBER HANES FUND

Contents

Illustrations

PHYSICIAN TO THE WORLD

The Yellow Terror

WHEN COLUMBUS and his men waded ashore on San Domingo in November, 1493, on his second voyage to the New World, they were determined that, come what might, the settlement they were about to establish would be impregnable. With the destruction of the earlier one at La Navidad fresh in their memories, they chose with great care a site that seemed to offer every advantage of topography and, with equally great care, set to work strengthening its natural defenses. When their task was finished they were well pleased, and with good reason. For they were certain that no conceivable attack by hostile Indians could possibly succeed.

Unfortunately, they were not equally well protected against another enemy that was to prove infinitely more destructive than any red men they were ever likely to encounter. They had been ashore only a short time when they were set upon by pestilential disease that affected them as no disease had ever done before. Adventurers though they were and certainly no strangers to danger and death, they nevertheless were like young children before this new invader, which attacked so mysteriously and killed so mercilessly. But they fought on and on, along with the new arrivals sent from Spain to fill the gaps. Finally, however, they came face to face with the certainty that only defeat lay ahead if they continued to fight. So those who were left gave up the hopeless struggle and moved away, and Isabella, named in honor of Spain's proud queen, lost its chance to become the cradle of white civilization in the New World.

It became, instead, a ghost town, with its dilapidated ramparts, its crumbling buildings, its great echoing emptiness, and its dead. And not until then did history's first recorded yellow fever epidemic come to an end. Like innumerable others that were to follow, it simply burned itself out, as a fire does, because of a lack of fresh fuel upon which to feed.

At Vega-Real, where Columbus led an assault which routed "a multitude of Indians," and at many other places where these men and their successors sought to set up colonies, yellow fever quickly nullified their most carefully laid plans and made their military victories hollow conquests indeed. Thus even at that early date the disease began earning its evil reputation as "the greatest single obstacle to the colonization of the New World."

In 1664 on the island of St. Lucia yellow fever wiped out all but 89 of a garrison of 1,500 soldiers, and the next year about 200 sailors succumbed out of some 500 stationed there. The third year the island received a third visit from the disease, which is said to have killed every man, woman, and child. St. Lucia's experiences were duplicated, except in detail, practically everywhere else in the West Indies. From that island area where the fires of yellow fever burned so fiercely sparks were blown to near-by and distant places. Many started blazes along the Gulf Coast and Atlantic seaboard. Others fell hundreds of miles inland. Still others flew eastward and landed in France, England, Portugal, Italy, Spain, and numerous other European countries.

As terrifying as was the disease itself, the mystery surrounding it made it appear much more so. Not knowing how to explain it, people feared it all the more. Why it appeared, or from where, remained an unsolved riddle. All they knew was that it came, often with terrifying suddenness, reaped its heavy harvest of lives, and then disappeared. During a major epidemic business houses closed and barred their doors. Its victims often lay where they fell, and soon the streets and highways were littered with bodies. For the prevailing belief that to touch a yellow fever victim or his garments was virtually an act of suicide kept even the closest relatives and dearest friends at a distance. A small speck of the characteristic black vomit was, in these people's fear-haunted minds, a deadly poison.

Goaded by the universal fear, those in an epidemic area resorted to ridiculous measures to keep infection away. Told that tobacco would help, they smoked until they became deathly sick. Striking out in other directions, they dipped sponges in vinegar and wore them over their mouths. They ate enormous quantities of garlic, wore tarred ropes tied around their waists, lighted huge bonfires, and turned public parks into semblances of battlefields by shooting off cannons to clear the air.

What has been described as the first sanitary legislation ever enacted in the Western Hemisphere was a measure passed about 120 years before the Declaration of Independence by the General Court of Massachusetts, which established a maritime quarantine to protect the colony against a yellow fever epidemic on one of the West Indian islands. Louisiana's State Board of Health, the first to be organized in this country, was set up as a temporary quarantining agency to check an outbreak in that state. Philadelphia's municipal Board of Health would not have been established as early as it was—in 1794—had the city fathers not been frightened into action by the great epidemic of 1793. Their fright was justified, if fright ever was. For hardly anything in the city's long history ever brought as much grief or left as firm an imprint upon the lives of the people as that outbreak did. Between August 1 and November 9 alone —a little over three months—it killed more than four thousand persons.

We are fortunate in having a firsthand description

of that epochal epidemic from the deeply sympathetic pen and understanding heart of Dr. Benjamin Rush, who knew it as few people did because he lived through it. In medical college libraries here and there are to be found yellowed and frayed but highly prized copies of the book he wrote shortly afterward.

"Between the eighth and the fifteenth of September I visited and prescribed for between a hundred and a hundred and twenty patients a day," the only physician-signer of the Declaration of Independence wrote.

Several of my pupils visited a fourth or fifth part of that number. For a while we refused no calls. In the short intervals of business which I spent at my meals my house was filled with patients, chiefly the poor, waiting for advice. For many weeks I seldom ate without prescribing for numbers as I sat at my table. . . . I rose at six o'clock and generally found a number of persons waiting for advice in my shop or parlor. . . . Having found myself unable to comply with the numerous applications that were made to me, I was obliged to refuse many every day. My sister counted 47 in one forenoon before 11 o'clock. Many of them left with tears, but they did not feel more distress than I did, from refusing to follow them. . . . In riding through the streets I was often forced to resist the entreaties of parents imploring a visit to their children or of children to their parents.

Dr. Rush described the "fear or terror" which "now sat upon every countenance." He wrote about streets and roads leading from the accursed community "crowded with families flying in every direction." A certain part of the city "became a desert." The poor, the first victims of the fever, "suffered . . . from poverty as well as disease," when "business began to languish." After the first week of September the contagion "spared no rank of citizens," and "whole families were confined by it." Once there were only three able-bodied doctors left to care for the six thousand victims of yellow fever. As those terrible weeks wore on, Dr. Rush became a comforter as well as physician:

During the first three or four weeks of the prevalence of the disorder I seldom went into a house the first time without meeting the parents or children of the sick in tears. Many wept aloud at my entry, or parlor, who came to ask for advice for their relations. Grief, after awhile, descended below weeping. . . . A cheerful countenance was scarcely to be seen in the city.

Once he received a great surprise. He entered a house and was greeted by a child who was smiling happily. That bright smile, "so discordant to my feelings and the state of the city," was well-nigh unbelievable. But then the explanation dawned upon him: One so young had no comprehension of the universal tragedy in which it was living.

The streets everywhere revealed marks of the distress that pervaded the city. More than one-half the houses were shut up. In walking for many hundred yards, few persons were met, except such as were in quest of a physician, a nurse, a bleeder or the man who buried the dead. The hearse alone kept up the remembrance of the noise of carriages or carts in the streets. Funeral processions were laid aside. A black man, leading or driving a horse, with a corpse on a pair of chair wheels, with now and then half a dozen relations and friends following at a distance from it, met the eye in most of the streets at every hour of the day, while the noise of the same wheels passing slowly over the pavements kept alive anguish and fear in the sick and well every hour of the night.

During the weeks of the late summer and early fall the people of the stricken city took courage from their knowledge of one of the peculiarities of yellow fever. For some reason unknown to them or even to their medically more enlightened doctors it had a way of coming to a sudden end with the onset of cold, rainy weather. So hopefully they waited. And waited and waited. The time for frosts and rains came, but it did not bring its accustomed showers and freezes. The weather remained "not only moderate but warm." Thus, under the impetus of ideal climatic conditions, the misery, the sickness, and the dying kept on well into the normal

cold-weather period. It is not surprising that "the stout-
est hearts began to fail," "hope sickened," and "despair
succeeded distress in almost every countenance." But
the long-hoped-for change came at last:

On the fifteenth of October it pleased God to alter the
state of the air. The clouds at last dropped health in showers
of rain, which continued during the whole day and which were
succeeded for several nights afterwards by cold and frost. . . .
The appearance of this rain was like a dove with an olive branch
in its mouth to the whole city.

Soon health conditions, as far as yellow fever was
concerned, were back to normal. In six weeks "nothing
but fresh graves and the black dresses of many of the
citizens afforded a public trace of the distress which had
so lately prevailed in the city."

In Santos, Brazil, during yellow fever epidemics ship-
masters hardly dared bring their craft into port for fear
they would not have enough crewmen left to get them to
the next port of call. Indeed, in more than one instance,
Mears tells us in *The Triumph of American Medicine,*
"vessels coming into port lost . . . and very quickly, their
entire crews from the disease, officers and men, before
they could be unloaded." One vessel he mentions "lay
anchored in the harbor for a period of 18 months, with
cargo perishing in the hold."

During Memphis's worst yellow fever epidemic,
which lasted from early August to mid-December, 1878,
more than 18,500 persons became its victims. Some five
thousand of these cases ended fatally. Twenty-five
thousand people fled from the city during the first ten
days, and another 5,000 did so before the epidemic
ended. Normal life came to a standstill. Business establishments had neither employees nor customers. River
traffic went past as quickly as possible. The railroad
stations were as deserted as the docks, as trains rushed
by at top speed. The dead, long unburied, lay in the
public buildings and the streets, getting in the way of

those who tried to carry on some semblance of their normal activities. J. M. Keating, of the Memphis *Appeal,* was one of these who remained and survived.

" 'In the midst of life we are in death' was never so vividly illustrated to me as now," he wrote.

Our fair city is literally a charnel house. The sights are awful and the scenes sad to a degree blood-curdling. Every day we put away hundreds and wonder where they come from. The city is deserted. Young and old, rich and poor, white and black—they all go alike, the victims of the relentless scourge.

The Memphis epidemic had a counterpart in near-by Granada, Mississippi. Practically all places of business, except drugstores and undertaking establishments, were closed. Prison doors were unlocked and thrown open, as jailers and their former charges alike rushed off pell-mell to join the flood of refugees. As at Memphis, trains went through at full speed, their windows closed tightly and their passengers and crew members almost holding their breath, lest they breathe a fatal germ.

Sensing the news importance of the epidemic, the enterprising James Gordon Bennett, Jr., proprietor of the prosperous New York *Herald,* offered almost unheard of sums to members of his staff to go to Granada and write about it. But there was no eagerness to accept his extravagant proffers. When his figure reached $1,000 a day, however, one of his veteran reporters, Alfred H. Spink, conquered his fears and started for the stricken community. He could stand anything for $1,000 a day, he thought. But he was mistaken, and what he saw and the fears it all inspired caused even huge sums to lose their lure. He was there just seven days. Then he wired Bennett he had had enough and more than enough —he would not stay another day. Bennett urged him to stay on and, to make his urging more effective, offered him more money. But Spink was not interested. Not even $10,000 a day would make him change his mind, he wired back.

But there was one who did stay. He was a relatively obscure telegraph operator whose name historians of Granada's great ordeal of fever failed to give. Day after day he sent to the New York *Times* terse, dramatic reports of what was going on around him. On the twenty-first day of the outbreak he ticked out a dispatch stating that only 300 white people were still left out of the town's 2,500 residents and that half of those 300 were sick. Two days later he cut that total to 200, of whom three fourths were sick. "Surely the end cannot be far," his message concluded, "and the chapter must soon be closed."

It soon was, as far as he was concerned. A few days later he wired the *Times:* "No one has dared to enter the town for several days. When we are gone, God only knows what will become of the stricken." Another dispatch had to do with rumors that the War Department was about to send tents to provide emergency shelters for the people of the town. But what good would they do without workmen to erect them? "There are not twenty-five active men in town." Later he sent this: "The *Times* specials are written in a house where there is one corpse and four persons are sick with the fever."

From then on the dispatches were quite brief. On August 29, when the epidemic was just a little over a month old, he reported yellow fever deaths during the previous day and night at the average rate of nearly one an hour—twenty-two deaths in twenty-four hours—and added: "In spite of all the doctors can do, death seems to reign supreme." He was still at the sending board two days later when he, too, succumbed.

The epidemics in Memphis and Granada were local manifestations of a general yellow fever outbreak that swept up the Mississippi Valley from New Orleans to Cairo, Illinois, and appeared in varying degrees of severity in nearly a hundred cities and towns. Besides the loss of life, which was incalculable, its cost in illness, demoralization of trade, and other ways has been estimated at a fifth of a billion dollars. New Orleans alone is said to have suffered a trade loss of some five million dollars. Fund-raising campaigns were put on in those parts of the country that had been fortunate enough to be out of its path. John Greenleaf Whittier and Henry Wadsworth Longfellow were among the notables who sent their autographs to be auctioned at relief rallies.

Soon after that epidemic started its rapid progress northward, a brand new towboat set out from New Orleans for Pittsburgh, trailing a string of barges. Before it could reach Vicksburg, the engineer and firemen died of yellow fever, and it was necessary to turn back to the home port to bury them and obtain replacements. Starting out again, it arrived at Memphis without incident. But there, its reputation as a yellow fever vessel having preceded it, it was refused permission to dock. A little north of Cairo, the engineer substituting for the one who had died developed yellow fever, asked someone else to take over his work, and went home to die. Upon approaching Gallipolis, Ohio, most of the crew, who by this time were incapacitated by the disease, flatly refused to take the accursed craft any farther. Moreover, they insisted upon going ashore immediately, disregarding their own illness and scorning the protective guard that had been thrown around the dock to prevent the entry of carriers. That weak quarantine line proved pitifully ineffectual, and the fevered crewmen wandered at will, starting a local epidemic which brought death to thirty residents. And when at long last the ill-starred *John D. Porter* pulled alongside its Pittsburgh pier, there were twenty-three names on its death list. To its surviving crew members and to authorities on yellow fever it became known as the craft that had "distributed poison through a journey of more than 1,000 miles."

New Orleans, Portsmouth, Mobile, and any number of other places experienced conditions similar to those described. Business was demoralized. People fled in panic from their homes. A state of hysteria gripped the community currently affected. The young, the middle-aged, and the old stopped at nothing, however extreme or ridiculous, to keep infection at a distance. Over-worked doctors struggled valiantly with the mounting flood of illness. Panicky quarantines were imposed by frightened city officials outside the fever-cursed areas. And, as Dr. Rush wrote of his own city, the only persons not sorrowing for loved ones or fearful of impending death were those too young to know what it was all about.

There are those now living to whom such experiences were once familiar. They could write, if they wished, as one Alabama woman wrote some years ago:

I am old enough to remember at least three times when yellow fever stalked—a veritable terror—in the land and state. The railroads spent many thousands of dollars for guards to put you off if you happened to be from an infected district. Large sums were also spent for disinfectants and for new concoctions that were supposed to be cures, while still other large sums were spent by people running from the dread disease.

But those whose memories are well stored with ex-periences of this kind have become rare. Much more significant, they are comparatively old. For scenes like those enacted in Philadelphia, Memphis, and Granada have not occurred on American soil or anywhere else, except in small, widely scattered, and medically blighted areas, for decades. Yellow fever is no longer listed in the indices of the state and national vital statistics agencies. There is no reference to it whatsoever in current mor-bidity reports. In brief, save for isolated cases here and there due to ignorance, backwardness, or carelessness, this disease is as foreign to the people of our day as witch-craft and the divine right of kings.

Smallpox, crippled as it is in its killing power, never-theless still exists, even in epidemic form, a century and a half after Jenner discovered the smallpox vaccine. Diphtheria is still a serious health problem, although science long ago gave the world the antitoxin which cures it and the toxin-antitoxin which prevents it. Tuberculosis, no longer the captain of the men of death, nevertheless has killed many more Americans since Pearl Harbor than all the frightful engines of destruction devised by our enemies, in spite of the fact that considerably more than half a century has passed since Robert Koch discovered the tubercle bacillus and caused an eagerly credulous world to believe that the disease would be wiped out in a single generation.

But there was no comparable lag between the discovery of a means of dealing with yellow fever and the virtual conquest of that disease. For that a none too grateful humanity is indebted to William Crawford Gorgas.

CHAPTER I

A Confederate Boyhood

ONE MORNING in the late summer of 1853 First Lieutenant Josiah Gorgas, on duty at Mount Vernon Arsenal, near Mobile, Alabama, heard a woman's voice through an open window in the building next door. He was sure he had never heard it before. He was equally sure it was the most beautiful voice he had ever heard. He stopped his work and listened more intently. Then it became apparent that the owner of that voice was reading aloud to some children. Hearing it again the next day, he again stopped his work to listen. The third day he heard it again. In time he found that he could hear it every day if he wished, as this reading to those youngsters had become a daily occurrence. The more he heard it the better he liked it and the more eager he became to know this woman. He literally fell in love with the voice before he saw its owner.

He did see her, of course, as soon as an opportunity came. And then he fell in love with Amelia Gayle herself. He learned from his friends that she was the daughter of a former governor of Alabama and a belle of Mobile society. Like thousands of others, she had fled from there to escape a yellow fever epidemic and had become a guest of an army family at Mount Vernon Arsenal. Rarely gifted, highly educated for a young lady of her time, and possessing a friendly, cheerful disposition, she had already become as great a favorite in the army community as she had been in Mobile.

She learned about him, too. She learned that he was one of the most brilliant junior officers on duty at the arsenal, a veteran of the Mexican War, in spite of his comparative youth, and already an ordnance expert whose opinions were listened to with great respect by his military superiors. A native of Pennsylvania, he had been transferred to Mount Vernon from Fort Monroe, Virginia, a few months before.

Amelia Gayle fell in love with Lieutenant Josiah Gorgas as quickly as he fell in love with her. Their courtship was brief, and they were married before the year's end.

Their first child, "a splendid specimen," was born on October 3, 1854, in the old Governor Gayle mansion in Mobile. By rather a remarkable coincidence, in view of the part which that baby was to play in establishing the mosquito theory of yellow fever transmission, the physician called in to launch this young life was Dr. Josiah Nott. A noted practitioner, Dr. Nott in his own quiet way had already become partly convinced that this particular insect was an instrument in the spread of that disease and was even then trying to test this theory by study and experiment.

There was no dearth, on either side of the family, of prominent persons for whom the baby might be named. Besides his maternal grandfather, who had been a member of Congress and Federal judge as well as governor, there were the two Atkinsons—Thomas, an officer in the Revolutionary War, and Stephen, who had accompanied William Penn to America; and William Rittenhouse, who had owned the first paper mill in the American colonies. Had he been a girl, the doting family might have named him Sarah, after another relative, Sarah Haynesworth Gayle. Francis Scott Key found this Southern beauty so charming during a visit to Alabama as a special emissary of President Andrew Jackson that he gave her a jewel case made of wood taken from the sturdy deck of the gallant *Old Ironsides*. But none of these names seemed to fit. So they named him William

Crawford, after an uncle, and began calling him Willie. That nickname stuck with him until he reached manhood.

During the next several years the pattern of Willie's life was set by distant forces, usually those working, directly or indirectly, from the War Department in Washington. He and the other members of the family moved here and there at the behest of officials whose responsibility it was to see that army officers did not stay anywhere too long for the good of the service. Like other army families, they were able to remain in one place only long enough to make friends and begin to feel at home. Willie was just two years old when moving orders took them from Mount Vernon, which they liked very much, to Kennebec Arsenal, in Maine, which they did not like so well. He was four years old when the next move came—this time to Charleston, South Carolina. Two or three years later they were transferred to Frankfort, Kentucky. Those frequent moves, without his having any say as to where they would be sent next, were most unwelcome to Josiah Gorgas. For, devoted to his family as few men are, he dreamed of settling down somewhere, accumulating enough money and property to keep poverty at bay, and making a home.

While the wandering Gorgases were living in Maine the elder Gorgas started keeping a journal, a typescript copy of which is now in the Library of Congress. In the initial entry, dated January 1, 1857, he dedicated it affectionately to his children and promised that it would be "devoted to their gratification and instruction." As might be expected, Willie was the main actor in innumerable adventures described in its pages, and the father's fond dreams for the child's future left their mark on any number of entries.

The Willie Gorgas of his father's journal was not particularly different from other children. He won praise at the age of two for his nice table manners and impressed Lieutenant Gorgas with his fondness for his mother's jelly about the same time. While still quite young he listened "with absorbed attention" to the singing of two gifted ladies of the community who were fond of bringing their music to the Gorgas living room. As he grew older he was delighted with a new table someone had given him and even more so with a donkey an uncle had brought him from Sicily. And he protested in boy-like fashion against having his hair cut.

"Splendid specimen" though he had been at birth, he had more than his share of the diseases to which childhood is especially susceptible and also some—typhoid fever, for one—which are more likely to attack older people. His father called him "poor Willie" while he was undergoing the double affliction of toothache and a painful swelling of the cheek, and journal entries for the last two or three years of the 1850's tell of his being "quite ill" with an unnamed malady, experiencing intense pain about the head and the muscles of the neck, and being "hollow-eyed" after an attack of jaundice.

Josiah Gorgas's journal entries show much more than solicitude over Willie's health. They also show the father's pride in youthful manifestations of superior qualities of mind and character. For Willie was not only "very good" and "obedient" but also "very bright." He tackled a disagreeable task "like a little hero." Although he fell off the seat once or twice during the service, he "behaved very well" at church. And there is generous praise for his willingness to help his mother and the servants about the house and for the good sportsmanship which marked his participation in a variety of games with his young friends.

Early in 1861, while the Gorgases were at Frankfort Arsenal, they had to make one of the cruelest decisions possible. Every day brought fresh and disturbing news of a widening breach between the North and South. It became more and more certain that the outbreak of

war between the two sections could be prevented only
by a miracle. And Josiah Gorgas had little hope that
such a miracle would occur. Like thousands of others
in his situation, he pondered deeply the problem of de-
ciding which side he should choose whenever the inevitable choice would have to be made. What did a high
sense of duty require of him? Which section had first
claim upon his loyalty? What would be the effect of a
wrong decision upon his personal fortunes? (He could
not disregard that consideration entirely, with the responsibilities of a growing family upon his shoulders.)
What of the happiness of those he loved most dearly?
No wonder this son of stern Pennsylvanians, who had
served for so many years with distinction in the United
States Army and had every reason to expect a brilliant
and honored career in that service, spent many days and
nights in mental torture. For, struggling against all
these considerations were his spontaneous and genuine
love for the South, his sincere conviction that it was
espousing principles in which he believed firmly, and
his marriage to the daughter of an Alabama governor,
even more devoted to Southern principles than himself.

Amelia Gayle Gorgas did not make any secret of her
devotion to the South. Nor could she have concealed her
true feelings had she tried. Her early childhood in Mobile, her school days in Tennessee, and her association
with her father's personal and political friends, all
staunch Southerners—these things and many, many
others made it impossible for her to hold any but strong
Southern views. And, as though that were not enough,
as a child she had become a warm admirer and friend of
that most Southern of all Southerners and prophet of
the seceding South—John C. Calhoun. While the Gayles
and Calhouns were living in Washington, she and the
great Nullificationist had taken many long walks together. He had even taken occasion during those walks
to practice some of his famous speeches upon his youth-

ful listener—speeches reeking with the philosophy of states' rights, secession, slavery, and the other principles that were now about to be fought over in one of the bloodiest of all wars. Perhaps her most cherished memory of the great South Carolinian had to do with one of those Washington jaunts which took them by the White House. They were walking along the street, the short-legged child doing her best to keep up with the long-legged man, when Calhoun pointed a gaunt, bony finger toward the Executive Mansion and said: "Amelia, if I had been willing to sacrifice my principles, I would be occupying that house this very moment." And two of her most treasured possessions were gifts from Calhoun—the inkwell he had given her after using it for several years in the writing of some of his great state papers and a bracelet made from strands of the Calhoun locks. How could she possibly have been other than a dyed-in-the-wool Southerner?

But Amelia Gayle Gorgas was also a loyal wife, fully conscious of her duty to her husband. Never for an instant did she forget that he had much to draw him to the North—family, birth, friends, and a sense of duty to the army that he had served in war and peace. She remembered that war between the North and South had been a strong possibility in 1853, when they were married, and that she had deliberately married a Northerner who conceivably might not be willing to fight against his own section and people. At that happy time, she remembered, she had been ready to follow him wherever he might feel it his duty to go. So now that the test had come, she did not flinch or falter or seek to make a reluctant Southerner out of him. She told him time and again that he must not consider her feelings but must make his own decision, confident that she would respect it and follow him wherever it might take him.

In the end Josiah Gorgas decided to go with the South. In spite of his wife's urging him to do his duty regardless of her, he inevitably was influenced by her deeply rooted Southern sympathies. However, there is no reason to believe the decision would have been different without that influence. Willie was too young, of course, to be consulted about this choice of loyalties. But, young as he was, it had his full approval. The Confederacy never had a more ardent defender than he.

Having reached his great decision, Josiah Gorgas lost no time in putting it into effect. He immediately submitted his resignation to the Secretary of War and, on the day it became effective, April 3, left with his family for Charleston. After arranging for them to spend some time there with relatives, he hurried on to Montgomery to report to Jefferson Davis. Realizing that he was gaining the services of one of the most brilliant ordnance officers ever to hold a commission in any army, Davis made him Chief of Ordance, with the rank of brigadier general.

Thus it was that Willie and his mother were in Charleston on the most momentous day in the city's history. Like practically everyone else, they were awake and watching at half-past four on that memorable Friday morning, April 12, when a commissioned officer of the Confederate Army stationed at Fort Johnson carefully pointed a heavy gun at Fort Sumter, dimly outlined in the early morning gloom, and fired. Sitting at a window in the Charleston Armory, they saw the heavy projectile rise to a great height, follow a slightly curved course, and burst directly over the fort. A few seconds later—"before the sound of the shot had blown shoreward," as a New York *Times* writer described it—that first shot was followed by a second one, and another streak of light momentarily brightened the harbor in its swift flight toward its intended objective. The solitary cannon roared again, and a third shot was heard by Willie Gorgas and those other tense listeners and watchers on shore. Then the air became thick with shot and shell as thirteen other Confederate batteries swung swiftly into action, centering their fire upon the still silent fort where Kentucky-born, Georgia-wed Major Robert Anderson of the United States Army was in command of a garrison of fifty-five gunners, fifteen musicians, and thirty laborers.

Major Anderson kept the guns of Fort Sumter silent until seven o'clock. Then, after two hours and a half of nonresistance, he gave the command to return the Confederate fire, and Captain Abner Doubleday, known to sports enthusiasts as "the father of baseball," fired the first shot of the war from the Northern side. The battle then began in earnest. Willie was deeply impressed by all of this. Turning to the gentle, anxious woman at his side, he asked earnestly: "Mother, isn't it solemn?"

He did not see much of his father during the next four years, practically all of which the Gorgas family spent in Richmond. He was too young to understand why meals often had to be eaten hurriedly or missed altogether, why there was practically no social life, and why Josiah Gorgas had to spend so much time at his work. But his mother knew and understood. She knew that her husband had been called upon to perform a miracle, a miracle that had to be performed if the Confederate armies were to have a chance of escaping immediate and disastrous defeat at the hands of their well-equipped and well-armed enemies.

Not for many years did Willie know how well his father performed that miracle—how, in spite of all but insuperable difficulties, he built a huge ordnance department and kept the Confederate armies supplied with cannons, rifles, and ammunition that made it possible to keep the war going for at least a year longer than it could possibly have lasted had less than a miracle-worker been in charge of that job. But, when he did learn of it, it made him immeasurably proud of his father. That pride grew as he grew older and in time amounted to virtual worship, rivaled only by his love for his mother.

Willie did not see as much of his mother as he wanted to, either. For she was working for the Confederate cause as tirelessly as her husband. Born with a genius for making herself useful among the sick and injured, she spent every hour she could spare from her household duties at work in the hospitals. That devoted and unselfish service drew warm praise from her hard-pressed husband, who called her "untiring in aiding, visiting and relieving those poor sufferers" and averred that she had done "an infinite deal of good to these poor people."

A laborer working under the elder Gorgas was so seriously injured in an accident that it was necessary to amputate a leg. Willie learned from his parents where the operation was to be performed and made up his mind to see it. Accompanied by a sister, equally curious, he climbed up to a window as it was getting under way and watched the surgeon and his assistants while they performed their gruesome task. Not satisfied with that, the two children went a day or two later to the place where the amputated leg had been buried and dug it up. After one quick look, they hurriedly buried it again and got away from the place.

War's grim aspect was also impressed upon the youngster soon after Stonewall Jackson died from a shot fired by one of his own men during a crucial stage of the war. When the grey-uniformed body was carried to Richmond to receive the new nation's homage, among the famous and humble who filed by for a last look at the kindly face as it lay in state in the capitol were Willie, his father, and his sister Jessie.

Jackson was of course only one of many leaders of the Confederacy whom the child got to know. High-ranking officers were constantly in Richmond for conferences with his father, the President, and others; and they frequently were guests in the Gorgas home. The

JOSIAH GORGAS, BRIGADIER GENERAL, C.S.A.

Gorgases and the Davises became particularly warm friends. They attended the same church—St. Paul's Episcopal—and Willie's father and mother and Jefferson Davis joined at the same baptismal service.

The most famous of Willie's military hero friends of course was General Lee. His impending first visit brought enthusiastic shouts of pleasure from the youngster, but the visit turned out to be something of a disappointment. Although the General took him upon his knee and made much of him, he was not greatly impressed. Lee was different from the picture of a great military leader which the child had created in his mind and did not impress him as at all "heroic."

One of the most memorable occasions during those four war years, as far as Willie was concerned, occurred early in March, 1864. More than a thousand Confederate prisoners of war had just been exchanged and arrived in Richmond on a Sunday morning to be welcomed by the President and other dignitaries and enjoy a feast before leaving for camp to resume military service. The speech-making and other ceremonies took place on the capitol square, and Willie was on hand to see and hear everything that went on. Like most of the others, he carried something for the tired soldiers—a demijohn of cold tea.

He also showed his admiration for the Confederate soldiers in another way. After seeing ragged, barefoot men passing through Richmond on their way to and from the front, he determined that he had no right to enjoy comforts which were denied his country's defenders. So he insisted upon going barefoot all winter himself. When spring came the skin on the bottom of his feet was as thick and tough as the sole of a shoe.

Once he witnessed a minor battle actually in progress. On May 15, 1864, the Confederate forces beat off the enemy at Appomattox Bridge and regained control of the Danville railroad. Accompanied by his father, he climbed to the cupola of the War Department Building and excitedly watched the exchange of fire, mainly artillery. The smoke of the guns and the bursting of shells were plainly visible in the distance.

But watching distant battles was far too tame a business for this patriotic young Confederate. He wanted to have his part in the fighting too. So he set up a toy cannon on the roof of the Gorgas home, pointed it in the general direction of the Yankees, and fired, revealing an altogether too optimistic conception of the range and destructive power of toy cannons but showing how completely he believed in the Confederate cause.

Those childhood years in the capital of the doomed but gallantly struggling Confederacy made a deep impression upon the boy. He frequently referred in later life to the experiences they brought and to the spirit that animated those who were carrying on the struggle, both soldiers and civilians. One of those times was November 4, 1916, when, in a message to his family, he recalled that he was writing on the birthday of his younger brother Dick, who was born in Richmond during the last winter of the war. That set up a train of memories spanning half a century.

We were all in Richmond together in '64. The men at the head of affairs at that time no doubt knew that the Confederacy was doomed, but the rank and file still had the utmost faith in ultimate success. Mother impressed upon me that I would soon be old enough to go to the war, though I was then only nine years old, and she always spoke of this baby as another soldier for the Confederacy. War is certainly a terrible thing and debasing in many respects, but it also brings out strongly some phases of altruism. I do not believe my father and mother from '61 to '65 gave any thought to themselves or to their family. Everything was swallowed up in their devotion to the Confederacy.

In that same message he related an example of personal sacrifice for the cause:

In '64 food and supplies of all kinds were very scarce in

Richmond. A friend living in the country had given my mother a turkey, which was to be eaten on Christmas. I had very dim recollections of the taste of turkey and looked forward to the feast with great expectation. The care of this particular turkey fell to me, and he got all the odds and ends that could possibly be spared from the household. As Christmas approached, he was in prime condition. We knew that the Army entrenched before Petersburg was suffering more from want of food than we in Richmond. About a week before Christmas Mother proposed that we send our turkey to the soldiers at Petersburg. She painted the suffering and wants of our protectors so strongly that I finally agreed to the sacrifice. I do not think anyone in the whole Confederacy made a much greater sacrifice to patriotism than I did in December, '64, in agreeing to part with my gobbler. I went out and had a good cry on its neck.

As the war dragged wearily on, the news reaching Richmond from the battlefields grew more disheartening, making it more and more certain that the military collapse of the Confederacy was only a matter of time. But the Confederate leaders still refused to admit that the candle of their hopes had gone out. They had no choice, however, when, on April 2, 1865, the news came that General Lee's lines had been broken and that he would not be able to re-establish them. The implication was inescapably clear: Richmond would have to be evacuated as soon as possible.

Davis and his Chief of Ordnance happened to be together many times when bad news arrived. This was one of them.

"We have just received, Gorgas, the worst news that we could have," the President told him. Then he read him the message.

"He was standing when he spoke and then sat down and placed his hand upon his head for a moment," General Gorgas recounted later. "After further conversation he got up, buckled on his sword and pistol and dismissed us. He looked, as he stood, thin, spare, erect, every inch a chief. He was sorrowful but self-possessed, hopeless but self-restrained, to the last."

Anticipating this news but not expecting it so soon, General Gorgas had arranged to move his family two days later to Danville. But now there was no time for that. The best he could do was to arrange for Mrs. Gorgas and the children to remain in Richmond with a relative while he accompanied the retreating army out of the city. During the next several hours he helped move most of the family's belongings to their new home, assisted by Willie and using a horse and wagon obtained for that purpose. The slow-moving team made trip after trip, with Willie either in the driver's seat or sitting proudly atop a load of furniture.

General Gorgas, Mrs. Gorgas, and the children did not wish to say their farewells anywhere except in their own home. So the final stages of moving were postponed until the next day. The horse and wagon having been returned to their owner, the elder Gorgas had a solemn talk with Willie. He had a job for him to do, an important job. He explained that he was going to leave in a few hours and perhaps would not see his family again for many months. During his absence he wanted Willie to help his mother all he could and to try to see that nothing happened to her. There was almost certain to be a big fire the next morning, set either by the retreating Confederates or by the advancing Federals. The arsenal would start burning, and that would set off many explosions. Then it would be dangerous to walk along the street. Rioters, taking advantage of the relaxation of authority, would add to the danger. Negro mobs, incited by agitators and drink, might attempt physical violence upon any white people they saw.

Willie was told to watch a certain house near the Gorgas home. When it started smoking, he was to go to the cowshed, get the family cow, and, with the other members of the family, begin the dangerous trek to their new home. He was especially enjoined to let nothing happen to the cow, a valuable piece of property of which they would have need.

About midnight General Gorgas bade his family good-by. The emotional strain told upon both husband and wife, relieved only slightly by the presence of two ladies of the neighborhood to whom Mrs. Gorgas had been kind and who, out of gratitude, had promised him that they would help her all they could. Willie, however, was oblivious to all of this. He had fallen asleep and did not wake up when his father leaned over and kissed him. When General Gorgas recalled those brief moments of farewell some weeks later, he remembered his wife "standing like a brave woman over the remnants of her household goods." And he remembered how soundly Willie was sleeping.

As the elder Gorgas had predicted, the city was aflame the next morning. The arsenal, crowded to the doors with ammunition and other war material, was one of the first buildings to catch fire, and the resulting explosions brought a realistic sample of front-line war into the Gorgas neighborhood. Stirred but not frightened by these ear-thumping bursts, Willie watched the creeping devastation of flame and shell.

After a while he saw smoke pouring from the house his father had told him to watch. Then he got busy. Conscientiously following instructions, he helped his mother and sisters get together the few articles they were to carry with them and then ran to the cowshed. With great difficulty he managed to get a rope around the frightened animal's horns and led her out into the street, choked with the homeless, the adventurous, and the curious. The explosions and general confusion made the cow much more panicky and harder to manage than she had been in her stall, and it was all he could do to control her. After the strange trek got under way, the burning arsenal became more of an inferno than ever. Shells began bursting on the fringes of that confused mob, and the animal tried to go in every direction except the right one. Willie, however, summoned his last bit of strength and struggled manfully to control her desperate lunges. He succeeded in doing so for awhile. But unfortunately not long enough for him, the cow, and the other members of his small party to get safely to his Aunt Maria's. There were many near misses, each bringing a trial of strength between boy and animal. Then a powerful shell landed directly beneath her. She made another desperate bolt for freedom, throwing the bravely struggling youngster against a cobblestone and stunning him so completely that he let go the rope. When he got back upon his feet, the cow was nowhere to be seen.

The pain of that bump soon ended, but not his remorse over letting the cow get away. In vain his mother told him he had done everything she or General Gorgas could have expected of him. He could think only of his shame at having failed his father at a time when the elder Gorgas had reposed special trust in him.

Life in Richmond was quite different after its fall, and Mrs. Gorgas did not stay long. Some friends invited her and the children to visit them in Cambridge, Maryland, and they spent some time there. Then they moved to Baltimore, hopeful that it would not be long before they could rejoin General Gorgas.

Willie was as much of a rebel as ever and never missed an opportunity to show his loyalty to the South and its leaders. As the boat on which he and the others were traveling to Baltimore approached Fort Monroe and he remembered that his father's friend and former chief was imprisoned there, this ardent young Confederate came rigidly to attention and remained so until the grim walls which kept Jefferson Davis a prisoner dropped out of sight.

The Gorgas family finally ceased its wanderings and, happily reunited, moved in 1866 to Brierfield, Alabama, where General Gorgas invested his scant savings in a blast furnace in the expectation of spending the rest of his life as an iron manufacturer. That, however, was not to be. Innumerable difficulties plagued the enterprise from the start, and the beginning of production was delayed time after time, while the heavy expenses ate rapidly into its limited capital. But that was not all, nor the worst. When at last the plant began turning out iron in marketable quantities, there was very little market for it, and even the most desperate measures were insufficient to stop the rapid descent into bankruptcy. The entries which Josiah Gorgas made in his journal during those months of mounting fears, heroic labor, and final failure are the very essence of disillusionment and personal defeat.

Naturally, Willie found Brierfield an entirely different place from Richmond. Many of the advantages which even a state of war could not prevent the family from enjoying in the Confederate capital were virtually unheard of in this slow-moving, backward Alabama town. However, he quickly adjusted himself to the change; and, while his father tried unsuccessfully to make and market iron and his mother served as the good angel of the community, he found much pleasure in the healthy, normal activities of a growing country boy. The son of one of his father's laborers became a bosom friend, and the two youngsters had great times together. They especially enjoyed swimming in the creek that ran near the Gorgas home.

One of his Brierfield playmates was a young girl of about his own age, and these two, much too young for romance, became almost as inseparable as Willie and the ironworker's son, who also took a great liking to her. The two boys were downcast, therefore, when she told them she was to leave Brierfield, where she had been living with her grandmother, to go to live with her father, who had just married again. After she left they missed her even more than they had anticipated. Moreover, they were sure she was unhappy in her strange new world and was missing them as much as they were missing her. As their loneliness increased, they decided to do something about it. The outcome was the organization of a two-boy "rescue" expedition to go for her and bring her back. Setting out on muleback, they finally reached the town where her father had taken her and had little trouble persuading her to go back to Brierfield with them. The three rode triumphantly back, all astride that single mule.

Willie's association with distinguished Confederates continued in the quieter atmosphere of Brierfield. General Joseph E. Johnston was a frequent visitor and became a great admirer of the lad. He happened to be there when Willie shot his first bird, and, to celebrate the event, gave him a powder flask and shot pouch. The proud father wrote of "the glow of joy" with which Willie told of that first success with a gun.

This personal acquaintance with war heroes stimulated a love of soldiering which had manifested itself some time before and was in time to develop into a virtual passion. Frequently his mother, watchful for evidences of the strong religious convictions which had enriched her own life, was delighted to find him sprawled on the floor or curled up in bed reading the Bible. She would smile approvingly and express to her husband the hope that Bible reading would become a lifetime habit with him. That hope received a great jolt when she learned the real reason for this interest in the Scriptures. It was not the noble religious teachings that held his interest by the hour. It was the battles.

Notwithstanding the changes which the passing years had brought, the Willie of the Brierfield days was little different in one respect from the Willie about whom his father had written in his journal before the War between the States. He was still "tolerably mischievous." And his mischief-making was still essentially harmless and altogether good-natured.

Usually his sisters were the chief victims of his pranks, as when he turned loose a live possum in their bedroom and sent them in headlong flight from the room, screaming with fright. Another time they missed their dolls and were almost as heartbroken over their disappearance as real mothers would have been over the disappearance of real babies. They looked anxiously for them all over the house and were about to give up the search when one of the girls happened to glance out the window. There they were, hanging from a tree like two thieves, their pretty hair disheveled and knotted and their pretty dresses all disarranged, faded, and crumpled. Willie, it is hardly necessary to say, was the author of his sisters' maternal anguish. He thought it all great fun.

Despite the success of numerous money-making enterprises in which he had a part, the youth showed an unmistakable distaste for business and gave little thought to a career of this kind. Equally distasteful to him were the professions in which several of his relatives had already distinguished themselves. His one great enthusiasm was for the army, and the passing years made him more and more determined that, come what might, he was going to become a soldier.

The lack of adequate educational advantages at Brierfield soon brought the family face to face with a serious problem. As Willie approached the limit of schooling the community afforded, what to do with him next formed the subject of many an earnest discussion in the Gorgas living room. It was finally decided to send him to a school in Greensboro, Alabama, which had earned an excellent reputation for high scholastic standards and emphasis upon character development. The entire family then got busy getting him ready for his departure. This stir of activity made the parents realize as they never had before what his absence would mean to them in loneliness and anxiety over his well-being. As the day of leave-taking approached, Josiah Gorgas also had thoughts of an entirely different kind: the tragedy of his own financial failure and what it probably would mean to Willie's prospects. While he was thinking of these things, strange emotions rushed upon him— emotions to which he gave words when he penned that day's entry in his journal:

> Willie has not gone to his school yet, but Wednesday next is fixed for his departure. I think he begins to feel a little sober over it, though he looks forward to the change with boyish pleasure. As he lies asleep before me now, how earnestly I pray for his future welfare! How my heart yearns toward him, and how glad I would be to shield him from the troubles of life! It makes me understand and, in some measure, respect the desire people have to accumulate in order that they may leave their children in affluence. It is the natural desire of the parent to protect and watch over the offspring—to work hard and bear the brunt of the struggle of life that the child may be saved the same struggle in some degree.

Willie made a good record at the Greensboro school. He showed a decided bent for public speaking and participated wholeheartedly in school programs. He would also entertain his family with his oratorical gifts while at home on brief vacation visits. While the others gave him respectful attention, he would recite in true schoolboy fashion the pieces he had learned.

He was back in Brierfield the following summer. As in the past, he made himself useful about the house and plant. We read in his father's journal that he and a companion "returned from a day's shooting proud of a crow, a lark and a dove," that he "rode after butter in the afternoon," that he "stayed in my office until 12 M.," and that he had a part in any number of other happenings that marked the swift passing of the vacation period.

That fall (1867) brought another leave-taking. This time his destination was New Orleans, much farther from home than he had ever been before, except for brief visits. This departure, too, brought sadness and a fore-boding of great loneliness to the parents. But, once he was gone, they found comfort and satisfaction in the ex-cellent reports that came from his teachers, all showing that he was doing a first-rate job of acquiring an educa-tion and bringing enthusiastic predictions that he was headed for big accomplishments.

About this time one of those distant events which so often helped to shape his career began making its in-fluence felt. At the outbreak of the War between the States the leaders of the Episcopal Church had been on the point of establishing an Episcopal university, but the ambitious project had been temporarily abandoned under the exigencies of war. Now, however, their efforts had been renewed and had met with enough success to bring them close to the realization of their dream. A beautiful site was selected at Sewanee, Tennessee, the institution was named the University of the South, and the opening was set for September, 1868. An outstand-ing bishop was chosen as its official head, and, upon the urging of Robert E. Lee and many other friends of the war period, Josiah Gorgas was named headmaster of the Junior Department.

The former Chief of Ordnance was delighted. Here was a position of distinction paying a salary which would insure the family an income adequate for its modest needs. Much more important, it would enable him to give Willie a university education at slight cost and with-out making it necessary to send him away from home.

Willie liked the arrangement too and began making plans to matriculate as soon as he could meet the en-trance requirements.

CHAPTER II

The Army Doctor

ENROLLING as a preparatory school student at the University of the South on July 15, 1869, Willie became a member of the institution's second class, which consisted of seventy-nine youngsters from twelve states.

These youngsters became not only students but workmen. A handful of wooden buildings had been erected to serve as classrooms and living quarters, but they were sufficient for only the barest necessities of instruction. Whatever else might be needed the boys had to provide themselves. So, moved by the exuberance of youth, they took up with a will where the carpenters had left off, cutting down trees, building football fields, and helping in the construction of the gymnasium. Willie took part in this extra-curricular activity as wholeheartedly as any of the other seventy-eight.

Near the end of their first academic year the steamship *Agnes* arrived in New Orleans from Honduras, bringing with it a case of yellow fever, which started one of the worst epidemics in the city's history. It lasted about seven months and brought death to 588 persons. When the stricken city appealed for medical supplies and volunteers to aid in caring for the sick and burying the dead, four students at the University of the South answered that call, unequipped though they were to render scientific medical aid. One of the four was Willie Gorgas.

Only two of them survived. On the way back Willie turned thoughtfully to his friend and classmate and said to him: "Mat, I am going to try to find something that will drive this terrible thing from the earth. There must be some way to get rid of it, and I am going to spend my time trying to find it." He meant every word. His first encounter with yellow fever had stirred his interest in the disease and aroused a wish to aid in its conquest. But it had not dimmed in the slightest degree his determination to become a soldier. To get into the army remained his burning ambition.

Unfortunately for one with such an ambition, he was a lamentably poor scholar. Those excellent reports which had come to his parents from the Greensboro school were not duplicated here. The parents, who had formerly taken such great pride in his scholastic record, were distressed and puzzled. They were at a loss to understand the great change that had come in his attitude toward his studies. His unexplainable loss of interest in his school work was reflected most directly of course in his reports. Whenever they would arrive, his father and mother would look them over carefully, shake their heads sadly, and hope that something would happen to bring about a change for the better.

One day Willie happened to overhear them while they were talking about his low grades. Then, for the first time apparently, he realized how unhappy they were because of his lack of interest in his studies. That realization brought an attack of remorse and shame. Never again, he determined then and there, would he hurt them in that way. From then on high scholarship would be his goal. That determination brought almost immediate results, which must have caused his instructors amazement. Of course his parents were delighted. General Gorgas wrote in his journal:

Willie has turned scholar since nearly a year ago, and is perhaps the first scholar here. The medal for scholarship from Alabama was awarded to him. It is a very beautiful gold medal. His mother and sisters are very proud of it and him, to say nothing of my feelings on the subject.

He did not become a bookworm, however, and managed to find time for other interests. He joined the Episcopal Church, the faith in which his father was finding much comfort in his declining years. He developed a veritable passion for sports, especially baseball, and never missed an opportunity to play, becoming in time a formidable performer with the bat and in the field. And all the time there was growing in him the hope and determination that he would become a soldier.

He wrote frequently to his mother during her extended visits with her Alabama relatives. A few of those missives, fortunately, have been preserved. They tell about his activities both on and off the campus—about chestnut hunts, baseball games, the arrival of new students, a face-blacking contest, a visit to a cave (where he got "wet and muddy all over"), the fun he and his playmates got from setting kerosene-soaked cloth balls afire and batting them about the campus, a house-burning, a lynching, and a "Professor Gray," who was vigorously spanked by a crowd of shingle-wielding students when he entered a building to make a speech, which spanking "made him abuse the boys not a little."

None of these letters mentions a certain encounter which he had with a Tennessee mountaineer during his student days at Sewanee. But the incident's authenticity is attested by members of the Gorgas family and illustrates the sterner side of the youth's nature much better than accounts of hunting trips and cave explorations.

This particular mountaineer, conspicuously under the influence of the whiskey that has brought fame of a sort to the Tennessee and Kentucky mountain regions, was riding in a railway car with Willie as his seat companion when the train stopped at a station. Thinking, in his muddled condition, that this was his getting-off place, the Tennessean staggered clumsily to the platform, and Willie politely surrendered the entire seat to two ladies who had just entered. Upon reaching the platform the

WILLIE GORGAS AS A STUDENT IN THE PREPARATORY DEPARTMENT
OF THE UNIVERSITY OF THE SOUTH, ABOUT 1870

inebriate discovered that the train was still several miles
from his destination. Thereupon he staggered back to
the seat he had vacated and, seeing it occupied, roughly
demanded of the ladies that they move. Willie's indignation rose. He clenched his fists, gritted his teeth, and
lunged. The disturber landed heavily in the aisle, and
the appreciative ladies applauded their champion.

Willie remained at the University of the South for
six years, receiving his A.B. degree on August 5, 1875.
While he was a student, his alma mater had grown from
a small school of junior-college grade into an outstanding
institution of higher learning. Three years before his
graduation he had the great satisfaction of seeing his
father promoted from headmaster of the Junior Department to vice-chancellor of the entire university.

Those who knew Willie Gorgas at the time of his
graduation remembered him in later years as tall, mentally and physically alert, soft-voiced, gentle, and tend-
ing to slimness. The hair which later was to turn snowy
white was then black. His skin was of a healthy, ruddy
tint, emphasizing that the frailities which had caused his
parents such great concern in his childhood had been
outgrown and emphasizing also the invigorating powers
of the collegiate sports in which he had participated so
heartily. The laughing, twinkling eyes through which
shone a cheerful, friendly disposition were, however, not
strangers to sternness, and his normally cordial, subdued
voice could be raised in an instant to express suddenly
aroused anger. While anything but pugnacious, he was
never known, either then or later, to run away from a
fight or fail to give a good account of himself while engaged in one.

To most young men graduation from college or university brings the troublesome question: What next?
But it did not worry William Crawford Gorgas, A.B.,
'75. There was no doubt whatsoever in his mind as to
what he wanted to do. His desire for a military career

was a complete answer to it or to any other question that might be raised regarding his future. West Point was still his goal, as it had been for years.

But his enthusiasm for the army was not shared by his father, who had learned the hardships and disappointments of such a life from the best of all possible schools. Josiah Gorgas had recorded in his journal some time prior to Willie's graduation his hope that his son would not spend the best years of his life in endless shifting from army post to army post. His heart was set upon Willie's becoming a lawyer, but his urging brought no response except distinct disinterest, although he pointed out the excellent opportunities that would be open to the youth if he would associate himself with a maternal uncle, who had become one of the leaders of the New Orleans bar. At last, to satisfy his father, Willie agreed to give the law a trial and dutifully began reading Blackstone in his uncle's office. But his heart was still in the army, and reading law became more distasteful by the day. After one of the unhappiest years of his life, he gave it up gladly and forever.

General Gorgas must have known almost from the start that in trying to direct the youth's enthusiasm into nonmilitary channels he was waging a losing fight. Eventually, he realized, his son probably would have his own way. And, like the good loser he always was, he was prepared to wish him Godspeed. On the very same day that he wrote in his journal "It grieves me to see him so infatuated about West Point and so opposed to the law" he also wrote that he was doing his best to help him obtain an appointment to the United States Military Academy.

Others also were helping. J. P. B. Wilmer, a New Orleans admirer, wrote President Grant that Willie was "a young gentleman of great promise, intellectually and morally" and that he had "enjoyed the best domestic discipline from his birth." General J. B. Hood, former

Associate Justice John A. Campbell of the United States
Supreme Court, and C. C. Augur, a former officer in
the Federal Army, likewise urged the President to name
him to a cadetship at West Point. General Gorgas's
enemy of the Civil War period wrote as follows:

NEW ORLEANS, LA.
January 17, 1875.

DEAR PRESIDENT GRANT:

I write this letter in behalf of our old friend Gorgas of the
Ordnance formerly. Gorgas is entirely above and without the
scope of politics. He is the head of the University of the South
and is devoting his whole mind to the good work of organizing
and building up the institution under his charge. His son is
a young man of about twenty—clever and well educated and
with fine physique. All his life he has been earnest and determined to get to West Point. There is no vacancy now in his
district, and his only remaining hope is that you may give him
an appointment at large.

I am very well aware of the great number of applications
for these appointments, and of the vigor and persistency of
the pressure brought to bear upon you in individual cases, but
I hope you will find yourself at liberty to consider this youngster's case, and, if the thing is possible, to give him the appointment. I am sure it will be worthily bestowed and thoroughly
appreciated by all of his friends.

I am, with great respect, your friend and obedient servant

C. C. AUGUR.

But these earnest pleas were all fruitless. West Point
appointments were eagerly sought in the troubled years
that followed the war, and the requests for them far outnumbered those available. Had the supply-and-demand
ratio been reversed, it is entirely probable that an appointment at large would have been given Willie. But
it is not surprising that President Grant was unwilling
to disappoint some other aspirant in order to please the
man whose administrative genius and knowledge of ordnance had delayed for months, perhaps years, Grant's
military triumph and had cost him the lives of thousands
of his best troops. So Willie's pleas and those of his

supporters were passed over in favor of others. However, they did not relinquish their efforts until his
twenty-second birthday, when he automatically became
ineligible.

The door to a military career thus appeared to have
been slammed in his face. There seemed to be nothing
to do but to try to forget how earnestly he had wished
such a career and direct his energies into other channels.
But William Crawford Gorgas was not willing to give
up so easily. There must be some way. There was. The
army needed doctors. He could study medicine and join
the medical corps. That is what he determined to do.

The father did not object to a medical career as
such. He did not falter in the face of the financial sacrifice it would involve for him, struggling along with his
college executive's small salary. But his old, never entirely quieted objections to the army as a career reasserted themselves. Nevertheless, he again yielded to
Willie's entreaties, hoping that during the long period
of medical training the youth would change his mind
about the attractiveness of army life. He gave his con-
sent to a three-year course at the Bellevue Medical College in New York City and agreed to help as much as
he could toward Willie's expenses. Willie began his
medical studies in September, 1876.

Those three years at Bellevue were difficult ones.
General Gorgas was able to send small sums from time
to time during the first two years, but after that the
young man had to get along as best he could without
money from home. The struggle once became so difficult that he seriously considered leaving school for a
year and getting a job so as to repay what he had borrowed but finally ruled that out as unwise. It was better,
he decided, to prepare himself for his profession first,
regardless of the hardships, and then repay what he owed.
Difficult as they were, those years had their share of pleasure too. He took up dancing. He went in for rowing

and spent much time on the river. And he enjoyed normal, harmless, semiromantic affairs with the nurses at the hospital where he worked.

He duplicated in medical school the excellent work he had done at the University of the South. Surprisingly enough, in view of his avowed lack of interest in medicine except as a means of getting into the army, he began experiencing a keen enthusiasm for his studies. The care of the sick, he discovered, had an appeal of its own which he had never suspected. Dr. William H. Welch, who, like him, was later to become president of the American Medical Association and an executive of the Rockefeller Foundation, was a member of the Bellevue faculty, and professor and student developed a great admiration for each other.

To keep down expenses, young Gorgas lived in a cheap boardinghouse at 303 East 30th Street, not far from the college, sharing a room with a friend, John Bowen, of Paris, Kentucky. Their Irish landlady, a Miss Eliza Kelly, acted as "mother" to her boarders, most of whom were medical students. As they paid only about five dollars a week each for room and board, they had to act as their own maids and housekeepers.

"Monday was the inevitable hash day," Dr. Benjamin J. Baldwin, of Montgomery, Alabama, recounted many years later, drawing upon his well-filled memories of his own student days at Miss Kelly's. "Wednesday prunes prevailed. Friday we knew before we gathered in the dining room in the basement that fish was to be the main course. On Sunday we had codfish balls of course and ice cream for dinner. Upon the appearance of ice cream a sweet smile always graced the gentle face of 'Old W. C.,' as we called him."

From this fellow-Alabamian we obtain other glimpses at Willie Gorgas's life as a medical student:

I had been in Bellevue a year when "W. C." came to New York, and the "country" had worn off me a little. I remember so well when Gorgas first entered the Bohemian crowd at Miss Kelly's. He was like a sweet, modest, precious country girl just come to town. All of us loved him from the beginning.

Saturday nights "on the Bowery" and in the "peanut gallery" of the old Union Square Theatre were times for us to cast off the goblins of the dissecting room and forget the harrassing, jaw-breaking names of muscles and bones. They were harmless revelries. We were not saintly, but we were not bad. Just big, free-hearted boys with enough of the "Old Nick" in us to go out for a good time once a week.

Bowen of Kentucky, Robertson, of North Carolina, Wood, of Alabama, Bibb, of Texas, "W. C." and I generally made one group, of which there were many "on the Bowery" those Saturday nights.

Bibb stood six feet high, weighed 210 pounds, and was red-headed and as strong as an ox, with the Texas propensity of "fishing for a fight." We often used "W. C.'s" gentleness to keep Bibb's "ruffles" down.

On one of those Saturday night theatrical excursions, Gorgas and a handful of his medical cronies were seated, as usual, in the "peanut gallery" witnessing a performance of *Two Orphans*. The misfortunes of the two sisters, one of them blind, were so appealing that the emotional Bowen, lost in the illusion of the play, forgot that it was only make-believe. His sympathy mounted as the play continued. When finally the blind girl fell into the clutches of the stage villain, he completely lost control of his sympathies. Leaping to his feet, he jumped onto his seat and thundered at the too-realistic thespian: "You scoundrel! Take your hands off that girl, or I'll blow a hole through you!"

Naturally, this outburst all but broke up the show, especially when he placed his hand on his empty hip pocket, as though about to carry out his threat. The entire gallery was in bedlam. Other theater-goers shouted: "Sit down, you idiot!" "Can't you see it's just a play?" "What's the matter with you?" Willie Gorgas was sitting on one side of the excited young Kentuckian, and Bibb, the big Texan, on the other. They managed to quiet him.

The severe economic strain was eased somewhat in the fall of Gorgas's senior year. A friend of his, a member of the house staff of the New York Insane Asylum on Blackwell's Island, obtained another position and offered his old one to Gorgas, who, like other senior medical students, was encouraged by the school to get an outside job of this kind in order to obtain practical experience. Finding that he could combine work and study in such a way as not to neglect the latter, he gladly accepted. Although his new job paid no salary, it did provide all normal living expenses. That of course was a great help.

It was about this time that the young Alabamian almost had another personal conflict with yellow fever. A particularly serious epidemic was raging in Memphis, and the city's urgent appeals were answered by volunteer nurses and doctors from all parts of the country, many of whom contracted the disease a few days after their arrival and quickly succumbed to it. Although he had not had it and was therefore a nonimmune, Willie resolved to offer his services and assembled a corps of trained nurses to accompany him. Bowen also went along.

They had no trouble at all in getting as far as the outskirts of the city. But there a quarantine station had been established, and those in charge, while expressing appreciation of their desire to help, nevertheless firmly refused to allow them to enter when they found that there was not a single immune in the whole party. Thus thwarted, Willie returned to his medical studies.

What he had learned about yellow fever in preparation for this trip, however, soon proved useful. His father resigned the vice-chancellorship of the University of the South in 1878 to become president of the University of Alabama, and scarcely had the family moved from Sewanee to Tuscaloosa when the university town had an epidemic. Soon after it started Willie began writing frequent and long letters home, recommending proce-

dures which he considered advisable. Those letters revealed a knowledge of yellow fever remarkable in one
so young and so medically inexperienced. Obviously,
he had done a vast amount of reading on the disease.

Willie, who was now known to all but the family as
"W. C.," won the admiration of his classmates and many
others by going swimming in the frigid waters of the East
River long after ice formed on its surface. He had plenty
of company in warm weather of course, but, as it turned
decidedly chilly with approaching winter, he was left to
swim alone. When his friends chided him, he retorted
that Andrew Jackson used to take a swim in the Tennessee River every day in the year and insisted that "what
Andrew Jackson did I can do." He did it, too, until
almost the first of March. At times he was as red as an
apple when he would make a dash for his dressing room.

His three-year medical course ended in June, 1879.
Along with the other members of his class he received
his diploma in Commencement exercises at the Academy
of Music.

"I got about the handsomest basket of flowers given,"
he wrote his mother. "It could not have cost less than
fifteen dollars and was given by one of the dear little
nurses. I am afraid the little lady must have spent the
savings from two months' salary, and, what is worse, I
shall have to break myself one of these days returning
it."

The last obstacle barring the military-minded Willie
from an army career appeared to have been removed, but
he postponed that decisive step for awhile. For one
thing, he felt the need for more hospital experience. For
another, he still faced the vigorous opposition of his
father. "I have no objections to your passing the army
examinations, nor would I object to a couple of years'
service," General Gorgas had told him in one of his
letters. "But it would not be a life to look forward to as
a permanent thing. It is not in the army that the sphere

Dr. William Crawford Gorgas, House Surgeon
at Bellevue, about 1882

of the doctor is ennobling. I hope that something better
will present itself before you graduate."

So he waited. A short time after his graduation he
accepted an internship at Bellevue Hospital. He had not
been there long when he had a chance to go to China as
a member of the staff of a missionary hospital operated
by the Presbyterian church. He declined the offer, determined to let nothing interfere with his plan to go
into the army.

He did not wait much longer. In June, 1880, almost
exactly a year after his graduation, he entered the Army's
Medical Department with the rank of first lieutenant,
carrying a salary of $133 a month, plus commutation.
Soon after his enlistment he was sent to Fort Clark, in
Texas. Then he was on duty for a while at Fort Duncan,
in the same state. And then Fort Brown, still another
Texas post, was his home. From 1885 to 1888 he was
stationed at Fort Randall, in North Dakota. Then came
a period of service at Fort Barrancas, Florida.

Had Gorgas been less enthusiastic about an army
career, he probably would have bitterly regretted many
times his failure to listen to his father's advice and become a civilian physician or lawyer. For the sort of life
that was forced upon him during his first two decades in
the army was enough to confirm the older man's most
doleful predictions. He must have been reminded many
times of the barren Brierfield of his childhood as he lived
the life and performed the duties of an army doctor.
His residence, whether in the sun-baked plains and val-
leys of Texas or in winter quarters near the Canadian
border, was typical of what Uncle Sam usually provided
for his armed defenders, fairly comfortable but crude
and frontier-like, with as few of the cultural advantages
as were to be found in the sleepy little Alabama community where he had played with the iron worker's son.
At one time he was seventy-five miles from the nearest
railroad, and the post's nearest neighbors were Indians

and half-breeds. Civilization, as represented by such up-
lifting influences as social life, clubs, libraries, churches,
and the like, was nonexistent. Even had there been
greater opportunities for cultural and social intercourse,
there would still have been a deadly monotony about the
life imposed upon the residents of these outpost en-
campments. But drawbacks of this kind brought no
diminution in Gorgas's enthusiasm for the army. So
great was his love for his work that such things were
mere trifles.

His unusual personal qualities did much to absorb
the jolts and jars of these conditions and make them
bearable and even enjoyable. As a child he had been
gifted with a sunny, cheerful, friendly manner and an
easy, complete adjustability to circumstances. These
characteristics became even more conspicuous after he
entered manhood and tackled the tough problem of
treating the many illnesses that were encountered in and
around an army post. Nothing, however trying, seemed
to get the better of him. He would work for hours and
hours without a suggestion of complaint or dissatisfaction
with his lot. He rapidly developed the rare medical virtue of feeling, and showing that he felt, a deep personal
interest in every patient and had an uncommonly inti-
mate knowledge of and sympathy for others' personal
troubles. Overshadowing all other characteristics of the
man in those early-manhood years were his tremendous
capacity for friendship, a strong devotion to his friends,
and a deep, disarming courtesy to all.

These qualities proved valuable assets indeed, for he
soon learned, as other army doctors had learned before
him, that he held a nonofficial commission to serve the
medical and near-medical needs of many who had no
legal claim to such service but were entitled to it under
the broad terms of the Hippocratic oath. In the un-
settled frontier country to which routine transfer orders
sent him, medical care was a haphazard sort of thing.

Doctors were scarce, sometimes to the point of virtual nonexistence, and whenever a baby was about to be born, a serious illness occurred, or somebody met with an accident, there was a search through the country-side for someone who knew how to cope with the current emergency. Under conditions like these the medical men on duty at a frontier army post were regarded as no less essential to its people's safety than the soldiers who protected them against Indians and marauders. Theo-retically, such medical services were entirely outside the army doctors' line of duty, could be refused if they saw fit to refuse them, and were subject to such charges as they might wish to make. Actually, these appeals almost never went unanswered; and, the economic status of the patients being what it was, they received practically no compensation for this work.

Gorgas soon learned that the peacetime army doctor often faced dangers as serious as those faced by troops in wartime. On two separate occasions while on duty at the North Dakota post he came perilously close to losing his life in blizzards. And of course he was constantly exposed to all manner of diseases while fighting them in his patients. But nothing mattered. He was in the work he loved.

Among his friends at one army post were a fellow-officer and his wife, the parents of a young baby, their first. When the mother asked him to advise her re-garding the baby's health and general upbringing, he laid down the cardinal rule that under no circumstances must she take it up and fondle it when it cried. Let it cry, he adjured. Crying would not hurt it. And in time it would learn that it did no good to cry and would stop crying. The mother took these instructions to heart and resolutely fought the maternal impulse to run to the cradle whenever the child would indicate its unhappiness in the orthodox baby fashion. Then one day, while the baby was lying on the porch, crying loudly, the crying suddenly ceased. Frightened lest something terrible might have happened—thoughts of kidnaping rushed through the mother's mind—the members of the family ran to its crib. There they found Dr. Gorgas, archenemy of this sort of thing, with the suddenly quieted child in his arms.

That same characteristic—acute sympathy for the unhappy and a desire to do something for them—was an outstanding mark of the man, motivating many an act of generosity and kindness during those army post years, as well as later. Persons in humble positions benefited from it no less than those more fortunately situated.

One of them was Henrietta, his colored washwoman. Henrietta was seriously injured in a train accident and would not think of letting anyone but Dr. Gorgas examine her. His examination convinced him that her life could only be saved by a double amputation above the knee. After he had convinced her of this, she insisted that he perform the operation himself, although both of them knew that she had no money to pay for it. As he always did when a request like this was made of him, he agreed to do so. Thanks to his skill and Henrietta's fighting spirit, the operation was entirely successful, and she made an excellent recovery. But then she faced a serious economic problem. Earning a livelihood had been difficult before, but what could an ignorant colored woman do to earn money now, with both legs gone? What happened next was typical of Gorgas. He gave her a pair of artificial legs. Thus restored to something like her former ability to get around, she returned to her former work, and again the Gorgas garments were entrusted to her care.

The story, unfortunately, has an anticlimax which reflects no credit upon Henrietta. So forgetful did she become of his kindness that she sent him an exorbitantly large bill. When he protested, she insisted that it was not at all unreasonable, since "it ain't everybody what

can git their washing done by a woman with two wooden
legs."

Friends of that period of his life have left other
glimpses of the Gorgas of the army post days. They tell
of his persistent but largely unsuccessful attempt to
master the art of the dance. They tell of his much greater
success as a hunter and fisherman, and of his delight in
long horseback rides, reminiscent no doubt of those he
enjoyed years earlier astride that donkey his uncle had
brought him from Sicily. They tell of his peculiar reading habit—how he would read no less than three books
simultaneously, devoting twenty minutes at a time, first
to a heavy scientific volume, then to a volume of general
interest of the better sort, and finally to something as
light as he could find, as likely to be a detective story as
anything else. He believed, he told them, that he could
retain what he read better that way than by sticking to
one type of reading to the end of the book. And those
friends of the army post days have taken particular pleasure in describing the one and only real romance of his
life.

On August 3, 1882, he was transferred from Fort
Clark to Fort Brown, near Brownsville, Texas. There
were many cases of yellow fever in that part of the country, including several among the army personnel and
their families, and he was as completely nonimmune then
as he had been several years before when he, with his
friends, made a vain attempt to go to the aid of the yellow fever sufferers of Memphis. But his nonimmunity
proved no greater deterrent to his determination to aid
victims of the disease in 1882 than it had done in 1878.
His official superiors took cognizance of it, however, and
forbade him, along with the other nonimmunes, to enter
the yellow fever wards under any circumstances.

At the outskirts of Memphis some three years earlier,
only the presence of armed guards had prevented him
from entering the stricken city. Now there were no

guards to enforce the "Keep Out" order. Of course in-
fraction of the rules—this one especially—would result in
the imposition of disciplinary measures, if discovered.
But that would come *after* his crossing of the forbidden
portal. Then it would probably be too late to return
him to his old duties among the nonimmunes.

A superior officer visited the hospital one day on a
routine inspection trip while Gorgas was supposed to be
on duty. Not finding him, the officer began a personal
search, which ended when he came upon the missing
medical lieutenant in the forbidden sector calmly performing a post-mortem upon the latest yellow fever
victim. An order for his arrest followed promptly but
was rescinded a few hours later. Because of his exposure
to the disease, however, he was ordered to move his
quarters from the hospital proper to the section reserved
for yellow fever patients. That, of course, was no punishment at all but exactly what Gorgas was hoping for.
Thus began, inauspiciously enough, his lifetime association with this disease.

Some time later Gorgas was called to the quarters of
Col. William J. Lyster, commander of the post, to treat
the colonel's sister-in-law, Miss Marie Doughty. She was
suffering from a severe chill, one of the telltale symptoms of yellow fever, and a definite diagnosis was made
in short order. A few days later she developed the characteristic "black vomit," indicative of a last-stage condition, and her early death appeared inevitable. So certain did it seem indeed that her relatives began to plan
her funeral and employed someone to dig her grave.

The eighteen-year-old son of one of the officers succumbed to yellow fever about this time, and Gorgas and
another physician, who had conducted funeral services
on a number of occasions, were asked to conduct this
one. Upon leaving the cemetery the other physician
pointed to a freshly dug grave and said to Gorgas, "This
is Miss Doughty's grave. Will you read the burial service

for her this afternoon?" Gorgas promised to do so. But
that was a promise he was not called upon to keep. For
not only did Miss Doughty fail to die in time for her
funeral to be held that afternoon as planned, but she
immediately began such a brisk recovery that she was
soon able to sit up. Two days after her improvement
started, Gorgas, still a nonimmune, notwithstanding his
deliberate self-exposure to the disease, contracted yellow
fever and became quite ill. However, his illness was considerably shorter than his patient's, and they became
convalescent about the same time.

As it happened, Gorgas and the family with whom
Miss Doughty was then living were close neighbors, and
the two convalescents, freed by their illness from normal
duties and responsibilities, official and social, found it
increasingly pleasant to be together. As time went on
they were more and more in each other's company, dis-
covering and developing innumerable common interests
and enthusiasms. The rapidly budding romance received
considerable undercover encouragement and assistance
from an elderly woman who had volunteered her services during the epidemic and had nursed both of them.

Several weeks after their recovery Gorgas invited
Miss Doughty to go with him to the cemetery. They had
no difficulty in locating the spot where she was to have
been buried and found that it was now the grave of
another yellow fever victim who had not been as fortunate as she in upsetting the doleful predictions of
apparently certain death.

Miss Doughty's brother-in-law was ordered some
time later to Fort Clark, while Gorgas's superiors saw
fit to keep him at Fort Brown. Her departure brought
a great emptiness into his life and, to relieve it somewhat, he made a trip to Fort Clark. He had not yet told
her what was now plain to him—that he was very much
in love. Nor did he tell her then, although he had
plenty of opportunities during the many hours they

spent together on long horseback rides and in other activities for which they both felt great enthusiasm. Nevertheless, those few days of reunion brought him appre-
ciably nearer a declaration of the true state of his heart.
From then on his letters to her were much more frequent. Their tone changed markedly too. In one of
them he wrote:

I am conscious of the many disadvantages under which I
labor in winning the place I wish in your esteem, particularly
that of being entirely separated from you. Words are poor
means of expression or of winning regard. I think if I could
be thrown with you from day to day, and have you appreciate
how dear you have become to me, it would be something in my
favor. But that is my misfortune, and I have to appeal to you
not to let it work to my disadvantage. I am very glad of this
opportunity of speaking on the subject nearest my heart. Our
relations have not been such that I felt at liberty to obtrude
my feelings upon you in writing unless you gave me some
opportunity. Any change in them, you must be aware, is entirely in your hands. If I have trespassed in this matter, please
pardon me. The greatest object I have just now is to stand
well with you.

His expressed desire to "stand well" with her evidently found a ready echo in her desire to "stand well"
with him. But she steadfastly held out against a definite
promise of marriage.

In the fall of 1884 Miss Doughty accepted Amelia
Gayle Gorgas's invitation to visit her at the family home
in Tuscaloosa and was very much surprised to be greeted
at the train by Gorgas himself, whom she supposed to be
many hundreds of miles away. She was so charmed by
the gracious manner and warm hospitality of her suit-
or's mother and so delighted with the other members of
the family, as well as with the lovely Southern university
town, that her self-questionings regarding the true state
of her heart and the wisdom of the proposed marriage
began slipping away. The widow of the recently deceased former Confederate ordnance officer was equally

charmed by this attractive, vivacious girl from the once-despised North and put in some highly effective work as a match-maker.

The two young people were walking across the University campus with Mrs. Gorgas one morning when she, with an excellent sense of timing, suggested that they take a walk, without her, through the piney woods to the Warrior River. Upon reaching it, they sat down on a tree trunk to rest. While they rested they talked, and what they talked about was marriage, more than ever before "the subject nearest my heart." We do not know how long they talked like that in the cool shade of a clump of Alabama pine trees, but we do know that his pleading was eloquent and effective. For when they started back to the campus, he had won the answer he had been seeking for more than two years.

"It would not be true to say that Yellow Jack was the best man at our wedding," Marie Doughty Gorgas once remarked, "but it would be perfectly true to say that, in a sense, he was an usher."

At the wedding Gorgas experienced more than the usual amount of bridegroom's nervousness. When the minister asked the time-honored question, "Do you take this woman to be your lawfully wedded wife?" he became confused, hesitated long enough to cause an embarrassing silence, and then demanded of the by-now confused preacher: "Will you please repeat that?"

His interest in yellow fever having been stimulated by his struggle with it in his own body and by the part it had played in his marriage, Gorgas now threw himself with even greater zeal into his study of this disease and his search for its causative agent. He devoted much attention to the eminent but ridiculed Dr. Josiah Nott, who, it will be remembered, had attended his mother at his birth. He followed dutifully the careers of Koch, Lister, and Pasteur and tried to find in the fruits of their labors an answer to the age-old question that was agitating his mind.

And when he completed this study, he found himself exactly where he had been when he began it—still unconvinced by Dr. Nott's reasoning and seeing little to accept in the theories of latter-day Dr. Notts who kept hammering away on the dictum that a mosquito bridged the wide gap between the sick and the well and that, if that link could only be effectively broken, yellow fever would disappear from the earth. He was eager to play a part in its disappearance but held to his earlier conviction that the mosquito-transmission theory was altogether unsound and unreasonable.

His determination to leave the mosquito alone did not prevent him from winning considerable recognition as a yellow fever expert, and he was selected for special duty here and there whenever Yellow Jack would strike. He was so successful in handling an epidemic at Fort Barrancas, Florida, that the Inspector General warmly praised him for his "fearless and skillful management" of the anti-yellow fever forces.

It was a natural next step for him to be placed in charge of the yellow fever camp at Siboney, near Havana, during the Spanish-American War. One of his patients there was Dr. Victor C. Vaughan, like himself a major and, also like himself, a future president of the American Medical Association. The two men became warm friends. "It was largely through Dr. Gorgas' skill in the management of yellow fever that the death rate in our army was so low," Dr. Vaughan wrote some time later. "The sight of his kindly face was a stimulant that did much to tone up the muscles exhausted by the exercise imposed upon the body by *el vomito negro*. His kindly words to his patients served as a better tonic than any name in the pharmacopaeia."

In Cuba in wartime, as on the mainland in peacetime, Gorgas continued to reject the mosquito theory of yellow fever transmission. He still simply could not see its reasonableness and acted accordingly. As a result, the commanding officer at Siboney decided, at his urging, to do what the people of Philadelphia, Memphis, and hundreds of other places had done—to fight yellow fever with the lighted torch. The little military community, with its valuable medical supplies and large stores of equipment, made a lively bonfire. After it had burned itself out, it was hopefully believed that the flames had destroyed the germs of yellow fever as effectively as they had consumed the blankets, wooden beds, clothing, and other hospital paraphernalia which had burned so briskly that day. Gorgas was soon to learn that they had not.

CHAPTER III

Man against Mosquito

WHEN MAJOR GORGAS was named sanitary officer of the City of Havana in 1898, he undertook the hopeless-appearing task of breaking a grip which yellow fever had had upon the city for a hundred and fifty years. And we have his own word for it that he knew just about as little about the key to the problem— the cause and method of transmission of the disease—as his medical ancestor, Dr. Benjamin Rush, knew about it when he worked so valiantly but so ineffectively to save the lives of yellow fever victims during the Philadelphia epidemic of 1793.

"When we went to Havana we knew no more of the sanitation of yellow fever than we knew a century before," he wrote twenty years later. "The army which went to Santiago suffered as severely from yellow fever and other tropical diseases as any military expedition to the tropics had suffered before that time, and its death rate, had it remained, would have been just as high as was that of the French army of similar size, which was exterminated in the island of Haiti just one hundred years before."

It was true that Pasteur's work in the field of bacteriology had given added impetus to the germ theory of disease transmission. It is also true that as early as 1809 Dr. John Crawford had contended that man could, and did, contract numerous illnesses by receiving into his body minute particles from the bodies of other forms of animal life; that in 1848 Dr. Nott had strongly suggested that the mosquito played an important role in that grim

drama of disease and death; that in 1854 Beauperthuy
had come out squarely as a proponent of the mosquito-
transmission theory; that both Dr. Rush, describing the
Philadelphia epidemic, and Noah Webster, writing of
New York's 1795 experience with the disease, had referred to the marked increase in the number of mosquitoes then infesting these two communities; and that
while Gorgas was in medical college Dr. Carlos Finlay
had reported enlighteningly upon his work with mosquitoes as yellow fever vectors to the Royal Academy of
Medicine, Physical and Natural Sciences, in Havana. But
these enthusiasts had not been taken seriously, and to all
practical purposes medical science was then as completely
unarmed for a combat with yellow fever as if these men
had never mentioned the subject.

The occupation of Havana by the United States
Army offered an excellent opportunity to perform an
invaluable service to the American people. If that city
could be eliminated as a focus of infection, it seemed
reasonable to hope that yellow fever would virtually disappear from Mobile, Charleston, New Orleans, and other
cities in the southeastern part of this country. The cost
of such an effort, if successful, would be trivial compared
with the results to be obtained, even as figured entirely
in terms of dollars and cents, without regard to what
the saving of lives and prevention of illness would mean
to those immediately concerned.

Ignoring the preachments of Dr. Nott, Dr. Finlay,
and the others and forgetting what Dr. Rush and Noah
Webster had written about the unusually large number
of "moschetoes" in Philadelphia and of "musquetoes"
in New York, Gorgas and his fellow sanitarians paid no
attention to the mosquitoes in and around Havana and
set to work cleaning up the city.

They soon found they had undertaken a man-sized
job. Sanitary conditions had been bad for decades before the war, and during the five years immediately pre-

ceding the occupation they had become much worse.
The people's minds had been on war and not on sanitation. Even such simple, backward measures as had
formerly been enforced after a fashion had died from
inattention. As a result, almost everything imaginable
was to be found in the streets, from dead bodies of
human beings and animals to human excreta and decayed
food in a raw or semicooked state. Those rotting things
stank to high Heaven. But the easygoing natives didn't
mind. They stepped over them, sniffed the revolting
odors, and continued on their way.

Gorgas and his men determined to put an end to all
this. They first attacked the filth where it was most
conspicuous—on the streets. The beggars with their
running sores disappeared. The bodies of dead animals
were dragged away and buried. The sick who had been
expelled from the hospitals when the Spanish officers
commandeered them for use as barracks vanished from
the parks and plazas. The vultures, which had lived on
those rotting bodies and other rotting things so long, left
to find some other place more like the Havana they had
seen disappear under the efficient clean-up of these energetic men from the American mainland.

But the clean-up work did not stop with the streets
and parks. While some squads were making them im-
maculate, others were attacking filth in more out-of-the-
way places. Residents of private homes became familiar
with the Gorgas workers and inspectors. These filth
sleuths surveyed backyards and trash piles. Business
establishments were carefully examined and required to
stay clean. Factory managers, accustomed to the slow-
moving ways of the Spanish, discovered that these ways
were no more. Probably no city has ever been so thoroughly cleaned inside and out as Havana was. Gorgas
had ample reason to be proud of his work. Newspapers
on the mainland were enthusiastic in their praise, printing, side by side for contrast, pictures of the city before
the clean-up and afterward.

The general health of the people improved markedly. Smallpox was entirely eradicated. Typhoid and dysentery showed striking reductions. In 1898, the last year of the Spanish occupation, there were 21,252 deaths from all causes in the city, and its general death rate stood at 91.3 per 1,000 population. In 1899, the first year of American occupation, deaths dropped to 8,153 and the death rate to 33.67 per 1,000 population. The next year deaths dropped again, this time to 6,102, while the death rate fell to only 24.40 per 1,000 population. Havre, Munich, Dublin, Kingston (Jamaica)—all had higher death rates than this Cuban city with a world-wide reputation for wretched health conditions.

Nevertheless, "the great result at which we aimed seemed to be as far away as ever." The ambitious sanitary program had had no effect whatsoever upon yellow fever except apparently to make it worse. Both cases and deaths increased sharply, the latter from 136 in 1898 and 103 in 1899 to 310 in 1900, when more Havana people succumbed to yellow fever than in 1890. The newspapers that had been publishing such glowing stories about the clean-up and all those contrasting photographs now began printing another kind of news, news of one of the worst yellow fever epidemics—somebody called it the very worst—the troubled island had ever experienced. A staff correspondent of one of the leading news services, overpainting the picture somewhat, even went so far as to write that there was not a single block in the city that did not contain from one to seventeen cases. Gorgas was aghast.

The disease seemed to take a diabolical delight in confounding and discomfiting the sanitarians. Besides striking again with unabated fury, which was bad enough, it also scorned all the accepted rules regarding its behavior. For example, those parts of the city inhabited by the wealthy became centers of the epidemic, while the abodes of the poor and filthy appeared to have developed a relative immunity.

Wise as we are in the present-day knowledge of the disease, we find no mystery in this sudden upsurge. For several years prior to 1898 Havana had been a garrison occupied by Spanish troops. Normal intercourse with the rest of the world had been curtailed, and immigration had been greatly reduced. Thus the population consisted mainly of those who had been born there and therefore were immune. It was this, and not the fact that filth and yellow fever are boon companions, which accounted for the relative absence of the disease just before Gorgas's clean-up drive. It simply had had no fuel to feed upon. And then, with the departure of the Spanish troops at the end of the war and the confidence that the United States would assure a period of peace and security, the ships of the world had started bringing to Havana large cargoes of immigrants. In 1900 alone there were 25,000 of them. And practically none had ever been exposed to yellow fever. Here, then, was the fuel that the germ had been waiting for. Under such circumstances, a serious outbreak was all but inevitable. It was Gorgas's misfortune that it occurred just after his clean-up campaign.

This also explained why the disease seemed to seek out the well-to-do, the socially favored, and the physically clean. The newcomers—that is to say, the nonimmunes—avoided the slums, choosing the better sections of the city, where they could live in an environment more in keeping with that which they had enjoyed at home. This was particularly true of the Americans. It was natural for the epidemic to be worst there.

Distressed though he was by the failure of his clean-up campaign, Gorgas refused to give up. Still convinced that he was working along the proper lines—he remained convinced of that for a considerable time—he intensified his drive. Perhaps he had not been thorough enough. Possibly he had overlooked some dirty spots after all. So the city-wide housecleaning went on and on. And so did yellow fever. Thus all of his carefully thought out theories regarding yellow fever control were completely blasted. He was, it need hardly be emphasized, a bitterly disappointed man. And so was Governor-General Leonard Wood, who had supported him wholeheartedly.

The carefully kept yellow fever records were not alone in emphasizing to Gorgas the failure of his campaign. Infinitely more poignant as reminders of that failure were the deaths of close personal friends whose passing would have brought intense grief under any circumstances. Among them was a Captain Page, who began having chills while attending the funeral of another yellow fever victim and died less than a week later. Another was the superintendent of the San José Asylum, who died within a month after his arrival in Cuba.

The yellow fever death which seems to have made the greatest impression upon him, however, was that of a major on the staff of General William Ludlow, the military governor of the city. A short time after his wife left the island for a visit with her family in Cincinnati, this officer became sick and, in accordance with a promise made before she left, Gorgas immediately cabled her. She received the message while attending a dinner party. Quickly abandoning her vacation plans, she left at once to rejoin her husband and arrived about two days before he died. Then when the end did come, she fell upon him, covered as he was with the repulsive *vomito negro,* and much of her body and clothing became covered with it. This, of course, was an attempt at suicide, since she, like nearly everybody else, believed yellow fever to be transmitted by physical contact with its victims and particularly with *vomito negro.* Gorgas rushed to her and, assisted by some nurses, forcibly removed her from the room.

Appearing to have regained her composure somewhat, the woman later talked over with Gorgas and Mrs. Gorgas plans for accompanying her husband's body back to the United States by the next boat. Some time after that, still composed and apparently regretting her impulsive attempt to join him in death, she went to her own room, asked for and received something to induce sleep, and prepared to retire. Gorgas and Mrs. Gorgas were just getting ready for bed when a messenger arrived with the news that she had killed herself. When he forced the door to her room, he found her lying on the bed as though in quiet, peaceful sleep. The left arm had dropped naturally to her side. The other, still holding the pistol that had ended her life, was lying across her breast. She had shot herself behind the ear, and the hemorrhage had been so sharp that the body was completely blanched. From where Gorgas stood as he entered the room, he could not see the wound. But he did see and comment upon the articles of wearing apparel which she had carefully arranged on a chair by the bed—the dainty feminine garments in which she wished to be buried. As he looked at her lying there so white and motionless, she reminded him of a marble statue like those he had seen in world-famous museums.

The next day Gorgas and other friends of the couple followed two coffins to the small military cemetery at Camp Columbia, about five miles from Havana, and saw them buried side by side. Naturally, the double tragedy had a most depressing effect upon the entire military community.

Mystifying as the sharp upswing in the yellow fever curve was to Gorgas, General Wood, and practically all the other yellow fever workers, there was no mystery about it to Dr. Carlos Finlay, who was then serving with Gorgas and two other experts as a member of a special commission for the diagnosis of all suspected cases of this disease. With the assurance born of years and years of study and deduction, he had been certain from the start that the whole anti-yellow fever campaign was entirely wrong—that it was based upon a complete misconception

of the nature of the disease and the method of its transmission, and that the measures being taken to curb it
would prove as futile as the old methods of building
bonfires and shooting off cannons. Many years prior to
Gorgas's and the American Army's arrival in Havana he
had reached the firm, unyielding conviction that the
civilized world would be cursed with periodic epidemics
of yellow fever as long as it failed to concentrate its anti-
yellow fever campaigns upon a single tiny insect which
the rest of the scientific world insisted upon ignoring—
the *Stegomyia* mosquito, since renamed the *Aëdes
aegypti.*

Others of course had also leveled accusing fingers at
the mosquito as an important, if not the only, agency in
the transmission of yellow fever. But those others—Dr.
Nott and the rest—had accused the mosquito as a whole,
without naming a particular species. Inasmuch as there
are said to be more than three thousand different varieties of mosquitoes, the contribution of these gentlemen
to the cause of yellow fever control, while definitely helpful and certainly leading medical attention in the right
direction, nevertheless left most of the distance still to
be traveled. It was just as though a detective insisted
that a certain crime had been committed by one or more
in a community of some three thousand population but
could not give you any idea as to which of these residents was, or were, guilty.

But Dr. Finlay, like a master criminal-seeker, had
walked confidently into the mosquito community, so to
speak, and unhesitatingly placed his hand upon one of
the three thousand-odd varieties. He had done that as
early as 1881. And during the years that had passed he
had labored indefatigably, first, to establish his theory
firmly by experimental study and, second, to convince
others that it was sound. But thus far he had accomplished neither of these aims.

It is true, he could and did make out a strong circumstantial case in support of his theory. Didn't yellow fever always, or practically always, break out in those parts of the world where this particular variety of mosquito was known to be especially prevalent? Wasn't there a more than coincidental relationship between their association in certain latitudes? Didn't yellow fever rage in unchecked epidemics near the seacoast in warm countries and yet never appear in near-by communities situated atop mountains where the weather was too cold for this type of mosquito to survive? (Hadn't it long been known, for instance, that Guayaquil, Ecuador's seaport, was a veritable pesthole as far as yellow fever was concerned, while the people of Quito, the nation's capital up in the mountains, never gave it a thought, except when they had to go to Guayaquil to catch a ship? And wasn't Mexico City with its 7300-foot elevation practically as free from yellow fever as Ottawa or Detroit, in spite of its being just a few hundred miles from Vera Cruz, which had been fighting yellow fever since soon after the disease first appeared in the New World? Hadn't the mosquitoes in Philadelphia and New York made such a great impression upon Dr. Rush and Noah Webster that both had referred to them in their accounts of these cities' great epidemics? And, finally, had not Sir Ronald Ross and others demonstrated that malaria was transmitted by mosquitoes?

All of this sounded logical enough, but the skeptical insisted upon a practical demonstration. They admitted that yellow fever and mosquitoes seemed to appear together. Nevertheless, they would remain unconvinced, they told him, as long as he failed to produce a single case of yellow fever that might reasonably be attributed to mosquito bite. There they had him stumped. For, whenever theory ended and scientific proof was called for, he was, and always had been, unable to carry his end of the argument.

Time after time during all those years he had al-

lowed a mosquito to drink its fill of blood from a yellow
fever patient and then watch it as it plunged its proboscis
into the skin of a healthy person. More than a hundred
times he had waited for the telltale yellow fever symptoms to appear, and every time he had waited in vain.
No reasonable person could blame the scoffers for remaining unconvinced, however plausible his theories
might sound and however greatly they might be drawn
to the man by his enthusiasm and his admirable personal qualities.

One of the skeptics was of course Gorgas, who had
met Dr. Finlay soon after his arrival in Havana and had
become his warm personal friend.

"Dr. Finlay is a most lovable man in character and
personality," he wrote some years later,

and no one could be constantly thrown with him as I was daily
for several years without becoming warmly attached to him and
forming the highest estimate of his scientific honesty and
straightforwardness. I can recollect in those years of our very
pleasant and cordial relations having spent a good many hours
trying to show Dr. Finlay the absurdity of his mosquito theory
of the transmission of yellow fever, but the doctor was a veteran
who had already had sixteen years' experience in meeting arguments of other men like myself who knew that his theory was
an absurdity, and he would not be convinced.

Fortunately for the hard-pressed Dr. Finlay, he and
his theory were soon to receive aid from a wholly unexpected source. This timely ally was Dr. Henry Rose
Carter, yellow fever expert of the Marine Hospital Service. For a long time Dr. Carter had been studiously seeking an answer to this question: How long after a case
of yellow fever develops in a building does that building
become dangerous for a nonimmune to enter? Incon-
clusive though his experiments had been, they had convinced him that this danger did not appear at once and
that therefore there was a period immediately following
exposure to this disease in which a building remained

uninfected. This conviction had grown stronger and stronger, although he still realized that the yellow fever cases under his observation had been both too small in number and too ill-suited to this type of study to constitute a particularly impressive argument in its support. Thus he was in much the same position as Dr. Finlay. Convinced himself, he lacked the means of convincing others.

But he worked on doggedly, sure that sometime, somehow, he would be able to give the doubters the proof they demanded. In that spirit he began making a first-hand study of a small yellow fever epidemic that broke out in the summer of 1898 in and near the town of Orwood, Mississippi. Unlike those he had previously studied, it was largely confined to a rural community in which each house was sufficiently removed from the others to enable him to study it separately. His study was just getting under way when he was transferred to another part of the country, but he was determined not to let his long-hoped-for opportunity pass. Before leaving he arranged with two local physicians to continue the house-by-house records he had begun.

Those records were completed in October, 1898, but Dr. Carter was unable to assemble this information and reach any conclusions regarding it until the winter of 1899-1900. Then he proudly proclaimed these important discoveries as the fruits of his labors: (1) that not a single case of yellow fever had developed among persons who entered those Mississippi farmhouses within ten days or two weeks after their occupants developed yellow fever; (2) that, on the other hand, a large percentage of those who entered those houses after that ten-day-to-two-week period developed the disease; and (3) that it was by no means necessary to come into contact with a yellow fever patient in order to contract this form of illness—that one could even wait until after the patient had died or recovered before visiting the house and still become infected. To this man of science, if not to others, all this meant that the yellow fever patient himself was not dangerous, except for the environment he created, and that even this danger did not exist until he had had the disease from ten days to two weeks.

Why this ten-day-to-two-week gap? How could one explain this period of noninfectiousness of a person suffering from one of the most infectious of all known illnesses? Dr. Carter was sure he knew the answer. Yellow fever, he was convinced, could not be contracted like influenza and measles by direct transfer of the germs from the sick to the well. Like malaria, this form of illness had to employ a third agency, which obviously did not become infectious immediately but in turn had to wait for the disease to develop in its own body before it could be transmitted to others.

Meanwhile, the growing seriousness of the yellow fever situation in Havana had caused Surgeon General George M. Sternberg to send a board of army medical officers headed by Major Walter Reed to Cuba to see what could be done about it, if anything. The task to which it was specifically assigned was to investigate the claims of an Italian scientist named Sanarelli who had recently created something of a sensation by announcing that he had discovered the organism responsible for yellow fever. In addition to Major Reed, this group consisted of Dr. James Carroll, Dr. Aristides Agramonte, and Dr. Jesse W. Lazear, not one of whom was then known to the general public.

The Reed Board soon disposed of the Sanarelli claim by proving that he had made no contribution whatsoever to the conquest of yellow fever. The organism which he claimed to have discovered was shown to have no causative relationship to the disease and was definitely identified as the long-known hog cholera bacillus. With that particular task behind them the members of the board began to look around for other ways of attacking the yellow fever problem.

Dr. Carter was acting as Havana's quarantine officer at the time, and naturally he and Major Reed were in frequent consultation. Gorgas and Finlay, both members of the commission to diagnose suspected yellow fever cases, were also participants in these consultations. It was inevitable that two enthusiasts like Finlay and Carter should do everything possible to bring the other members of the little group around to their way of thinking. Carter was more successful as a salesman of ideas than Finlay, who, for all his lovableness, lacked the personality for that sort of thing. Another thing greatly in Carter's favor of course—something which Finlay lacked —was the record he and his medical friends had kept of those Mississippi cases. Their tables spoke a language a scientist could understand, even though he might differ with Dr. Carter regarding their interpretation.

As time went on both Gorgas and Reed started wondering whether they had been right in condemning the mosquito theory as unsound. Gradually they began to concede that there might be something to it after all. Determined to find out, Reed got busy planning experiments of his own. He was called back to Washington, however, before they could get under way, and Dr. Lazear took charge. Delighted that his theory was at last to be put to the test, Dr. Finlay gladly turned over to him the mosquito eggs he had been growing for his own experiments. Then he waited impatiently for the results of the demonstration, supremely confident that they would bring him and his theory immediate and complete vindication.

In that, however, he was grievously disappointed. Although eleven persons were bitten by some of his mosquitoes in August, 1900, after the insects had bitten yellow fever patients, only two of them (Dr. Carroll and another volunteer) developed the disease—certainly not enough to convince anybody that the mosquito was responsible for the epidemic which was then causing

Gorgas such great concern. The experimenters were again plunged into dark discouragement. It seemed that they were off on the wrong track again.

A few weeks later, however, Dr. Lazear became seriously ill with yellow fever after allowing himself to be bitten by a mosquito. His condition rapidly became worse, and he died, a martyr to science if ever there was one, on September 25. Gorgas spent considerable time with him, and just before his friend went into the final delirium that ushered in his death, the Alabamian obtained a fairly coherent account of what had happened. Weak and wracked by fever as he was, Dr. Lazear went to great pains to emphasize that he had been bitten by a *Stegomyia*, the variety which Dr. Finlay had been accusing for years as the one responsible for the transmission of yellow fever.

Dr. Reed was shocked when news reached him of his friend's death. Returning to Havana, he set in motion a series of additional experiments and sent out a call for volunteers. Those taking part were promised the best of medical care should they develop yellow fever, immunity certificates after recovery, and two hundred and fifty dollars in cash. The offer was not open to anybody to whom these inducements might appeal of course. The successful applicants had to be carefully selected. It was not enough that they had never had yellow fever. They also had to be relative newcomers to Havana and to have resided previously in nonendemic areas so as not to have developed immunity to the disease from long-time association with it. This requirement automatically ruled out all local residents.

There remained only American soldiers and immigrants, most of whom had recently arrived from Spain. The latter at first seemed more interested than the former, as they had come to Cuba with the conviction that they would probably have yellow fever sooner or later and were strongly appealed to by the inducements offered, especially when they learned that the promised immunity certificates would enable them to receive twice as high wages as they could hope to earn as nonimmunes. So the application offices soon began to look like a corner of Spain itself.

After a while those inducements began to appeal pretty strongly to the Americans as well. Gradually it dawned upon them that they were passing up a good thing. They too were likely to develop yellow fever sooner or later even if they did not participate in the experiments, since they appeared destined to spend an indefinite time in Cuba. Being treated by the best yellow fever experts and enjoying nursing care rivaling that obtainable at the most expensive civilian hospital would beat having to take their chances as ordinary patients on the yellow fever wards. And what a gold mine two hundred and fifty dollars seemed to those drawing army pay! Truly those dirty, ignorant Spaniards had been getting something they didn't deserve—something good Americans wanted. The good Americans decided to do something about it.

Soon the Spanish immigrants, passing an old kiln near the Reed headquarters, began seeing things they had never seen there before—bones. About the same time they began hearing disconcerting rumors about them and why they were there. What they heard, thanks to the soldiers' cleverly staged rumor-spreading, was that those bones were all that was left of the men who had already participated in the Reed experiments. What they did not know was that the Americans had scoured the countryside in search of bones—any kind of bones— and placed them there in that old kiln in a war of nerves.

The ruse was highly successful. By the time the inspired rumors had made the rounds of the immigrant colony, two hundred and fifty dollars, free hospitalization, and immunity certificates had lost their appeal. With European competition at an end, the soldiers found a bull market for their services.

Not all of the Americans volunteering for those experiments were prompted by such sordid motives of course. It is remembered to their eternal credit and to the credit of the American Army that some were moved solely by a desire to help rid mankind of yellow fever. Conspicuous among this heroic group were John R. Kissinger and John J. Moran, who refused to accept a penny. Major though he was, Reed touched his hat and said: "Gentlemen, I salute you."

Camp Lazear, named for the martyred member of the Reed Board, quickly came into being. It was not a camp in the usual sense of the word but consisted of a small frame building, fourteen by twenty feet, carefully screened with wire netting so as to be absolutely mosquito-proof. This building was divided into two compartments of equal size separated only by a wire-net partition extending down the center. In order to prove that yellow fever germs were not carried by the wind, as many believed, care was taken to keep the entire structure well ventilated.

Meanwhile, Reed had obtained from Gorgas some interesting details regarding Dr. Lazear's illness and death. Among other things, he had learned that the *Stegomyia* mosquito which had infected Dr. Lazear had bitten a yellow fever patient within three days after that patient became ill and that ten days or longer had passed between the time that patient was bitten and the time Dr. Lazear received his fatal infection. Determined to put this knowledge to good use, Reed selected for his experiments only *Stegomyiae* which, at least ten days previously, had bitten persons who had just been admitted to the yellow fever wards of one of the Havana hospitals. After turning loose fifteen of them on one side of that wire-net partition, he admitted one nonimmune to that side and two other nonimmunes to the other side. Half an hour later the first man had been bitten seven times.

To insure his subject's being sufficiently infected, Reed had him returned to the mosquito-infested compartment a few hours later. He was then bitten five times. The next day he went back and was bitten three times. At the end of the fourth day he developed yellow fever, while the other two men, with only the wire-net partition between them and the mosquitoes, remained perfectly well. This proved, Reed contended, that the bite of the infected mosquito, and nothing else, caused the disease. But that was only the beginning of Reed's experiments, which Gorgas was watching with growing interest.

Reed's next step was to disinfect that infected room, not by the orthodox method of using powerful germicides to kill disease germs but by the revolutionary though simple one of capturing and removing those fifteen *Stegomyia* mosquitoes. To prove that no other form of disinfection was necessary, he placed nonimmunes in both rooms. The two men continued perfectly well. Reed, delighted, was sure he was making real progress at last.

These demonstrations were impressive, and even the skeptics began to be convinced. But, some of them contended, only a part of Dr. Finlay's thesis had been proved. Admitting that the *Stegomyia* transmitted yellow fever, what proof did he have that it was not also transmitted in other ways? Wasn't it also transmitted by contact with clothing and other objects which the yellow fever patient had infected? What was the major's answer to that?

He set about to find it. About eighty yards from the structure where the earlier experiments had been carried on another type of building began to take shape, small and so nearly airtight as to provide very little ventilation. Its screened windows and doors prevented mosquitoes placed inside from getting out and those on the outside from getting in.

Into this building Reed had orderlies carry one of

the most grisly collections of sickroom paraphernalia
ever assembled, all carted over from the yellow fever
hospital at Las Animas. There were mattresses on which
yellow fever patients had spent their last anguished
hours, foul with human excreta, body discharges, and
other products of this disease. There were sheets, pillows,
and pillowcases deeply colored with black vomit. There
were pajamas hastily removed from the bodies of those
who had just succumbed to yellow fever. Determined
to make the test conclusive and the results a complete
answer to those who might still have lingering doubts,
Dr. Reed asked the superintendent of the hospital to
see that basins of black vomit and other excreta from
yellow fever sufferers were poured over the gruesome
pile just before the experiment began. If that did not
make these things dangerous to touch, then nothing
could.

An attendant opened up the chests containing these
foul-smelling things, and Dr. Reed looked on while they
were scattered about the building. An officer and several
privates donned the dead men's soiled pajamas and spent
the next twenty nights in the building, sleeping on and
under the soiled bed clothing. To protect their general
health they were not required to stay there during the
day. Not a single one of them contracted yellow fever.
Not a suggestion of a case could be attributed to this
exposure.

Here was the dramatic proof Reed had been seeking.
Even the most determined skeptic had to admit that
only a miracle could have prevented practically all of
those nonimmunes from contracting yellow fever had it
been possible to contract it by contact with articles used
by its victims.

The Reed Board did not stop there, however. It had
entered a fascinating field of experimentation and was
determined to explore it farther. Blood taken from a
yellow fever patient within the first three days after the

onset of the disease was injected hypodermically into the blood stream of a nonimmune, who developed yellow fever a few days later. Thus it was demonstrated that the disease could be transmitted directly from the sick to the well, without the intervention of the mosquito. This thought then sprang into the agile minds of the investigators: Perhaps the blood of a yellow fever patient contained, not a parasite, but a toxin. They determined to find out.

Blood was taken from this second patient, also within three days after the onset of the disease, and injected into the arm of a third person, a nonimmune. Within the usual incubation period he too developed yellow fever. Thus it was proved that the virus in the patient's blood was capable of multiplying. Therefore it was a living germ and not just a toxin or chemical body.

Then the yellow fever sleuths struck at the enemy from another direction. Blood was taken from a patient, selected, like the others, because he had had yellow fever less than three days. However, instead of being injected at once into the arm of a nonimmune, it was passed through a Pasteur filter so fine that anything which could be seen under the most powerful microscope could not get through. Then it was injected into the bloodstream of a nonimmune, who developed yellow fever. Here then was another important bit of truth to be added to the Reed collection: The yellow fever germ is submicroscopic. There was no chance of studying it as one studies the malaria parasite or the tubercle bacillus. It had to be attacked, if at all, like other enemies that move about in the darkness of invisibility.

The Reed Board was not yet quite through. It had one more important experiment to make. This one was relatively simple. Still another yellow fever patient, less than three days sick, was asked to let these experimenters have some blood. It was heated to 55 degrees Centigrade and then injected into the arm of a nonimmune. He did not develop the disease. Then another sample of blood was taken and heated, and then a third, and a fourth. All were injected into the bloodstreams of non-immunes, and all failed to produce any symptoms of yellow fever. Thus the Reed knowledge chest received still another important item: The living germ in the blood of the yellow fever patient cannot survive a heat of 55 degrees Centigrade.

When at last the results of all these and other experiments were studied and their lessons digested, Reed had a complete answer to the baffling riddle that had so completely foiled Dr. Finlay and prevented him from winning converts to his theory. He had failed to take into account two vital conditions which must be present before mosquito transmission is possible, namely, that the mosquito must bite the yellow fever patient within the first three days of his illness, and that—as Dr. Carter had demonstrated indirectly in the Mississippi epidemic— the mosquito thus infected must then wait ten days or two weeks before biting the second person.

Complete vindication of his theory after all these years made Dr. Finlay a happy man. It made little difference to him that the Reed Board, rather than himself, had brought it about.

CHAPTER IV

Triumph in Havana

DURING ALL THESE epochal experiments Gorgas had remained modestly in the background—"a very interested spectator," as he once called himself. But with the end of this phase of the yellow fever campaign and the beginning of another he again assumed the leadership.

He and Reed, who had by now become warm personal friends, spent many hours discussing ways and means by which the knowledge just obtained might be put to practical use in ridding Havana of yellow fever. Almost the first conclusion they reached, rather a discouraging one, was that it appeared impossible to destroy enough adult *Stegomyia* mosquitoes to prevent them from causing periodic yellow fever epidemics. For Havana, their natural habitat, was full of them. It is no wonder that the two men shook their heads sadly and asked whether they were any nearer a solution of their greatest problem than they had been before Reed, Lazear, Agramonte, and Carroll left the mainland.

Remembering how extremely light the first two cases of yellow fever experienced by the Reed Board subjects had been, Gorgas decided to attack this disease in the same way that smallpox and typhoid fever have been attacked so successfully—by vaccination, or the development of artificial immunity through deliberately contracted light cases. So, early in 1901, a mosquito inoculation station was set up at Las Animas Hospital, with Dr. Juan Guiteras in charge, and the word went out that volunteers would receive such immunity free.

The Reed Board, as its last official act, presented to Gorgas and his Sanitary Department a solitary female *Stegomyia*, the only one it had left. Because of the cool February weather and its effect upon the supply of both mosquitoes and yellow fever cases with which to infect them, the continued life of this particular insect, who already had several yellow fever cases to her credit, was regarded as well-nigh essential to the uninterrupted progress of the yellow fever campaign. She was therefore looked upon as a valuable piece of property and indeed with something approaching veneration. To those working with and around her she became known as Her Ladyship.

Fearful lest the winter cold, so destructive of mosquito life generally, should prove too rigorous for Her Ladyship, Gorgas sent to the United States for an oil stove with which to heat the room where she was kept. In the center of the room, large and flooded with Havana's brightest sunshine, was placed a table on which was placed the large jar in which she was confined. On a string suspended from the top dangled a lump of white sugar, her chief article of diet. Occasionally, for variety, she was also treated to small pieces of banana. Water, kept fresh by frequent changes, was also within easy reach. To insure a plentiful supply of fresh air, a light but sufficiently strong covering of mosquito-netting was placed over the top of the jar in lieu of the usual metal cover. Every few minutes during the day some member of the staff would take a look to see that she was all right, and the highest official around the place, as well as the lowliest orderly, felt a personal responsibility for her well-being.

"When she dies," Gorgas told a friend and medical-school classmate, "we are preparing to have a grand funeral ceremony. I'll send you an invitation to be one of the chief mourners."

Her Ladyship's demise came sooner than either

Gorgas or any of the others anticipated. Early one morning she caught her wing in the mesh of the mosquito netting over her jar and struggled so desperately to free herself that, when discovered by a distressed attendant, she appeared at death's door. Gorgas dressed as quickly as possible when he heard the news and hurried to her. So did Dr. Ross and the others who shared his anxiety over her fate. With the aid of such a distinguished group of medical men as might be expected to battle for the life of a President or the occupant of a European or Asiatic throne, the valuable insect's wing was carefully liberated, and she herself was placed, like a priceless solitaire, on a soft bed of cotton. Attendants, prodded to unaccustomed activity by their own solicitude and by the urgings of their superiors, got the imported oil stove into quick operation, and soon the room was at above-summer temperature. But all these zealous efforts were fruitless. Her Ladyship went the way of less favored mosquitoes, dying about nine o'clock that morning. She is said to have had at her "bedside" when the end came more doctors and nurses than had ever gathered to make peaceful the last earthly hours of any human resident of the city of Havana, rich or poor.

The extreme measures taken to save the insect's life were found to have been justified when an effort was made to find another to take her place. This was entirely unsuccessful until after the new breeding season set in. In the meantime the vaccination work had to be suspended.

With several infected mosquitoes at last available, Gorgas and his fellow-workers allowed them to bite sixteen persons. Exactly half of them developed yellow fever. To his distress, several became dangerously ill, and no less than three died. One of the three was Miss Clara Maass, a nurse on the staff of Las Animas hospital, who had taken a deep interest in the experiments.

This was an entirely different result from what had

been so confidently expected. Obviously, some other means of dealing with the yellow fever problem must be discovered if Havana and the rest of the civilized world were to enjoy freedom from the disease. Gorgas began looking for it.

Acting on the knowledge that to spread yellow fever the mosquito must bite the patient within the first three days after the onset of the disease, he determined to prevent that from happening, if possible. To that end, he issued an official order requiring all suspected yellow fever cases to be reported at once to the Health Department. Cases thus reported were seen as soon as possible by a special diagnosis commission, and whenever it concluded that a suspected case was really yellow fever, the patient was required to make up his mind in a hurry whether he preferred to be taken to Las Animas hospital for treatment or to submit to the necessary procedures in his own home. If, in spite of the excellent treatment record made at Las Animas, he chose to remain where he was for the duration of his illness, then his home immediately ceased to be his castle and became instead a citadel of the Havana Department of Sanitation. Those permitted to visit him were obliged to enter and depart through a double door, or, more accurately, a set of single doors separated by a vestibule. Leaving nothing to chance or the whim of the patient or his family, the Department detailed men to twenty-four-hour duty, requiring them to sit in the vestibule on eight-hour shifts and see that no one but authorized persons visited the sick room. Equally important, these men saw to it that the outer door was firmly closed before the inner one was opened.

Theoretically, this was a perfect plan and certain to succeed. Actually, however, it proved disappointing and had very little effect upon the yellow fever situation because, in spite of the regulations, many cases were not reported promptly. A delay of even as little as two or three days, which was not at all unusual, could easily cause the infection of many mosquitoes, each capable, at the end of the usual period of incubation, of forging new links in the baffling chain of yellow fever infection.

To attack the enemy on still another front, Gorgas decided to pay more attention to the *Stegomyia,* without, however, relaxing his vigilance in trying to keep mosquitoes away from patients. Having spent much time in studying the peculiar habits of this particular member of the mosquito family, he knew that it tended to stay within a small area. (Dr. Carter's experiments in rural Mississippi had demonstrated that it was dangerous to be in a house where a yellow fever case had occurred even after the patient had died or recovered.) So he and his staff would wait until either death or recovery had brought a case to a close—which they were safe in doing, since the disease would run its course before a mosquito could become infectious after biting the patient—and then fumigate not only that particular house but also the houses on both sides of it. Fumigation was rather an elaborate procedure, beginning with the careful plugging of all cracks and crevices with paper and paste and ending with the burning of some product—usually sulphur or pyrethrum—to destroy the mosquitoes.

Although even the experts knew much less about the *Stegomyia* mosquito, or mosquitoes in general, in 1901 than the average person knows now who takes the trouble to do a little reading on the subject, Gorgas was aided greatly by a single bit of knowledge, i.e., that all mosquitoes pass through a so-called larval stage, lasting from eight to nine days, in which they must live in water. He realized, therefore, that collections of water were essential to their survival and development. Moreover, he knew enough about the *Stegomyia* to know that this particular kind of insect required a particular kind of water—not the brackish kind on which certain others thrive, or the kind found in the sheltered flow of slow-

moving streams, where still other types find ideal breeding places, but the kind one finds in commonplace receptacles in and around the average home. He was soon to
learn that the cisterns, tanks, and other containers in
which the easy-going people of Havana collected rain
water for domestic use were veritable *Stegomyia*
incubators.

Other peculiarities of the *Stegomyia* he also knew
well, peculiarities which set it off from the three thousand-odd other types as definitely as a cat or dog is distinguished from other members of the animal family.
Instead of merely showing a mild preference for places
inhabited by human beings, for instance, it has an extreme fondness for such places, such a strong one, in
fact, that it is almost never found anywhere else. You
can examine as carefully as you wish the premises of an
unoccupied house with its cisterns full to the brim of
rain water, but you will look in vain for *Stegomyia* mosquitoes in that neighborhood. But let a family move in,
and in almost no time these same cisterns will be swarming with larvae, and adult *Stegomyia* mosquitoes will be
flying all about the place as soon as they can reach that
stage. On the other hand, you look in vain for *Stegomyia*
larvae in streams, mud puddles, water-filled holes made
by animal hoofs, and such places, even though there may
be a dozen families living in the houses near by. But
leave a vase or pan containing water around the premises, and it will soon seem alive with *Stegomyia*. In brief,
the water in which the *Stegomyia* will lay its eggs must
be in artificial containers and must also be in or near
a building inhabited by human beings.

The *Stegomyia* is discriminating in another sense
too. It does not try to get its fill of blood just anywhere
on the body but heads straight for the ankles or the soft
tissue under the wrist. With an instinctive wisdom
denied to most of the other members of the insect family, it avoids the tough-skinned areas as carefully as a

general in wartime avoids the heavily fortified sectors of
the enemy's line.

And of course it is the female alone that bites, since
the male lacks the hard proboscis needed to cut into the
skin. Neither male nor female requires human blood
to sustain life. Fruit juices, nectar, and any number of
other products of a similar nature, usually readily available, are sufficient for that. But such are the mysterious
processes of reproduction that the female must have
human blood before she can lay her eggs.

Gorgas was interested in this mosquito's other characteristics, of course, because he was operating upon the
military plan of learning all you can about your enemy.
But he was most interested in its choice for egg-laying
purposes of water in artificial receptacles situated on the
premises of inhabited dwellings. Thanks to that, he
could concentrate upon fighting the *Stegomyia* where it
was known to be, instead of making a general assault
upon mosquito-breeding all over the city, an all but impossible task. His strategy thus decided upon, Gorgas
launched his attack, the like of which the world had
never known.

To their great surprise and disgruntlement, the
people of easy-going Havana awoke one morning to find
that it had become a misdemeanor to have mosquito
larvae on their premises. The city was divided into
twenty districts, and each district was placed in charge of
a Sanitary Department representative, who was required
to make a monthly inspection of every house in his territory and report immediately any violations of the regulations against mosquito-breeding.

Whenever conditions in or around a particular house
were reported as in flagrant violation of the anti-larvae
ordinance, Gorgas had authority under the law to im-
pose a fine upon that householder. This was collected
by the regular Cuban courts and deposited in the treas-

ury. In the interest of friendly feeling and a spirit of co-operation among the natives, however, it was provided that he could remit a fine whenever, in his opinion, the condition responsible for its imposition had been corrected. Being more interested in the improvement of sanitary conditions than in making more money available for Cuban politicians, he adopted a liberal policy in this respect, and actually very few fines remained unremitted. In fact only fifty of the approximately twenty-five hundred that were imposed during the last nine months of 1901—just 2 per cent—failed to go back sooner or later to those from whom they had been collected.

The usual procedure was to inform an offending householder that an inspector had discovered mosquito larvae on his premises and that he had been fined five dollars but that the fine would be returned as soon as the nuisance was abated. In all but a few cases this notice brought the offender to headquarters in a hurry with assurances that there were no longer any breeding places for mosquito larvae in or around his home. The sanitary officials would not take his word for it, of course, but would send an inspector to make another examination. If this showed sufficient improvement, the fine was remitted.

Occasionally the procedure was less simple than that. From time to time the recipient of a notice would ignore it, whereupon the fine was turned over to the judge of the district for collection. When this official's representative called and made it plain that he meant business, the offender usually became frightened and promised immediate correction of the condition. Upon this being satisfactorily carried out, as evidenced by an inspector's report, the action was dropped, and the offender had learned a good lesson in co-operation with the sanitary authorities.

The new regulations did not require the destruction or removal of all water receptacles. That would probably have brought on a revolution among the people Gorgas was trying to aid, for all but a very small percentage of them had no water for household use except that collected in rain barrels, while practically all of them had vases, basins of various kinds, and any number of other utensils in which water was kept for purposes of beauty, utility, and convenience. His objective was more direct—to prevent these receptacles, large and small, from becoming breeding places for *Stegomyia* mosquitoes.

Gorgas ordered that all rain water receptacles be constructed in such a way that mosquitoes could not have access to them. To meet that requirement, the tops were completely covered save for a small opening left for the admission of rain. This opening itself was covered with wire netting, and at the bottom of every receptacle workmen attached a spigot so that the water could easily be drawn off without tilting the barrel. Carpenters were kept on hand at all times for this purpose, being paid out of public funds.

This of course was a fairly simple task and easy of accomplishment, as it was little trouble to spot and cover large outside rain barrels and cisterns. The problem became more difficult, however, when the anti-mosquito campaign moved indoors. Here a host of troubles arose to plague the inspectors and others engaged in the work.

The city was again divided into districts, eight of them this time, and again each district was put in charge of an inspector, whose main job was not, as before, to report violations of the sanitary regulations but to cooperate with householders in the observance of these regulations and to instruct them as patiently as possible regarding ways and means to prevent mosquito breeding. He was required, for instance, to call attention to the serious potentialities of the harmless-appearing earthen vessels in which practically every Havana family kept its drinking water—ideal breeding places and certain to contain many larvae, if neglected. Then he was required to empty them, deliver a brief dissertation on the breeding habits of mosquitoes, and explain that mosquito propagation would be impossible if all vessels were emptied once a day and the accumulated larvae carefully washed out. He also had to make a careful survey of the houses and premises to ferret out other mosquito incubators—things like flower pots, tin cans, and those small glass cups in which table legs and bed posts were kept immersed in water to prevent ants from reaching them. As the campaign got under way, it was found that roof gutters had to be watched carefully, as they proved to be prolific breeding places for the *Stegomyiae*. Leaves from near-by trees would fall on the roofs and collect in the gutters, forming miniature dams that blocked the flow of water and created artificial pools. These often did not disappear until long after the rains had ceased.

Mosquito larvae have to come to the surface of the water to breathe, and this necessity proved of the greatest value to Gorgas and his workers in their campaign of extermination. Seizing upon it, they poured a thin film of kerosene upon the surface of water which they found it impracticable to pour out. Then, when the air-hungry larvae would rise toward the surface for a good breath of air, they would encounter this oil, draw it into their breathing tubes, and die of suffocation. This procedure Gorgas called "very effective."

The work of the mosquito inspectors also earned his commendation, not only because it too was "very effective" but also because it was carried on under almost unimaginable difficulties. Even in the all too infrequent instances when the householders co-operated wholeheartedly, there were any number of breeding places which escaped the most watchful eye. A case in point was that of a Havana physician, who severely condemned the whole campaign as a complete failure because his own house was still full of mosquitoes, although he had gone to the greatest pains to see that every container around the place was emptied. Gorgas turned the matter over to one of his assistants, who accompanied the doctor to his home and made a minute inspection. That done, the assistant was as completely baffled as the physician, for not a single particle of water had been revealed. Returning doggedly to the search, he happened to think of a box of books, which it would have required a tremendous exercise of the imagination to associate with mosquitoes. Upon unpacking it he found at the bottom a paint bucket containing, not paint, but water. The female *Stegomyia*, impelled by the same sort of brute intelligence which enables her to select the tenderest part of the human body for her raid for blood, had followed a labyrinthian course between, around, and over the closely packed books to this all but inaccessible container. There she had laid her eggs. In due time her multitudinous progeny had been hatched, had spent the requisite number of days in the larval stage, and, pursuing an equally labyrinthian course, had emerged into the wide expanse of the doctor's dwelling.

This particular doctor had the public-spirited intelligence and community-mindedness of the professional man of his class. There were others like him, and of course they made Gorgas's work much easier than it otherwise would have been. But they represented only a small minority of the total population. Those of the lower social and economic levels gave him a world of trouble. By the very nature of their task, his representatives had to make demands upon the people which they could hardly be expected not to resent. It is not surprising that they became vocal with indignation when told that they had to destroy all possible sources of mosquito breeding, especially when they found how seriously this would interfere with their normal habits and conveniences. They would not have been the easygoing Latins they were had they not become resentful toward these meddlesome foreigners who were telling them what they had to do and threatening them with fines for infractions of rules which they regarded as the very essence of unreasonableness.

That the work of cleaning up the city went ahead in spite of all this was due almost entirely to Gorgas himself. Having studied the Latin temperament, he knew how to deal with it. More important, he was able to bring into play the gentleness of manner and long-suffering patience which had characterized him during his years as an army doctor, caring for the sick and wounded in far-flung frontier communities. His office was always wide open to anyone with any kind of grievance, whether real or imagined; and he was never too busy to explain in great detail why it was necessary to enforce the regulations against which his visitors were protesting. And seldom indeed did he fail to win a convert. Hot-headed Cubans would approach him in a mood of angry rebellion and depart ten minutes or half an hour later as docile and smiling as you please, eager to co-operate with the health officials. The Gorgas patience, the Gorgas gentleness, and the Gorgas persuasiveness worked miracles during those trying months in Havana.

Nor did he wait for people to come to him. As often as his regular duties permitted, which was surprisingly often in view of the heavy burden he was carrying, he would stroll about the city, now here, now there, to be sure that none of his inspectors had overlooked any possible breeding place for the elusive *Stegomyiae*. Whenever he had time, he would go calling upon these people, not as a captious official looking for trouble, but as a kindly visitor trying to make friends with the people of the city and doing his best to lighten the hardships inevitably imposed by the agency which he headed. In those unexpected visits he never missed an occasion to tell housewives and children about the work he was doing and the great advantages that would accrue to

them from the extermination of yellow fever. Their
reaction, on the whole, was gratifying indeed, and Gorgas
became one of the most popular men in Cuba.

This of course made infinitely easier the task of
those entrusted with the enforcement of the sanitary
regulations and had an excellent effect upon the reduction of the city's mosquito population. An inspection
made under his supervision in January, 1901, just on
the eve of his campaign, revealed no less than twenty-
six thousand mosquito-breeding places within the city
limits. One year later, when a second survey was made,
these larva hatcheries had been reduced to a mere three
hundred.

Such a drastic reduction could be expected to have
only one result, a sharp decrease in the prevalence of
yellow fever. And that is exactly what occurred. For
a full decade prior to the American occupation, yellow
fever had killed an average of nearly 500 people in
Havana every year. In 1900, two years after the city
came under American control, there had been 310 yellow fever deaths. From 1762 backward for two centuries
the Cuban capital had been visited periodically by devastating epidemics, and between 1762 and 1901 we have
it on the word of Gorgas himself, who had made a careful study of the mortality statistics, that "there probably
was not a single day when Havana did not have a case
of this disease within its bounds."

Yet as early as May 22, 1901, Gorgas was able to
write to Reed, then in Washington:

The fever situation is all that could be desired, I think. The
last death from yellow fever occured on March 13. Since that
time we have had a case April 21st, another on April 22nd. We
had no more cases then till May 6th, when we had one; and on
May 7 three more. Since that time, two weeks, we have had no
more; and, as the conditions, as far as non-immunes are concerned, seem more favorable for the spread of yellow fever, I
am in high fettle.

But that was only the beginning of the story of the conquest of yellow fever in Havana. Some five months later, on October 8, he had even better news for Reed:

"Our last case occurred September 26. Ten days without a case, this time of year, is pretty good. . . . Yellow fever in Havana will soon be a thing of the past."

In that cheering observation, Gorgas erred seriously on the side of understatement. For not only was yellow fever soon to be a thing of the past in Havana, but, even as he wrote that optimistic prophesy, it already was a thing of the past. That case of which he wrote was to prove the last to occur in 1901 and also the last for all time up to the present, except for one or two outbreaks which were quickly suppressed by prompt reimposition of measures based upon the Gorgas technique of 1901. With those minor exceptions, yellow fever ceased to be a factor in the health of the people of Cuba's capital city on September 26, 1901.

Never for a moment did Gorgas permit himself or any member of his staff to forget that they were engaged primarily in combat with the yellow fever mosquito. However, their warfare was by no means limited to that type. Rivaling the success of the campaign against the *Stegomyia* was that of the drive against the malaria-transmitting *Anopheles*. This latter campaign, less dramatic and spectacular than the other one, nevertheless would have been sufficient in itself to earn for Gorgas the undying gratitude of the people of Havana.

Strangely enough, in the light of the widely held impression that yellow fever constituted the only really serious disease problem there, the fact is that between 1898 and 1900, inclusive, malaria deaths outnumbered yellow fever deaths by nearly six to one (3,141 deaths due to malaria and only 549 due to yellow fever). Havana's yellow fever had been widely publicized and its malaria had not. Hence the misconception.

Like the story of Gorgas's conquest of yellow fever,

the story of his success in subjugating malaria is best
told in the language of normally dull vital statistics.
From an average of 1,047 a year in 1898-1900, malaria
deaths dropped precipitately to only 151 in 1901, 77 in
1902, and an average of only 44 a year for the decade
following the turn of the century. By 1912 they had
dropped to only four a year. In view of the fact that the
best hospitals in all Cuba were situated in the capital
city and its reputation as a health-building center had
caused the sick from all parts of the island to go there
for treatment, Gorgas was undoubtedly correct in insist-
ing that these four deaths were undoubtedly those of
nonresidents and that by 1912 malaria had become as
completely extinguished in Havana as had yellow fever
in 1902. By this time of course Gorgas himself had
moved on to other fields of battle, but the procedures he
had put into effect deserve the credit.

The success of the campaign against malaria was by
no means just a fortunate by-product of the drive against
yellow fever. True though it is that both diseases are
spread by the mosquito, there are, as already pointed out,
mosquitoes and mosquitoes, more than three thousand
varieties of them, some as different in their habits and
physical characteristics as the bear and the dog. The
campaign against the malaria-transmitting *Anopheles,*
therefore, had to be, and was, an entirely different sort
of campaign from that waged so energetically against the
yellow-fever-spreading *Stegomyia.* For the most part,
it was carried on in the suburbs because it is in such
areas of the city and in rural sections that one finds the
slow-moving, shaded streams which form the breeding
places of the silent, quick-striking *Anopheles.*

Personal credit, whether for the extinction of yellow
fever or for the conquest of malaria, was one of the
things in which Gorgas was little interested. He never
missed an opportunity to insist that he had had no part
at all, except as an interested spectator, in the mosquito-

incriminating work of the Reed Board. For Reed himself he had the greatest admiration, and this admiration
was fully returned. Of his own part in the great work,
he had this to say:

It seems almost providential that we had all the machinery
at hand whereby the discoveries of the Reed Board could be
immediately tested and demonstrated. Here was a large city of
250,000 inhabitants in which yellow fever had been endemic
for one hundred and fifty years. . . . Dr. Reed himself later
was strongly impressed with the advantage it had been to him
to have his discoveries given so thorough and conspicuous a test
and wrote me to that effect many times.

Two incidents reveal the extent of Gorgas's admiration for Reed. Some time after the mosquito battle of
Havana came to an end and Gorgas and his soldiers of
health had evacuated the city, he was walking down
one of the principal streets of our nation's capital when
he met a friend of his accompanied by the friend's young
granddaughter.

"This," said the friend, a high-ranking army officer,
"is General Gorgas, one of our great men."

But Gorgas would not have it thus.

"No, my child," he objected, "not a great man. Merely one who is trying to follow in the footsteps of a great
man, Walter Reed."

The other incident was related by one of Gorgas's
greatest admirers in his home state. Speaking at a meeting of University of Alabama alumni in 1921, Dr. Seale
Harris, of Birmingham, told of the unveiling, in the
presence of the man it honored, of a bronze bust of
Gorgas which had been placed in the Army Medical
Library in Washington.

Dr. Harris described Gorgas's extreme embarrassment as he squirmed and tried to retain his composure
under a heavy barrage of praise from the Secretary of
War and other distinguished speakers and how, after
the flood of laudatory eloquence had ceased, the recipient

of all these encomiums, still ill at ease, thanked them all
from a full heart. Then, said Dr. Harris, Gorgas pointed
to a portrait of Walter Reed and told the small assembly:
"While you have been praising me, I have been thinking
that, had it not been for the discoveries of Reed, my
efforts would have availed nothing."

Reed's admiration for Gorgas was no less great or
sincere. On June 27, 1901, he wrote enthusiastically:
"When I think of the absence of yellow fever from Havana for a period of fifty days, I begin to feel like re-
joicing that I was born. . . . You are doing a splendid
work for your corps and profession in Havana." On
July 29 of that year he wrote:

That you have succeeded in throttling the epidemic [of yellow fever] appears to be beyond question and is to your ever-
lasting credit as an energetic Health Officer, who saw his opportunity and grasped it. A man of less discretion, enthusiasm
and energy would have made a fiasco of it. . . . All honor to
you, my dear boy! Thank God that the Medical Department
of the U. S. Army, which got such a "black eye" during the
Spanish-American War, has during the past year accomplished
work that will always remain to its eternal credit!

I was simply delighted with your annual report. What a
glorious record! No wonder, my dear boy, that you should grow
eloquent in your closing paragraph. It made my heart beat
faster as I read it. You have done a splendid work in Havana,
my dear Gorgas, one that should always give you the greatest
pleasure to look back upon. You have my sincere admiration
and congratulations.

Others also were enthusiastic in their praise of
Gorgas for the remarkable job he had done. By special
act of Congress, he was promoted from major to colonel,
and, while the measure was awaiting Congressional approval, General Leonard Wood wrote as follows to Senator Edmund W. Pettus in support of the proposed
advancement:

It gives me great pleasure, as Major Gorgas' commanding
officer for the past two and a half years, to most earnestly in-

vite your favorable consideration to the recognition, as proposed
in this bill, of the excellent work performed by Major Gorgas
as chief sanitary officer of the City of Havana, a work of inestimable value not only to the inhabitants of the city and island,
but to the inhabitants of the southern states.

Secretary of War Elihu Root wrote in his annual
report for 1902:

Especial credit is due also to the Medical Department of the
Army and particularly Major Walter Reed and Major William
C. Gorgas for their extraordinary service in ridding the island of
yellow fever, described in my last report. . . . The brilliant character of this achievement, its inestimable value to mankind, the
saving of thousands of lives and the deliverance of the Atlantic
seacoast from constant apprehension demand special recognition
from the Government of the United States.

Although his brilliant sanitary achievements had reflected great credit upon the United States Army, the
somewhat embarrassed recipient of all this praise could
not forget that he was the son of one of the men who
had fought against that army in 1861-1865, or that he
himself, as an impressionable child, had lived in the
South during those trying years of the war and the
equally trying years of Reconstruction. How little he
had changed in his sympathies, as between the two sides
in that memorable struggle, he revealed in a hitherto
unpublished letter written from Havana during the
latter stages of the yellow fever campaign. After telling
his mother about the success of that campaign he wrote:

Let me have the Confederate cross. I will wear it on the
outside of my full dress coat. Because I wear the blue now does
not make me any the less an ardent Confederate. I differ from
most Southern men. I regret deeply that the Confederacy failed.
It seems to me that the Southern people would have been infinitely better off. We would have been one of the world powers
and would gradually have abolished slavery and our people
would have gone on increasing their wealth. As it is, the intelligence of the country has been impoverished and everything
that our people can save is taxed away for the benefit of the
Northern states.

The result of the war has been unfortunate for the North too. They have lost all patriotism. The men who fought the war have banded together purely for the purpose of plundering the treasury. I refer to the Grand Army. And the protective tariff has caused the concentration of wealth in few hands and the impoverishment of the masses.

But the matter was settled by the war and it seems hopeless to think of setting up a republic of our own now, and we just have to drift with tied hands to the destruction [to] which, it seems to me, our country is plunging. But let us cherish in every way the memory of those who gave up all for the Lost Cause, a cause which, if it had succeeded, I think, would have saved civilization from the destruction to which it is at present so rapidly drifting.

You promised when I was last at home to let me know when I could get those pictures of Lee and Jackson and one of Father in his Confederate uniform.

Obviously, the highly honored and middle-aged Major William C. Gorgas, U. S. A., was still a later model of the Willie Gorgas who mounted a toy cannon on the roof of his father's Richmond home and took pot shots at the Yankees.

CHAPTER V

The White Man's Graveyard

ON NOVEMBER 18, 1903, just fifteen days after Panama won complete independence from Colombia, Secretary of State John Hay and the new republic's first minister to Washington signed the Panama Canal Convention, giving the United States government the right to construct an interoceanic waterway across the Isthmus of Panama. After its ratification by the provisional Panamanian government and the United States Senate, it was officially proclaimed as in full effect on February 24, 1904. With the surmounting of that major obstacle, which had thwarted this nation and numerous others for decades, plans went ahead confidently for the construction of the canal.

But the last major problem involved in carrying out such a great undertaking had by no means been solved. Obtaining the right to construct the canal across Panamanian territory was one thing. Actually constructing the canal was something else. The French also had won the right to build a canal but had failed to do so. What assurance did the United States have that the diseases which had brought defeat to those earlier canal-diggers —particularly yellow fever and malaria—would not also defeat this ambitious new effort?

How many Frenchmen died during that ambitious but cursed attempt to link the two oceans is not known. It will never be known. For those who knew, if anybody knew, went to great pains to keep the knowledge from the people of France, to whom they looked for the golden flood of francs with which to continue the hopeless ven-

ture as long as possible. The effort to misrepresent the
mortality from yellow fever was especially flagrant, deaths
known to have been due to this disease having been
attributed to others lest the people back at home—
peasants and bankers alike—lose faith in the enterprise
and shut off that golden stream. Notwithstanding this
effort at suppression, however, an inquiring world has
learned something about the true state of these canal
workers' health—enough to enable it to get a fairly good
idea of the wretched conditions under which they lived
and labored.

M. Philippe Bunau-Varilla, one of the ablest of the
Frenchmen sent to Panama to help push the canal
through to completion, once declared that one fourth of
all those engaged in the venture succumbed to yellow
fever alone. How many of them were carried to their
graves by malaria and other agents of death he did not
say.

"We have no means of telling what was the sick rate
with the French during the period of construction under
the old French Company, from 1881 to 1889, but we
know that it was very large," Gorgas wrote in 1918. He
was convinced by "the best statistics which I could get
on the Isthmus" that the French lost every year by
death from yellow fever "about one-third of their white
force" and figured that, on an average day, one French
workman out of every three was disabled by illness. It
is no wonder that, in spite of the desperate effort at con-
cealment and the barefaced juggling of facts and figures
in the published reports, disturbing bits of truth made
their way across the Atlantic and that the venture finally
received its death sentence.

However, the story of that vain struggle against disease and death on the Isthmus of Panama can best be
told, not in mortality statistics of questionable reliabil-
ity, but in the experiences of some of those who were
there.

"In all the world there is not perhaps concentrated

in any single spot so much swindling and villainy, so much foul disease, such a hideous dung heap of physical and moral abomination," declared James Anthony Froude in 1885, referring, of course, to Panama. "The Isthmus is a damp, tropical jungle, intensely hot, swarming with mosquitoes, snakes, alligators, scorpions, and centipedes; the home, even as Nature made it, of yellow fever, typhus and dysentery."

Visitors to Panama were told about the two seasons—the wet season, lasting roughly from the middle of April to the middle of December, when people would die of yellow fever in four or five days, and the dry season, from mid-December to mid-April, when it took a much shorter time, usually from twenty-four to thirty-six hours.

When De Lesseps, builder of the Suez Canal and organizer of the French company, made his first visit to Panama in 1881, a fellow-countryman of his then living there tried to dissuade him from going ahead with the enterprise. Should he persist, the other man warned him, "there will not be trees enough on the Isthmus to make crosses for the graves of your laborers." Subsequent events showed that his friend had not greatly exaggerated the killing power of tropical illness.

Funeral trains became "as much an institution as passenger or freight trains," and "death was constantly gathering its harvest" while M. Bunau-Varilla labored on amid the increasing gloom. Thousands upon thousands of his fellow-workers were buried in a single cemetery, which he saw grow like a boom town in an oil rush. For weeks at a time burials there numbered from thirty to forty a day. The director of works, gravely ill, was forced to return to France, and M. Bunau-Varilla had to assume the burden of general administration with a working force decimated by disease and desertions induced by disease. Two talented engineers were sent him from Paris to lighten his so recently increased task, but fifteen days after their arrival both of them were taken to the cemetery after falling victims to yellow fever.

"The most erudite and devoted physicians must content themselves with administering, not remedies which will check the progress of the malady, but simple palliatives, the effects of which are more moral than real," he observed sadly as he contemplated the apparent futility of his own and others' efforts to cope with the onsweeping terror.

Out of each hundred individuals arriving on the Isthmus, it is no exaggeration to say that, on an average, not more than twenty were able to keep at their posts in the construction camp. And of this number how few—although preserving the minimum of health which was strictly necessary—had not lost some of their courage.

In his *Deux Ans à Panama,* M. Cermoise tells about a happy group of thirteen that sat down for dinner at the home of M. Henri Bionne, a gifted writer and speaker employed by the French company. Seventeen days later, while en route to France, the host developed yellow fever and died before reaching the end of his journey. Another member of that gay party took his wife and children to Colon, put them on board a steamer, and returned to Panama the same evening. The next day he developed yellow fever and succumbed to it a short time later. Finally a third member of M. Bionne's dinner party felt those telltale symptoms. And, like the other two, he died.

You still hear occasionally about "La Folie Dingler," which was much discussed on the Isthmus just after the Americans took over. Jules Dingler, one of the engineers the French placed in charge of the canal-digging, arrived in 1883. Scorning yellow fever and the other diseases that were playing havoc with the men working under him, he determined to set up here on the edge of the tropical jungle a mode of living modeled after that which means so much to the Frenchman at home. He selected with great care a site that could have been matched only with great difficulty along France's own famed Azure Coast. And on that perfect site, as far as beauty was concerned, he built a dream castle, where, he fondly planned, he, Mme Dingler, and their children would entertain their friends on a lavish Old World scale. But that was not to be, because, while this house of his dreams was being built, all the other members of his family were attacked by yellow fever. Not one escaped the disease or the death that so often accompanied it. And Dingler Castle remained a sardonic reminder of the wrecking of a man's dreams and the breaking up of a happy family. Dingler himself, crushed and grief-stricken, returned to France, dying shortly afterward.

Even the incomplete, deliberately misleading French records show that the Dingler experience, while perhaps unusual, was duplicated, except in detail, any number of times. Out of a railroad official's family of five, including himself, three died. A single ship arrived at the Isthmus bringing seventeen French engineers, only one of whom lived to return to his native land. Twenty out of twenty-five Sisters of Charity who began their duties at the Ancon hospital at the same time succumbed to the ever-present agent of death. In September, 1884, twenty sailors died of yellow fever in Colon harbor. Only a single member of the crew of a British brig was alive when the epidemic subsided. During the same epidemic 160 yellow fever cases occurred among the white men of the coast city, two out of every three resulting fatally. In the light of all this, is it surprising that to the Frenchmen at Panama this part of the world became known as "the white man's graveyard"?

After some eight years of struggle against innumerable difficulties, the conqueror of Suez and his army of workmen admitted that they were beaten. The battle of Panama—men against germs—ended in victory for the latter. The men packed up as much of their equipment as they considered it practicable to move back to France and hauled it to the coast for transfer to the waiting ships. The rest of it they left behind to rust and fall to pieces, solemn reminders of their defeat at the hands of their invisible enemies. And they left behind their dead, French warriors who had fallen in this long battle that had ended so disastrously.

This tragic lesson was not lost upon at least some of those who looked ahead to the time when American engineering genius and American workmen would be doing battle with the perils and pitfalls of the Panamanian jungles. To anyone who took the trouble to study the French debacle and the reasons for it, it was crystal-clear that there would certainly be an American debacle at Panama too unless sanitation received a great deal more attention than it had received in the past.

A few of those who could see this most clearly began a quiet campaign in behalf of Gorgas's appointment as a member of the Isthmian Canal Commission as soon as it became evident that the United States government was going to build the canal—even before it obtained from Panama the right to do so. The sanitation-conscious American Medical Association was particularly active in urging his claim to membership as a suitable reward for his work in Havana and as the best possible assurance that the all-important sanitation would receive full consideration in the canal-building program. Although his supporters could obtain no promise of his appointment to such a high post, it was generally assumed from the beginning that he would play an important part in the work of pushing the canal-construction work through to success.

In the fall of 1902, more than a year before the Panamanian revolution obligingly opened the door to the acquisition of full construction rights, Gorgas was relieved of duty at Havana and ordered back to the United States. This was done so that he might familiarize himself with the preparations already being made for the monumental engineering enterprise upon which the government was soon to embark.

News of his impending departure brought sincere and freely expressed regret to the people of Cuba. Forgotten, or at least cheerfully forgiven, were the inconveniences and the upsetting of cherished practices by the Gorgasmen, whose chief had instructed them to be firm, as well as courteous. Remembered—and remembered with gratitude—were the inescapable evidences of their work—evidences such as vastly improved health conditions, greatly increased prosperity blossoming from the swift inflow of tourists who were glad to visit Havana as soon as they were convinced that the disease curse of the centuries had been exorcised, and better living conditions generally. And, thanks to the Gorgas fondness for knowing people and his unaffected interest in them and their problems—in part a product of his small-town boyhood and in part an inheritance from his mother— many of them, important and humble, had grown to know him personally and like him immensely. One of the fruits of that great liking was an editorial in the Havana *Post*. After referring to the orders that had just come for his departure, it declared:

It is no exaggeration to say that no official, however popular and efficient he may have been, who has figured in the reconstruction of Cuba since the beginning of the American occupation, has left the island with such gratitude and good wishes as follow Major Gorgas.

He had also won golden opinions from his fellow-countrymen, especially those who had come to know him in the sick-room and on the yellow fever wards. A veteran of the Spanish-American War wrote to the editor of an American newspaper:

I occupied quarters at an American rooming house on Monserate Street. A man who was taken ill suddenly was reported to headquarters. An attaché of the health department, a contract doctor, was sent to investigate. He entered the house abruptly, visited the patient, and before leaving reprimanded us severely for not according him more attention and consideration, which, he said, were due him as our superior. The irate medico reported a suspicious case and in a short while Gorgas entered. The courtesy he showed on entering caused every man to rise and salute. With that smile he inherited from his mother, he admonished us to leave off the salute. He deplored the necessity of our isolation for a few days and departed with an expression on his countenance which impressed us with a feeling that we had come in contact with "the noblest Roman of them all."

As part of his preparation for his new responsibilities Gorgas was sent as the official representative of the United States Army to the first Egyptian Medical Congress and was instructed to stay in Egypt long enough to study the sanitary problems encountered in the construction of the Suez Canal. He returned home by way of Italy and France and while in the latter country talked to many engineers, medical men, and others about the part played by health conditions in the failure of the French attempt to link the Atlantic and Pacific oceans at Panama.

When he arrived back in the United States, he was even more firmly convinced than when he left that American wealth and American engineering skill would prove as ineffective in pushing the ambitious Panama Canal project through to completion as French wealth and French engineering skill had been, unless his fellow-countrymen were more successful than their predecessors in the curbing of disease, especially yellow fever and malaria.

Others, unfortunately, did not agree with him. Most of them conceded that sanitation and health-protection generally were important, but there was very little support for his contention that this aspect of the enterprise should be accorded an importance equal to that accorded engineering and administration. The effort of the American Medical Association to have him made a member of the Canal Commission was entirely fruitless. Instead he became merely the chief sanitary officer, occupying a position of distinctly secondary importance and exercising little real authority.

Those responsible for determining the membership of the Canal Commission were not satisfied with denying him and every other medical man a place at its council table. They, deliberately or otherwise, "packed" it with men whose entire backgrounds showed that they had little interest in health. At its head as chairman they placed Rear Admiral John G. Walker (retired). To serve with him they named Major General George W. Davis (retired); William B. Parsons, builder of the New York subway; William H. Burr, a Columbia University civil engineering professor; and Benjamin H. Harrod, Carl E. Grunsky, and Frank T. Hecker, all civil engineers. General Davis was appointed the first Civil Governor of the Canal Zone, and John F. Wallace, one-time general manager of the Illinois Central Railroad, became chief engineer.

Although naturally disappointed over the membership of the Canal Commission, those who realized how important sanitation was to the success of the venture assumed that it would receive proper support. They certainly had no reason then to suspect an official hostility to it. The realization that such hostility did exist came slowly.

An inkling of what lay ahead was not long in showing itself. It came some time before Gorgas sailed for the Isthmus in June, 1904, after making a preliminary visit there to look things over. He then learned, with a heart-chilling sense of foreboding, that the staff of assistants which his official superiors proposed to furnish him was much smaller than the absolute minimum he believed to be demanded by the size of the job to be done.

But that was not all. Time and time again Gorgas pleaded with Admiral Walker for permission to take with him an adequate supply of wire screen, cloth, disinfectants, and the other articles he knew would be needed for an immediate attack upon the disease germs. This, he was convinced, was essential to a proper start and would prevent the sacrifice of many lives. But the admiral gave him a cold and unrelenting refusal.

"Go on with your party to Panama," he told him. "Look the situation over. See what you'll need. Then make out an order for it. We'll see that you get it promptly."

In vain did Gorgas protest that he had just returned from Panama, that he had devoted considerable time to a study of the situation there, and that the list he had submitted was based upon needs clearly apparent from that study. The admiral again told him to go on to the Isthmus and do as he had been instructed. He made it clear that he expected from Gorgas the same kind of "Yes, sir" obedience to which he had been accustomed from his naval subordinates.

Thus balked at the outset, Gorgas had little choice except to do as he was told. He proceeded to Panama with his pitifully small party of helpers, trying to keep himself and them cheered up but suffering all the time from a gnawing realization that he was virtually being sent into battle without arms or ammunition. As he walked the deck of his steamer and tossed fitfully in his berth late at night, trying to get to sleep, he wondered if he had not been unwise to let the Canal Commission chairman have his way so completely. He could have defied the old sea dog. He could have refused to put a foot on the gangplank until he was assured that those all-important supplies had been stored away in the ship's hold. But he was a soldier. And obedience to authority ranked high in the soldier's code. He would hope for the best.

After landing he lost no time in giving Admiral Walker a chance to keep his promise about getting supplies to him as quickly as possible. Convinced that the list he had prepared during his earlier visit needed no changes, he immediately had someone make a neat new copy and saw that it was mailed to his official superiors in the nation's capital. But again he was to see how little they were interested in sanitation in Panama.

Joseph L. LePrince, who later spent many years on the malaria control staff of the United States Public Health Service, was in that group of unarmed disease-fighters who went ashore in mid-1904. He was with Gorgas for a long time afterward. And he had plenty of experience with broken official promises.

"That list," he said, "apparently glued itself to an invisible spot somewhere in Washington. We waited expectantly, with the patience of angels, for that shipment." And they waited and waited, while the mills of governmental red tape and official disinterest ground with maddening slowness.

CHAPTER VI

The Enemy Returns

THAT SMALL GROUP of new arrivals—Gorgas, Mr. LePrince, Dr. Carter, and the others—found that the old villain, yellow fever, was then putting on a good-behavior act, as though for their special benefit. The narrow strip of land which Panama had recently turned over to the United States for canal-building purposes seemed as free from the disease as anyone could have wished it to be. Undoubtedly this fact was largely responsible for the determined unwillingness of the canal authorities to pay much attention to sanitation or be in any hurry to send wire screens and other supplies urgently requested by the worried chief sanitary officer. With an optimism based upon ignorance, they believed that the present favorable health conditions would continue indefinitely and that, in spite of the French experience, yellow fever would not prove a serious obstacle to the construction of the canal after all.

But Gorgas knew better. Hadn't yellow fever been comparatively rare a short time prior to the start of his sanitary campaign in Havana several years before, only to burst forth, apparently out of nowhere, into one of the most devastating epidemics the city had ever experienced? Hadn't other yellow fever centers witnessed this same peculiarity of the disease? Hadn't they too enjoyed periods during which cases were almost as infrequent as in regions outside the yellow fever belt? Hadn't the population of the Isthmus, since the departure of the French, consisted almost entirely of native Panamanians who, like the natives of Havana, had developed a large

degree of immunity to it? Hadn't yellow fever therefore
virtually disappeared from Panama for the same reason
that it had previously declined to relative unimportance
in Havana—because it had found little fuel upon which
to feed? And, by that same token, would it not blaze
forth like the proverbial forest fire as soon as thousands
of nonimmunes—manual laborers, white collar workers,
administrative assistants, and others—flocked there from
all over the world? His knowledge of all these things
was back of Gorgas's insistent appeals to Washington for
the instruments of war for use in the battle which he
knew was inevitable.

"From the very beginning insuperable difficulties
arose in the way of getting supplies," he wrote several
years later. "Very little could be obtained on the
Isthmus, and the supply departments in the United
States were so slow in being organized that, during the
first year, very few requisitions that were sent to the
United States were filled."

This complaint was actually a model of understatement. Had he been less charitable he would have lashed
out at the obstructionists hindering his work and endangering the success of the great enterprise from their
cool, luxurious offices in the nation's capital. He would
have criticized bitterly the tragic farce of attempting a
sanitary job of this magnitude with a staff of only eight
persons, including himself—excellent leaders but utterly
lacking in personnel to carry out the program they
wished to get under way. He would have told of the
peremptory suggestion to "get a few niggers" when he
insisted upon some laborers to prevent the whole business from falling to pieces. He would have called public
attention to the reply he received to a cabled request for
urgently needed supplies—a message telling him curtly
that cablegrams were expensive and ordering him there-
after to use the mails.

"From the very beginning the Commission underestimated the magnitude of the sanitary operations, as well as their cost, and when the sanitary authorities urged upon them more extensive preparation and larger expenditure, they thought us visionary and more or less lost confidence in us," he once observed. "This was very unfortunate both for the sanitary authorities and for the Commission, and came very near being the cause of the complete collapse of sanitation."

How very near this Washington-directed policy of niggardliness and obstruction actually did come to causing the complete collapse of sanitation few people know, even now. Even fewer knew then. In fairness to the Washington bureaucrats, whose official shortcomings were many and grievous, it must be admitted that all of Gorgas's troubles were by no means chargeable to them. There was a maddening maze of red tape and incompetence on the Isthmus too.

Here is just one example of it, as observed by W. Leon Pepperman, who spent considerable time in Panama. Two hundred "service cocks" were urgently needed in the installation of the new water system for the city of Panama. In accordance with the usual practice, a formal requisition was presented to the storekeeper, who, however, replied that he could not furnish them. Thereupon they were ordered by cable from Washington. A day or two later the division engineer whose operations were being interfered with by the delay happened to be in the storehouse and, to his great surprise, saw about ten times as many "service cocks" as he had asked for. When he called upon the storekeeper for an explanation, the latter replied that he was required to keep two thousand on hand at all times and, since filling the requisition would have reduced his stock below that number, he had refused to fill it.

But it was the absentee-management men in far-away Washington who contributed most to Gorgas's discomfiture. Typical of his relations with the group as a whole were those with the Commission chairman during the latter's infrequent visits to Panama. Day after day, Gorgas complained bitterly, he would go to Admiral Walker with requisitions for seriously needed supplies and equipment. Instead of acting upon them immediately, the Admiral would have to "talk the matter over." Then he would get started on a dissertation about expenses and how necessary it was to save every dollar possible. And somewhere in his long exposition he would say: "Gorgas, there is one thing certain. Whether we build that canal or not, we will leave things so fixed that those fellows up on the hill can't find anything in the shape of graft after us." Then "he would take my requisition and stick it in a drawer." There it would remain indefinitely.

Obviously, the graft and waste which had contributed so much to the collapse of the French attempt to dig the canal had made a deep impression upon the admiral. As he indicated to others as well as Gorgas, he was determined, even at the risk of endangering the success of the whole enterprise, to take extreme measures to avoid those things as long as he was chairman of the Canal Commission.

But the full explanation of the admiral's lack of cooperation with Gorgas cannot be found in a determination to lean over backward to avoid extravagance and graft. Equally weighty was his cocksure conviction—in the face of an abundance of evidence that should at least have made a sizable dent in the prejudices of a reasonable man—that the mosquito played no part whatsoever in the prevalence of yellow fever. In vain did Gorgas spend hours piling proof on top of proof to convince him that he was wrong and that the mosquito-transmission theory was right. Walker would listen courteously and, at the conclusion of the Gorgas discourse, laugh violently, just as an adult might laugh at the fantastic theories of a child. It was not the mosqui-

toes that constituted the chief yellow fever peril in
Panama, he would insist, but filth. Clean up Panama and
Colon, he would argue, and there would be no danger
of yellow fever.

Patiently, vigorously, and ineffectively would Gorgas
remind him that Havana, some six years before, also had
been reeking with bad odors; that filth, dead animals,
decaying vegetables, and rotting food had all but blocked
its streets; that all this had been cleaned up, making
Havana as nearly perfect from this point of view as a
city could be; and that—how well he remembered this
and the effect upon his own peace of mind!—yellow
fever had continued to reap its rich harvest of human
lives. Every session with Admiral Walker brought added
evidence that his mind was tightly closed to all suggestions contrary to his own preconceived opinions.

Gorgas's letters to Admiral Walker and his fellow-
commissioners were even less fruitful, if possible, than
his interviews. When they were answered at all, it was
only after a long delay, and the admiral's replies were
plainly those of a man who did not speak Gorgas's language in matters of sanitation. At last, after several
months of this sort of thing, Gorgas made up his mind
to go to Washington and try to accomplish a miracle of
official mind-changing.

But there was another reason why he wished to
make that trip. Mrs. Gorgas had been stricken by a
serious malady which appeared to make her death a
matter of only a few months. She was then in New
York receiving treatment, but the doctors' reports were
far from encouraging. He was not willing to weight the
scales even more heavily against her recovery by having
her return to an unhealthful place like Panama. At the
same time he rebelled at the thought of being away from
her during those few short months of life which seemed
left to her. The obstinacy of his official superiors would
only have challenged his fighting spirit and added to his

determination to see this thing through, in spite of red tape, indifference, Admiral Walker, and all the other dragons in his path. But here was something else that had to be considered. He had written to a member of his family as early as August 15:

> The work is great work and very attractive to me, though I am much discouraged at starting. The Commission have their own ideas of sanitation and do not seem much impressed by mine. If I had myself alone to consider, I would stick it out. The work, even as it is, is much more important than anything I am likely to get in the United States; but with the probability of Marie's having only a year or two of life, I do not want her to lightly bury herself down here. If she does stay here, there should at least be some compensating advantage. So, when I go on, we are going to have some earnest talks and, if Marie agrees, I will ask to be relieved of these duties.

During that leave of absence, much of it spent in fruitless pleas for better co-operation from the higher-ups, he did have some "earnest talks" with his sick wife. We do not know the details of those talks, but we do know the outcome. Sick as she was, she insisted that he must not be influenced by her condition, that if he wanted to stay on the job he had undertaken so hopefully, he should do so. Pooh-poohing his unwillingness to let her "lightly bury herself down here," she prepared to accompany him on the return trip. The fate of the Panama Canal quite possibly hung upon that decision. Fortunately, it did not cost her her life. Instead of succumbing within a year or two, as the doctors feared, she survived her husband.

The labor battalions and white collar workers, hardly any of whom were immune to yellow fever, began arriving in 1904 and increased rapidly during the following winter and spring. And, as Gorgas had expected, the sullen armed truce between the disease and those inhabiting that narrow strip between the oceans came to an end. As time went on, it became more and more evident that the Isthmus of Panama was experiencing one of the worst yellow fever epidemics in its history. The morale of the workers, already under heavy pressure from the rapid spread of the disease among their fellows, received a particularly hard blow from the deaths of several highly placed officials. As the ever-alert Gorgas was quick to observe, "the rank and file of the men began to believe that they were doomed just as had been the French before them."

There was no satisfaction of the "I told you so" variety, or any other variety, for Gorgas in seeing his worst predictions rapidly coming true. For he realized what their coming true would almost certainly mean. His constant warning that this would happen would be conveniently forgotten by those who should have heeded it, and he would probably be blamed as mercilessly as if he had done nothing to prevent the outbreak. Even worse, if possible, the entire canal-digging project would be exposed to grave jeopardy. Worry drove sleep away while he watched the swift development of a virtual stampede among the disease-terrorized workmen. Some five hundred Americans, to say nothing of persons of other nationalities, quit their jobs and left Panama during April, May, and June, 1905.

Probably the only thing that prevented a tie-up of work on the canal was the high cost of transportation back home. The regular fare from Colon to New York was seventy-five dollars, but canal workers returning to the United States on brief leaves of absence were entitled to a special rate of only twenty dollars. Finding it impossible to raise the larger amount, some solved the problem by obtaining leaves of absence, taking advantage of the reduced rates on the ground that they were still members of the canal personnel, and failing to return.

Needless to say, those who remained on their jobs, whether from a sense of duty or a lack of funds, were far from contented. Many expressed their discontent by rebellious outbursts. In others the grimness of the situation was relieved greatly by a sense of humor. The observant Mr. Pepperman tells about a Commissary Department clerk who would sing snatches from the famous camp-meeting hymn beginning:

> There's a land that is fairer than day,
> And by faith we can see it afar. . . .

A casual passer-by, hearing just this much of the song, would naturally have assumed that the song-singing clerk was thinking of the celestial city which had inspired its author. However, such an assumption would have been altogether incorrect. For there would follow these words of that clerk's own composition: "Add seventy-five dollars to faith and you get there by a United Fruit Company boat."

Newspaper stories and returning travelers kept the American people fully informed and greatly concerned about yellow fever conditions on the Isthmus. Among those contributing to the general anxiety was John Barrett, retiring American minister to Panama, who told New York reporters a distressing story about the failure to solve the yellow fever problem.

"Despite the efforts of the present sanitary staff under the skillful guidance of Colonel Gorgas," he said, "yellow fever seems no nearer to being stamped out than it was a year ago. We have had more cases of the dread disease during the last thirty days than during any corresponding period for ten months."

Nor was the Gorgas peace of mind improved by editorial comment like this from the New York *Tribune*:

> It appears that the yellow fever scare on the Isthmus of Panama has not abated and that conditions are serious there. This appeared yesterday in the return by the Panama Line Steamship *Seguranca* of thirty young men who went to work for the Canal Commission. All were coming home because they were alarmed over the fever scare.

Although yellow fever was principally responsible for the panic which gripped the workmen, it was by no

means the sole cause. Bubonic plague added to the
anxieties of Gorgas and the others doing their best to
stem this onrushing flood of sickness and death. As conditions grew worse and worse, funeral processions became
about as commonplace as steam shovels, and the churches
were in almost constant demand for funeral services.
The demand for coffins—one item for which requisitions
were filled promptly—became so great that several of
these symbols of death were constantly to be seen piled
in doleful uniformity on the station platforms along the
Panama Railroad right-of-way. To remove this added
strain upon the workers' morale, the authorities finally
sent out orders that in the future they must be kept away
from public sight.

Coffins, indeed, played a big role in the lives of
America's canal-diggers during those months when it
appeared that disease and death were about to repeat
their early victory at Panama. Mr. Pepperman tells
about the arrival of five members of the Canal Commission after spending a week on a ship where the main
topic of conversation was the unhappy lot of those brave,
or foolhardy, enough to live on the Isthmus. As these
commissioners started down the gangplank, they saw five
mahogany caskets near a pile of coffins of more simple
design. They became somewhat perturbed when they
noticed that the ornate five had been stacked in dignified
array near their own baggage.

"Why," one of the big men inquired of a workman,
"are those caskets placed with our trunks?"

The employee sensed the anxiety behind the question
and increased, rather than allayed, it with his reply:

"Five commissioners, five superior coffins—a specula-
tion on the part of the undertaker."

A slightly different version of this incident—which
may or may not have actually occurred but at least illustrates the grim humor of those disease-darkened times—
has been told by Gorgas himself. According to his ver-

sion, it was Major LaGarde and not a dock employee who made this reply, not to five commissioners, but to six. Answering a question similar to that propounded in the Pepperman version, Major LaGarde is reported to have said with an air of great seriousness:

"Mr. Burr* didn't come down, you know."

Another anecdote born of those yellow-fever-ridden days and nights at Panama also had to do with Major LaGarde and somber symbols of death, though not with expensive mahogany ones like those just mentioned. Living in an atmosphere heavy with depressing talk of the disease and the deaths of its victims, officials and laborers alike soon developed a fever-phobia which kept them on the alert for the telltale symptoms. Particularly inclined that way was the current governor of the Canal Zone, General Charles E. Magoon. Feeling, or imagining he felt, illness coming on, he consulted Major LaGarde, who gave him an examination and put him to bed, with the admonition to stay there until told to get up. Wracked by his fears, General Magoon donned his pajamas in the unhappy mental state of a prisoner being shaved for his execution and prepared to lie down on what he regarded as his deathbed.

Life had been good to him, and that part of Panama, in spite of its yellow fever and death, was beautiful. Certain as he was that his own demise would come with the morrow, if not before, he felt a great urge to take a final look at it all before lying down for the last time. So he walked unsteadily to the window and looked out. What he saw was not the setting sun dipping into an expanse of blue water, or the beautiful trees for which that country was famous, or the luxuriant foliage that swung in graceful loops from their branches, or ships, or carriages, or people—not any of these things, but a somber black hearse. Jumping, naturally enough, to the conclusion that it had been stationed there by the method-

* The seventh member of the commission.

ical Major LaGarde to take the Magoon corpse to the
undertaker's, the frightened official quickly lost what
lingering hope he might have had of lasting beyond the
morrow, and with a groan, yielded to the imprisonment
of his bed. It was not until the next morning that he
learned the truth—that the hearse had been sent to take
away the body of a workman.

It was expressive of the state of the public mind
that coffins had become the subject of jests and that
people found a grim, sardonic humor in telling about
them. These jests failed to amuse the hard-pressed
Gorgas. At the time the stories were current he was in
little mood to be amused. He could not see the rapidly
increasing yellow fever deaths and the growing apprehension of those who remained on the job in spite of
them without having it impressed upon him time and
again how dangerously close the great Panama Canal
venture was approaching complete collapse. For he knew
what many others, including callous Washington bureaucrats, failed to grasp—that the inability to maintain a
reasonable measure of health among the workmen could
have no other result. And how bitter was the thought
that, unless yellow fever and the other killing and disabling diseases could be curbed before long, the full
weight of official blame would fall upon him, however
unjustly and however eloquently he might plead that
no one could have done any better with the supplies and
equipment doled out in such niggardly fashion by his
official superiors.

How woefully unavailing were Gorgas's efforts to
break through the steel wall of official disinterest and
how hopelessly the work of the Sanitary Department was
enmeshed in governmental red tape were known at the
time only to him and to the handful of others struggling
with this superhuman task. It was not until later that
these things were revealed to an astonished and indignant
public in the United States.

Here are just a few instances of the endless formalities which he found so destructive of efficiency:

An insane woman gave birth to a child. For obvious reasons, she could not be trusted to nurse her baby. The only thing to do, of course, was to obtain a nursing bottle and nipple—an extremely simple procedure, it would seem. But when the nurse applied to Major LaGarde for them, he had no choice but to turn down the request temporarily. For the nursing bottles and nipples requisitioned five months before had not yet arrived. So Major LaGarde made out a special requisition—one nursing bottle and one nipple—and took it to Gorgas for his endorsement. Then while the hungry infant waited for its milk, the requisition went to the chief of the Bureau of Materials and Supplies for his endorsement. Then it had to be copied and engrossed. Finally, two days after it became apparent that that particular infant would have to depend upon a nursing bottle and nipple for the means of sustaining life, a messenger was sent to a drug store to make the purchase. The records fail to reveal whether the child died of hunger before the simple but essential articles were delivered or, if not, what measures were resorted to to keep it alive during the two days of waiting and bowing to the exigencies of bureaucratic red tape. It was revealed, however, or at least estimated, that the cost of this nursing bottle and nipple was boosted by this complicated maze of official O. K.'s from the normal price of about thirty cents to a sum somewhat in excess of six dollars and fifty cents.

A second new-born baby and a second badly needed nipple also figured in this saga of bureaucratic inefficiency. Mr. LePrince tells about them:

There was so much constant delay in obtaining supplies needed to meet emergencies that even when a baby was born and needed a nipple at once for his milk bottle, the husky little chap yelled like thunder while nine copies of the requisition were made out, and he had the opportunity of yelling for about nine months more before that requisition caused the nipple to arrive on the hospital grounds. Whether or not he suddenly became quiet from surprise-shock when the nipple arrived, I cannot tell you, as I was not present when it came. The receivers had a task to trace the one-in-a-million paper bearing the requisition.

Then there was the matter of buying X-ray equipment for the Ancon hospital. Several months after the usual requisition for it had been sent on its way Washington-ward, but before the high and mighty members of the Commission had gotten around to giving it their attention and approval, the X-ray expert who had been employed to operate this equipment happened to be in the nation's capital and, as an act of courtesy and co-operation, requested permission to select the Crookes tubes which it would require. The request was peremptorily turned down. The visitor from Panama then repeated it, this time more vigorously, pointing out that his technical knowledge would be more helpful in making a proper selection than the limited information regarding the good and bad points of Crookes tubes possessed by the average purchasing agent. To add force to his appeal, he called attention to the fact that Panama was considerably distant from the United States and it would involve much time and expense to return material of this kind if it should be found upon arrival to be unsatisfactory. However, this reasoning made no impression whatsoever upon the official disinclination to grant the requested permission, and he was dismissed with the admonition to return the tubes sent if they should prove unsuitable. And they were unsuitable when they finally did arrive, after another long delay.

The Engineering Department was specifically authorized to exercise a certain amount of discretion in the choice of materials and supplies, but that discretion was denied the Sanitary Department. The laws of the Canal Zone provided severe penalties for any pharmacist found guilty of substituting one drug for another called for in a prescription, but those filling requisitions for medicines for canal employees made little or no effort to send what was wanted. Gorgas was accused, under circumstances that must have been extremely humiliating, of being disrespectful to those of higher rank when he asked for the reasonably prompt filling of requisitions for urgently needed materials. When he submitted an estimate of the cost of emergency hospitals, the Commission changed his figures. To carry through a drainage project and other malaria-control activities, he asked for twenty inspectors but got only eight. He asked for screens to mosquito-proof all the buildings in the Canal Zone—a wise move in the light of what he had learned at Havana—but the Commission, scorning the mosquito theory of yellow fever and malaria transmission, turned down the request. Thereupon he tried to obtain sufficient screening for the porches at Ancon Hospital at least. But the Commission rejected that request too, offering an alternative plan. Besides plainly revealing a dismal noncomprehension of hospital procedure, it called for an expenditure amounting to about ten times the cost of the screening that Gorgas had recommended.

Gorgas asked for a chief clerk at a salary of eighteen hundred dollars a year, hoping to obtain the services of a person who had done outstanding work with him in Cuba. The pound-foolish members of the Commission cut the annual compensation by three hundred dollars, and the man Gorgas had in mind for the job was not interested at that salary. So the best he could do was to hire a wholly inexperienced man. A similar request for permission to employ, at five thousand dollars a year, a health officer for the city of Panama was approved with the proviso that only three thousand dollars a year would be available for his salary. The result, as in the case of the chief clerk, was that the man he had in mind, a veteran of the Cuban health service, could not be employed;

and this important work was turned over to a virtual amateur. When he asked for one hundred properly trained nurses to care for the patients at Ancon and Colon hospitals, he received only forty, along with permission to establish a training school where green girls would be expected to work for extremely low wages in return for nursing instruction and experience. This of course left unsolved the pressing problem of staffing those two hospitals with well-trained nurses. He asked to be allowed to pay fifty dollars a month for trained attendants and orderlies. His recommended rate of compensation was reduced to twenty-five dollars a month for the trained attendants and fifteen dollars a month for orderlies. As a consequence, the only persons who would take the jobs were totally inexperienced, inefficient natives, who often proved a greater nuisance than help to the doctors. Approval of his recommendation for the prompt sanitary control of the cities of Panama and Colon was withheld for a long time on one flimsy pretext after another and was not given until after yellow fever had actually developed. To protect the laborers against the widely prevalent hookworm, he recommended a system of removable latrines for use in the larger labor camps. Only one member of the Commission even deigned to express an opinion regarding the recommendation, and it was unfavorable. That gentleman expatiated upon his disapproval to the extent of informing those interested that he was something of an authority on certain tropical countries and that in those countries sanitation as Gorgas interpreted it was unheard of—that buzzards and swine had proved entirely satisfactory in disposing of body wastes.

Gorgas requested permission to remodel a building at Toboga so that it might be used as a convalescent hospital and asked for personnel to man it. He hoped in that way to make room at the regular hospitals for more serious cases. A considerable sum was authorized for remodeling the structure but none for the employment of personnel. Months later the well-equipped but unstaffed hospital was still being occupied only by a caretaker, while convalescents crowded the other hospitals and greatly reduced their capacity to care for the seriously sick. Replying to a request for personnel to operate an institution soon to be opened for the care of lepers and the insane, the Commission authorized the transfer to that service of a physician and a nurse but made no provision whatsoever for replacement personnel in the institution from which they were to be transferred. When it became apparent that a serious yellow fever epidemic was under way, Gorgas asked for a general appropriation to be expended at his discretion in meeting the mounting need. This request was peremptorily refused. He then requested permission to order directly from a reputable medical supply firm in New York drugs and other supplies costing not more than thirty thousand dollars during the first month of the epidemic and up to fifteen thousand dollars a month as long as, in his judgment, the yellow fever situation should make such expenditures necessary. This request was likewise refused. Substituting its own remedy for the one Gorgas had recommended, the Commission instructed the Bureau of Materials and Supplies to make such purchases as might be needed. Eight months later, when the yellow fever epidemic had had plenty of time to run its course and claim its full harvest of victims, these supplies were still missing.

Windows and doors for the hospital at Culebra, requisitioned in January, had failed to arrive in March. Material to floor the porch of another hospital, also requisitioned in January, was likewise missing in March. Consequently, it was necessary to continue to carry the sick, by a roundabout route, upstairs and downstairs and through open parts of the institution whenever they had to be moved from one ward to another—a simple, easy

procedure had the missing floor been in place. Screens
were requested for the district hospitals to which yellow
fever patients and others were sent before being transferred to the larger central hospitals. Gorgas's superiors
in Washington turned down the request on the ground
that the screens were not necessary. He asked for materials needed in the disinfection of buildings, an all-
important part of his anti-yellow fever and anti-malaria
work. The request was approved only after the Commission had reduced by 75 per cent the amount requested. Even this pitiful 25 per cent was supplied in
such small quantities that its effectiveness was greatly
impaired.

Gorgas asked for fifteen thousand dollars for the
equipping of a research laboratory, plus a very small
sum—about one hundred and forty dollars a year—for
maintenance. (It was planned to staff it with personnel
detailed from duty at Ancon.) The Commission's answer
was a stern refusal. He asked that an ambulance be kept
on the hospital grounds at Ancon for quick service in
emergencies. The higher-ups insisted that another plan
of their own be followed. As a result, prompt responses
to ambulance calls were out of the question, emergency
or no emergency. He urged that, in order to attract the
type of doctors needed, annual salaries of eighteen hundred dollars be offered those beginning service in the
Canal Zone. In the interest of what passed for economy,
the Commission rejected this proposal and offered one
of its own—that hospitals be largely staffed by interns
rather than physicians, and that their salaries be fixed
at fifty dollars a month. Anyone in a position to know
the true situation could have foreseen the inevitable result: the complete impossibility of establishing a permanent, capable staff of well-trained, experienced medical
men and the necessity of substituting therefor a shifting
group of immature youngsters, none qualified to assume
a doctor's professional responsibilities and all looking

forward impatiently to their return to the United States at the end of their one-year internships.

Sometimes this sort of thing strained the Gorgas patience almost to the breaking point. But the Gorgas genius for saying the right thing under trying circumstances often saved the situation.

That priceless Gorgas gift was demonstrated when he complained to a certain official about the withholding of funds for an important sanitary project. That gentleman, as much opposed to the Gorgas conception of sanitation as most of the others with whom the long-suffering sanitarian had to deal, stubbornly stuck to his refusal to approve the requisition.

"Why," he contended militantly, "it's silly to spend all this money just to kill a few mosquitoes."

The Gorgas mind worked fast. In a flash, the Gorgas tongue shot back: "But, Sir, suppose one of those mosquitoes should bite you and give you a fatal case of yellow fever. Just think what a serious blow that would be to the building of the canal."

The mulishness that had prevented that official from seeing the wisdom of the mosquito theory also prevented him from seeing that Gorgas was pulling his leg. Greatly flattered, he withdrew his objections and approved the requisition.

Gorgas's harassments, unfortunately, were not limited to a yellow fever epidemic rapidly getting out of hand and to a completely unconcealed determination on the part of his official superiors to block his program at every turn. He also had to contend with Latin-American politicians.

Although the American sanitation authorities exercised considerable theoretical power in the matter of formulating and enforcing regulations for the protection of health throughout the Canal Zone, there was a vast lack of enthusiasm for those regulations among local officials. In many cases this was covert and was discovered

only when the enforcement machinery encountered difficulties. In others there was no secret about it, the un-
enthusiastic officials admitting their disinterest with
quite disarming candor.

"You and your ordinances!" the mayor of the city of
Panama once protested to Mr. LePrince. "Don't you
know the meaning of our local politics yet? Aren't you
aware that, if I enforce the sanitary regulations against
yellow fever mosquitoes, I'll lose the next election? And
are you not aware that I've held office through revolution after revolution? Can't you think of future elec-
tions? I will politely receive your requests, but I absolutely will not enforce any new ordinances, laws or regulations if doing so would be likely to interfere with
future votes."

While local dignitaries worried about "future votes"
and the scornful among Gorgas's fellow-countrymen
made fun of the mosquito theory, the log jam of Washington lethargy remained unbroken; and yellow fever
kept up its triumphant sweep. The outlook appeared
dark indeed for the ambitious canal project as the American experience with mounting disease and death seemed
about to duplicate, with slight variations, the French
experience. This was a cruelly bitter, discouraging time
for William C. Gorgas.

As a general thing, he kept his worries and fears to
himself. One of the most considerate of men, he did not
like to burden other people with his troubles. So he
struggled along with a thousand difficulties and did his
best, in his own quiet, efficient way, to overcome the ter-
rific handicaps under which he was obliged to work.
But he was only partially successful in keeping his
troubles secret. Those who knew him best knew almost
as well as he did how much he was worrying.

Outwardly unperturbed though he appeared, a
slight mannerism gave away the truth. From time to

time his observant intimates would hear him whistling softly under his breath. It might be an aria from grand opera. It might be the chorus, or just a snatch of the chorus, of a currently popular song. It might be a remembered line or two from a mountain ballad or a Negro spiritual learned years before in Richmond or Brierfield. But whatever it happened to be, they knew what it meant: a new and serious worry had arisen to torment him.

CHAPTER VII

Help from the A. M. A.

UNFORTUNATELY, local officials more interested in "future votes" than in sanitation were not the only persons in Panama who made duty a nightmare to Gorgas. His troubles were also vastly increased by the non-co-operative attitude of General George W. Davis, Governor of the Canal Zone and the only member of the Canal Commission who resided there, the others being satisfied with occasional brief visits.

One would naturally assume that his close association with the chief sanitary officer, his frequent opportunities to see the sanitation problem at first hand, and his great personal stake in maintaining good health conditions there would have made him a whole-hearted supporter of the effort to repeat at Panama the sanitary success attained at Havana. It was Gorgas's great misfortune that they did not.

As an engineer, General Davis stood in the forefront of an honored profession, and the magnificent Washington Monument, which he completed, will stand through countless generations as a monument also to his engineering genius. But, like his Washington-residing fellow-commissioners, he had no enthusiasm whatsoever for the work Gorgas was trying to do and insisted that money needed for sanitation would be much better spent if devoted to other phases of the canal-building enterprise. And he went to great pains to let people, especially Gorgas, know that he had no faith whatsoever in the mosquito-transmission theory. To his pre-Walter Reed way of thinking, as to Admiral Walker's, yellow fever was due to one thing and that alone—filth. Whenever Gorgas would tell him about his Havana experience and cite it as proof that the mosquito-transmission theory had justified itself, he would get no response at all except continued disbelief and a willingness to argue the matter till Kingdom Come.

"I'm your friend, Gorgas, and I'm trying to set you right," he would say. "On the mosquito you are simply wild. Get the idea out of your head. We all know that yellow fever is caused by filth."

Taking their cue from their superiors, those in immediate charge of operations also went to great pains to show their contempt for the mosquito theory and their conviction that Gorgas and those who agreed with him were mild cranks trying to waste the public's money on impractical schemes that had nothing at all to do with canal-building. Among them was a certain cocksure young architect. When Mr. LePrince called his attention to some broken places in a screen in the Administration Building and pointed to doors and windows that did not fit tightly, making it easy for mosquitoes to enter and leave the building at will, he showed not the slightest interest and no intention of having them repaired. Rebuffed but not discouraged, Mr. LePrince called his attention to them again and again. Becoming nettled, the cocksure young architect showed plainly that he was getting tired of the subject and considered the other man an obnoxious meddler.

"What if there are twenty deaths in this building?" Mr. LePrince demanded. "Who will be responsible for them?"

"Oh, I'll take that responsibility," the confident young architect promised, his manner that of someone betting on a sure thing.

We do not know whether the twenty Administration Building deaths which Mr. LePrince feared actually materialized. It is a matter of record, however, that

this young man with such a great contempt for mosquitoes was one of a number of persons in his office who
developed yellow fever and succumbed to it less than a
month after his haughty refusal to have the screens,
doors, and windows repaired.

Naturally, the deaths of those who sneered at the
mosquito-transmission theory brought Gorgas no satisfaction. Although every death was a potent argument in
his favor and weakened the arguments of his critics, it
also made more difficult his task of preventing the epidemic from getting entirely out of control. Too, he did
not seek vindication in such fashion.

Fortunately, another kind of vindication was just
around the corner, one which eventually was to give him
much satisfaction. The hand that brought it was that
of Dr. Charles A. L. Reed, of Cincinnati, one of the
country's most eminent surgeons, a close personal friend
of the Secretary of War and future President, William
H. Taft, a former president of the American Medical
Association, and, at the time we are considering, chairman of its Legislative Committee.

Having been rebuffed in their recommendation that
Gorgas be made a member of the Canal Commission and
disturbed by reports regarding the health of canal workers, officers of the A.M.A. quietly sent Dr. Reed to Panama with instructions to find out the truth about conditions there and tell his professional brothers and official
Washington about them in a complete report. Arriving
in Colon on February 7, 1905, he told very few persons
the real purpose of his visit but moved about the Zone
with eyes wide open, asking questions and seeing things
for himself. Quietly taking his leave fifteen days after
his arrival, he completed his report in time for its sub-
mission to Secretary Taft on March 1. Its publication in
varying degrees of completeness in newspapers from
coast to coast created a national sensation and brought
forcibly to the consciousness of the newspaper-reading

public the magnitude of the task which Gorgas and his associates had undertaken. Even more important, it emphasized the additional difficulties which the sanitary officials were encountering as a result of the non-co-operation and hostility of the Canal Commission, one member of which was spotlighted for special condemnation.

"As a result of this investigation," Dr. Reed told the Secretary of War,

I became impressed with the efficiency and the zeal of the sanitary staff; with the fact that very much has been accomplished in the way of sanitation under exceedingly adverse circumstances; that much remains to be done which cannot be done unless better facilities are afforded; and that very much more ought to be done and would have been done if the facilities had been properly furnished.

Having paid this warm tribute to Gorgas and his associates, Dr. Reed turned quickly from praise to blame and directed his attack at the shortcomings of the Commission, especially those of Commissioner Carl E. Grunsky. This part of the report was so withering in its criticism that it stands virtually alone in the entire annals of medicine. So long was it that it filled nearly six pages of small type when published later in the *Journal of the American Medical Association,* causing the reader to feel amazement that, in slightly more than two weeks, a single pair of eyes and ears could have seen and heard so much that was unfavorable to the Commission.

The Commission, "more especially Mr. Grunsky," was charged with robbing Gorgas of authority which should have been his by virtue of the job he was doing and which it had been the expressed wish of President Roosevelt that he exercise freely. As a result, the report declared, the chief sanitary officer had been made "subordinate in the seventh degree" to the original source of authority, specifically, to the Governor of the Canal Zone, the chief disbursing officer, the chief of the Bureau of Materials and Supplies, Commissioner Grunsky, the Canal Commission, the Secretary of War, and, finally, the President.

And this is the state of affairs on the Isthmus today. One can not but be impressed with the anomalous condition by which a man of Colonel Gorgas's distinction, the foremost authority in the world in solving the peculiar problems that are connected with sanitation on the Isthmus, being made a subordinate of a whole series of subordinates who are confessedly ignorant of the very questions with which he is most familiar.

The result of this humiliating subordination, made worse by bureaucratic red tape, is pictured in a paragraph subheaded "How the Machine Does Not Work":

It is interesting to inquire into the working of this wonderful mechanism. Thus, if Major LaGarde, superintendent of Ancon Hospital, makes a requisition for supplies, he must make it in due form, take it for approval to the chief sanitary officer, then to the governor of the zone, then to the chief disbursing officer; whence it goes to the commission at Washington; then to Mr. Grunsky as committeeman; then back to the commission; then, if allowed, bids are advertised for; awards made; the requisition is filled under the supervision of a purchasing agent notoriously ignorant of the character and quality of medical and surgical supplies; the material is shipped to the Isthmus, consigned to the chief of the Bureau of Materials and Supplies, who notifies the disbursing officer, who notifies Colonel Gorgas, who in turn notifies Major LaGarde, who applies to the quartermaster—the boss of the corral—for transportation, and as much of the stuff as, in the judgment of, first, the governor, next the chief disbursing officer, next the Commission, next and more particularly, Mr. Grunsky, ought to be allowed to the superintendent of Ancon Hospital finally arrives or does not arrive at its destination. This is no fanciful picture; it is exemplified in practically every ordinary requisition that goes forward. And what is true of Ancon Hospital is true at Colon, at Culebra, at Miraflores and at all points along the line that require supplies of this description.

In fairness to the Commission, Dr. Reed pointed out that this baffling labyrinth of red tape and approval-getting might be dispensed with in rare cases of an emergency nature and that certain purchases could be made in the open market at Panama, but always, he added, at greatly increased prices.

Dr. Reed's gift for scornful criticism was shown at its best as he went on to detail the Canal Commission's, and particularly the luckless Mr. Grunsky's, official sins. He told in incisive language about abuses of authority, interminable delays in furnishing urgently requested supplies and materials, and other examples of the Commission's apparently deliberate policy of impeding the work it was employed to promote. He mentioned the insane mother, her baby, and the thirty-cent nursing bottle that eventually cost the taxpayers six dollars and fifty cents; the rejection of the X-ray technician's request for permission to select the Crookes tubes for the Ancon Hospital, the sending of tubes which were worthless and had to be returned, and the inevitable result—that "Ancon Hospital is today without x-ray services, while the salary of the expert goes on"; the assumption by the Commission, "more especially Mr. Grunsky," of superior knowledge regarding microscope objectives, the scornful disregarding of the specifications of the laboratory chief, and the sending of objectives that, like those Crookes tubes, were utterly worthless; the continuous breaching by the Commission of the spirit of the law forbidding the substitution of other drugs for those prescribed by physicians; the arbitrary reduction of Gorgas's estimate of needed inspectors by more than 50 per cent; the refusal of the Commission, "more especially Mr. Grunsky," to furnish screens for buildings; the drastic reductions in the salaries of the chief clerk and the Ancon health officer, and the effect they had upon the type of persons available; the decision to convert the hospitals at Ancon and Colon into nurses' training schools so as to obtain the services of young, inexperienced girls willing to work at low salaries; the substitution of fifty-dollar-a-month interns for eighteen-hundred-dollar-a-year physicians; the

reduction in the compensation of attendants and orderlies to a level attractive only to ignorant natives; a certain commissioner's learned observation regarding the
superiority of hogs and buzzards over modern latrines
as means of disposing of body wastes; the refusal to let
Gorgas make emergency expenditures for needed supplies during the yellow fever epidemic; the reduction by
75 per cent in the order for pyrethrum, sulphur, and
other products for the disinfection of buildings; the rejection of a request for sufficient funds to build and
maintain a research laboratory; the commissioners',
"more especially Mr. Grunsky's," refusal to allow an
ambulance to be kept ready for quick response to emergency calls; and numerous other episodes in the troubled
history of the canal's recent past—all pointing to grave
shortcomings on the part of the Commission, "more
especially Mr. Grunsky."

"The Commission, one would naturally suppose, was
appointed to solve great general problems and to lay
down broad general principles relating to the gigantic
work to be done, leaving the execution of details to better
qualified persons employed for the purpose," wrote the
indignant A. M. A. official in a section of the report
which he or the *Journal* editor subheaded "Other Examples of the Littleness of the Commission." "Yet we
find in the published minutes of that body that, after
traveling 2,000 miles, it sat in solemn session at Ancon,
at an expense for salaries and incidentals of five hundred
dollars a day to the people of the United States, con-
suming much of its time with trivialities."

Among the time-wasting "trivialities" he listed were
the following:

A request from Dr. LaGarde for a waiter for the
Nurses' Home, which was not granted but, instead, was
"laid over for inquiry," and—presumably—the waste of
more valuable time.

A recommendation, also from Dr. LaGarde, that the

compensation of the assistant baker at Ancon Hospital be increased from thirty-five to forty-five dollars, which was "taken under advisement."

A request from Dr. J. W. Rose, director of hospitals, for authority to keep a pony in the Commission's stable at Ancon, which likewise was "taken under advisement."

A request from the chief sanitary inspector for authority to employ sixteen carpenters, which was turned down, although approval was finally given for the employment of eight, "with authority to increase the number as required to twelve."

A request from the superintendent of Ancon Hospital for permission to employ twelve additional nurses, which was granted.

Another request from the superintendent of Ancon Hospital for permission to hire an additional waiter and waitress, which was also granted.

A request from a staff physician for a personal servant, which was "disallowed."

"Numerous other instances could be cited from the published proceedings of the Commission to show that it consumed its time in carefully scrutinizing minutiae of administration that ought to have been entrusted successfully to the men employed for the purpose," the report charged.

Colonel Gorgas and Major LaGarde are both officers of high grade and extensive experience, are gentlemen of recognized integrity and ought certainly to have been accorded the generous confidence by which they could dispose of such questions of detail at their own discretion. They ought, therefore, to be entrusted with a contingency fund or emergency fund by which to make small purchases, but this was specifically disallowed to Major [sic] Gorgas, the intimation being conveyed to him by the Commission, more especially by Mr. Grunsky, that the request was in the nature of an impertinence.

Dr. Reed went to great pains to show incontrovertibly how the Commission, "more especially Mr. Grunsky," not only hamstrung Colonel Gorgas and the Sanitary Department with "unnecessary and unreasonable restraints," but also displayed "petty, almost despicable antagonism."

Turning finally to the disease that was threatening the success of the whole Panama Canal enterprise and bringing deep furrows to the Gorgas brow, the former A. M. A. president asked:

"Why is there yellow fever in Panama?"

Why indeed? Dr. Reed wanted to know.

Yellow fever is demonstrably a preventable disease, and as a consequence all deaths resulting from that disease must at once raise the question of responsibility. Panama has long and justly been recognized as a seat of yellow fever infection, just as was Havana before the brilliant sanitary achievements of Colonel Gorgas in that city—achievements which resulted in his call to the Isthmus. The real campaign against the disease in Havana, more particularly against the disease-bearing mosquitoes, lasted from January to September, 1901. As Panama is but a village in comparison with the Cuban metropolis, it was naturally expected that similarly satisfactory results would be realized there in the same, if not less, time. But yellow fever is still endemic in Panama. Why is this true?

Gorgas had fully realized the dangerous potentialities of the disease, even when only a few cases existed on the Isthmus, Secretary Taft was reminded, and before leaving the United States he had laid before the Commission a comprehensive plan for dealing with the expected epidemic and also for the protection of the canal workers against other forms of illness. This plan was five-fold, calling for (1) the installation of sewer systems for the cities of Colon and Panama, (2) installation of water supply systems for these two municipalities, (3) cleaning of the streets, including of course proper disposal of garbage and body wastes, (4) general sanitation of houses in the district, including their fumigation, the draining of pools, and banishing of the time-honored water barrels and cisterns, and (5) prompt isolation of all yellow fever cases. Certainly nothing had been omitted.

Both the Commission, "even including Mr. Grunsky," and Chief Engineer Wallace had expressed complete approval of these measures, the report pointed out. Then it leveled an accusing finger at Gorgas's seven official superiors, placing upon their shoulders full responsibility for what had followed:

Panama was then [when the sanitary work was begun] apparently free from yellow fever, but Colonel Gorgas, with his Cuban experience, and knowing the danger that was lurking in the immediate future, set about promoting these complete measures of prevention, while Mr. Wallace addressed himself to plans and specifications for waterworks and sewer systems for Panama. The plans of both of these men went promptly before the Commission, but it was not until that body had returned to the Isthmus, in August following, that they were given serious consideration; meanwhile the danger of which Colonel Gorgas had forewarned them had developed; for, on July 12, Charles Cunningham was stricken with yellow fever, from which he died two days later. Fourteen days after his death another case developed, which, however, went on to recovery. When the Commission arrived at Ancon on the occasion of its second visit, that is, on August 3, Colonel Gorgas again urged the prompt assumption of sanitary control over Colon and Panama and cited the case still in the hospital, and the fatal one that had preceded it, as danger signals of sufficient gravity to justify action. But the Commission, more especially Mr. Grunsky, had not yet determined the degree of humiliating subordination to which the Sanitary Department was to be subjected, and, under pretext of perfecting a plan of organization, deferred action for another three and one-half-weeks—valuable weeks—that is, until August 28. On this date the Commission, on the report of Mr. Grunsky, adopted Mr. Grunsky's plan of organization, by which, I have already shown, Colonel Gorgas was subordinated to the seventh degree below the original source of authority. Even then, with the cases of yellow fever staring them in the face, the Commission, at the instance of Mr. Grunsky, directed Colonel Gorgas, acting through Governor Davis, to refrain from any attempt to secure sanitary control over the cities of Colon and Panama, citing certain more or less diplomatic frivolities as a pretext for deferred action. It was only after four or five months had elapsed, only after the progressive development of yellow fever had reached the sensational point, and only after the personnel in the Canal Zone had become thoroughly alarmed over the situation, that Colonel Gorgas was permitted by those in authority over him to assume the sanitary control of the two cities, one of which, Panama, having by this time become very generally infected.

One would think that a rapidly spreading yellow fever epidemic would have spurred the Commission to action. However, all the evidence, Dr. Reed tells us, pointed the other way:

But even then his [Gorgas's] hands were tied, sometimes, and in important particulars, by the arbitrary exercise of super-imposed authority, but all the time, and in still more important particulars, by the fact that the water supply and sewer systems were not installed. Mr. Wallace had drawn the plans and specifications in July previous, and had taken care to specify only such pipe as manufacturers keep in stock, and that could therefore be procured without a moment's delay. But the Commission, more especially Mr. Grunsky, in total disregard of the emergency that was present, saw fit to indulge in some views about pipe, and as Mr. Grunsky is a civil engineer and needed to impress the fact on somebody, he summoned Mr. Wallace, confessedly one of the ablest of engineers but now his subordinate, before the Commission to explain why he had specified both eastern and western standards of pipe. The explanation given by Mr. Wallace that either one or both of these standards would answer the purpose and that it had been simply his desire to purchase the pipe promptly, if necessary, in small lots, and to get the pipe promptly on the Isthmus, seemed to make no appeal to either the Commission or Mr. Grunsky; and pipe of the western pattern alone was ordered. The delay in the consideration of this particular point consumed another precious two weeks, after which Mr. Wallace was authorized to proceed with the work. This he undertook with his characteristic energy and, allowing for all reasonable delay in procuring the pipe and in sending it to the Isthmus, promised the people of Panama that they should have water by December. He finished the work at the Rio Grande reservoir in a short time; the trenches for the pipe were dug, washed full of dirt and redug, but still there was no pipe. Mr. Wallace then cabled to Washington, urging that the pipe be sent, only, however, to receive a reprimand from Admiral Walker, chairman of the Commission, admonishing him that cablegrams from the

Isthmus were expensive. It is now nearly the first of March, and the schooner which brought the first consignment of pipe, not enough to complete the work at Panama, was discharging the cargo at Colon when I left. It is further understood that, before the work can go on, this same schooner must sail back to Mobile, await the arrival there of enough pipe to make a full cargo, then sail back to Colon and again unload—a proceeding that, at a conservative estimate, will consume at least two or three months. And all this by a Commission that controls a line of steamers plying weekly between New York and the Isthmus.

In the light of all these facts, in contrast with the brilliant results achieved by Colonel Gorgas in Havana, where he was given, not only a free hand but his own purchasing and distributing agents, the responsibility for the present existence of yellow fever on the Isthmus can be placed nowhere else than on the Isthmian Canal Commission, more especially on Mr. Grunsky.

Having presented his case, Dr. Reed called to Secretary Taft's attention this statement by President Roosevelt, made at the time Mr. Grunsky and his fellow-commissioners assumed their official duties:

I believe that each one of you will serve not merely with entire fidelity, but with the utmost efficiency. If, at any time, I feel that any of you is not rendering the best service which it is possible to procure, I shall feel called upon to disregard my feelings and forthwith to substitute for him on the Commission some other man whom I deem capable of rendering better service.

As Dr. Reed saw it, the President's duty was clear:

In view of the facts which I have presented, in view of the President's manifest and expressed wishes and their complete disregard by the Commission, but more particularly in view of the vital interests at stake, I have the honor not only to submit the suggestion, but really to urge that the time has arrived when the President ought to redeem his word and ask for the resignation of the Commission.

Naturally, these developments were followed with much interest by the man whose lot had been made so miserable by the Commission, "especially Mr. Grunsky." Writing to his mother on April 3, 1905, about a month

after the report was submitted, Gorgas described his reaction to it and its possible consequences:

Here all is expectation as to what the President is going to
do about the Commission. The latest rumors are that the whole
Commission is to be changed. I think that such action under
the circumstances would be wise, but I do not believe that very
active work can be done under the present organization. Seven
men are too many to do executive work. It would be much
better to have one man responsible. Our present Commission
are all high-minded men but with about as much knowledge
of executive [management] as Aileen.* It surprises me that
men who have been connected with big undertakings should
saddle us with such cumbersome, impracticable schemes. If
I remain, I think that I will be in much better position than I
have been. That is, be given more power, though of course there
is a possibility of my head going with the Commission.

Evidently President Roosevelt and his Secretary of
War had been doing some investigating of their own and
had formed essentially the same opinion that Gorgas had
reached regarding the Commission's value to the canal
project and the desirability of reducing its size. As early
as January 13, 1905, about six weeks before Dr. Reed's
return from the Isthmus, the Chief Executive had asked
Congress for authority to supplant the seven-member
Commission with one of only three members. This request had been denied by a Senate failure to act upon it.

Dr. Reed's report, coming shortly afterward, and the
reaction to it in all parts of the country brought a typical
Rooseveltian decision to take matters into his own hands.
Promptly and decisively, he made good his threat. Seven
resignations were demanded and received, and thence-
forth Admiral Walker, General Davis, and Messrs. Parsons, Burr, Harrod, Grunsky, and Hecker were powerless to hamstring sanitary work in Panama.

The Senate's failure to act having blocked the Roosevelt plan for a reduction in the Commission's membership, the Chief Executive attacked the problem of ad-

* One of the Gorgas children.

ministrative inefficiency and delay from another direction. Obliged as he was to make the new Commission as large as the old one, he nevertheless had, or assumed that he had, the power to make some of the memberships largely honorary, concentrating authority and responsibility in an executive committee composed of Theodore P. Shonts, chairman of the Commission; John F. Wallace, the chief engineer; and Charles E. Magoon, civil governor of the Canal Zone.

Meanwhile, Gorgas kept going ahead, doing the best he could with the scanty resources at his command. In spite of all the obstacles put in his way, he made progress, and the slurs cast upon him and his work by his enemies in and outside Washington had no effect upon his personal relations and friendships. He soon became in Panama what he had been in Havana—the most popular man in the area he served. An enthusiastic sportsman and an uncommonly good horseman, he found fleeting escape from his worries in various forms of physical activity, especially long horseback rides. Afoot and asaddle, he explored old trails and jungle wilds and visited places of historic interest, which assumed greater importance in his eyes by virtue of his extensive study of the history of this part of the world. He found a great thrill in standing on ground where Morgan, Balboa, and Pizarro had stood; and in those simple activities he gathered strength and courage for the tough going which lay ahead.

CHAPTER VIII

Brighter Days

WITH THE OUSTING of Admiral Walker, General Davis, Mr. Grunsky, and the others, it seemed certain that Gorgas's future would be relatively free from the troubles that had hamstrung him in the past. The worried chief sanitarian, still struggling with the yellow fever epidemic which, for obvious reasons, he had been unable to control, looked forward hopefully to the arrival of the new Commission members and the better order which their coming was expected to usher in.

This, however, was not to be. Shortly after Magoon arrived at the Isthmus it became evident that, notwithstanding the change, Gorgas's chief difficulty had not been eliminated. The new civil governor and executive committee member was as uncompromisingly opposed to the mosquito theory of yellow fever transmission as Admiral Walker and Governor Davis had been and had equally little patience with those wishing to attack the problem by mosquito-control methods. Nor did Gorgas derive any comfort from the chairman, Shonts. He too had no patience with those who thought of yellow fever control in terms of the mosquito. The idea of spending any considerable amount of public money for such measures as the chief sanitary officer advocated was, in the hostile opinion of these two, folly of the first magnitude.

When the new administration took over with Magoon's arrival in May, 1905, thirty-eight yellow fever patients were being treated at the hospital, and twenty-two deaths had already been attributed to this disease since the first of the year. Moreover, all signs were pointing to a sharp increase in both cases and deaths the following month. Those who thus read the signs read them correctly. The June cases shot upward to sixty-two and June deaths to nineteen, or more than twice as many as occurred in May.

The brave Gorgas effort to be optimistic and try to find a sunny side to the gloomy picture ran into new difficulties, and Canal Zone morale, already severely strained, received a hard, fresh blow to the midriff when, just about this time, of all times, sensitive ears got word that Chief Engineer Wallace had asked his Washington superiors for a leave of absence. Although that important little detail was left out of the announcement of his impending departure, it was generally assumed that he was going for good. This impression received official confirmation soon after he got away, and it was whispered around that he had been frightened into resigning by the sudden change in the yellow fever situation. When it became known that he had kept his personal coffin ready for use most of the time he had spent on the Isthmus and had even taken it back with him, Gorgas found in the men's rising fears a disease of the mind and emotions rivaling in dangerous potentialities the diseases of the body which it was his official responsibility to treat.

Making much of the chief sanitary officer's undisputed failure to drive yellow fever from the Isthmus and placing the blame for it, not upon Gorgas's inability to obtain the necessary weapons of warfare, where it belonged, but upon his tenacious clinging to the mosquito-transmission theory, Chairman Shonts began laying the groundwork for a complete "reorganization" of the Sanitary Department shortly after the new Commission assumed control. This was aimed primarily, of course, at the replacement of Gorgas and the others sharing his sanitary theories by men whose ideas on the subject were more in line with those of Shonts himself. Acting under the chairman's misguided inspiration, the Canal Commission in June, 1905, recommended to Secretary Taft that these men be relieved of their duties and that those "of more practical views" be named to succeed them. The Secretary of War forwarded the recommendation to President Roosevelt with his full approval.

Secretary of War Taft, like President Taft and Governor Taft, frequently showed a remarkable genius for doing the very thing that should not be done. That peculiar brand of genius was now in full flower. How he could bring himself to become a party to the overthrow of Gorgas less than four months after his personal friend, Dr. Reed, had climaxed a thorough investigation of the whole canal sanitation problem with the highest praise for Gorgas, leaves even the warmest Taft admirer baffled. The Taft role in this sorry business became even more indefensible when Shonts revealed the man he had in mind for the job which he proposed to make vacant by removing Gorgas. Shonts's choice for that highly responsible post was an osteopath, who had the advantage of being a friend of the Commission chairman and, as Shonts pointed out when the gentleman's fitness was called into question, had "been in the South" and had "seen yellow fever." Almost any Cuban peon could have qualified for the job to that extent.

Another person whom Chairman Shonts had in mind was a physician of high standing in his profession. Unlike the chairman's osteopath friend, this gentleman had considerably more to recommend him than the fact that he had "been in the South" and had "seen yellow fever." Indeed, he had had considerable experience with the disease. But he was as sternly opposed as Shonts himself to the mosquito-transmission theory and would have none of it. There was no question as to his determination to proceed on an entirely different, and contrary, plan of action. That, the mosquito-theorists were firmly convinced, would mean the complete scuttling of the whole sanitation program.

Losing sight of Gorgas's brilliant success at Havana and the high praise accorded him by Dr. Reed, President Roosevelt was inclined to follow the recommendations of his Canal Commission and Secretary of War and order Gorgas's removal. Indeed he found himself in such complete agreement with them that he virtually reached a decision to get rid of Gorgas and appoint as his successor, not the osteopath who "had been in the South" or the respectable physician to whom the mosquito-transmission theory was anathema, but the eminent Dr. Hamilton Wright, who had done notable sanitary work under the famous Joseph Chamberlain in the Straits Settlements.

But the President could not quite make up his mind to take this decisive step. Anxious lest he do something he would regret, he turned for advice to his friend, Dr. William H. Welch, dean of the Johns Hopkins University Medical School. The Chief Executive's appeal for help contained the mock-serious Rooseveltian warning that "I shall hold you responsible for every word you put in the letter."

Replying, Dr. Welch was generous in his praise of Dr. Wright and expressed the opinion that he could handle the job acceptably. But he told the President: "Your statement that you will hold me responsible for every word in this letter obliges me to add that, in my opinion, neither Dr. Wright nor anyone else is as well qualified to conduct this work as the present incumbent, Dr. Gorgas."

This statement halted, or at least slowed up, the anti-Gorgas drift of Roosevelt's mind. But the President was not yet willing to agree with Dr. Welch that Gorgas should be kept where he was. So again he turned to an eminent member of Gorgas's profession for advice. This time he appealed to Dr. Alexander Lambert, of New York City, with whom he had been on several hunting expeditions and who had done his best to persuade Roosevelt to make Gorgas a full-fledged member of the Isthmian Canal Commission. This time he wanted more information and a freer expression of opinion than would be possible in a letter. So he asked Dr. Lambert to call upon him at his Oyster Bay home.

The two old friends had a long talk that evening about sanitation, the progress of the canal, the mosquito theory, and Shonts's complaints that Gorgas was spending his time oiling streams and fighting mosquitoes, instead of doing an old-fashioned clean-up job. President Roosevelt made it plain that he was inclined to agree with at least some of these complaints and thought more attention ought to be devoted to bad odors and the removal of the conditions responsible for them. He made it plain too that it would take a great deal of convincing to make him disregard a recommendation of his Canal Commission which had received the approval of his Secretary of War.

With vast patience, Dr. Lambert explained to his distinguished auditor the real meaning of the mosquito-transmission theory and its significance in terms of health conditions in Panama. He assured the President that Shonts and the others who ridiculed that theory were as far behind the times as if they had been opposing the use of steam shovels in digging the canal. Bad odors were a nuisance, he conceded, but all the bad odors in Christendom could not cause as much malaria or yellow fever as a single mosquito, and Gorgas was everlastingly right in letting odors go and concentrating with every device possible upon those winged messengers of death that had been breeding by the millions in the swamps and water barrels and any number of other places in that disease-cursed country.

The problem of completing the canal was, generally

speaking, a problem of curbing disease, particularly malaria and yellow fever, he went on earnestly. Give the chief engineer and his foremen healthy laborers, give the white collar bosses employees able to stay out of the hospitals and on their jobs, and the construction of the waterway would be an easy matter, he insisted. Otherwise the United States could hardly hope to escape the disease-brought failure that cursed the French effort to link the oceans. His earnest plea could be boiled down to this choice: Keep Gorgas on the job and give him the authority he needs to do his work, and you can be reasonably certain the canal will be dug. Or yield to the plea of Shonts and the others for Gorgas's official head, and you will seriously jeopardize the success of the entire venture.

That evening's discussion ended exactly as Gorgas, who of course knew nothing about what was going on, would have had it end. Deeply impressed as he had been by Dr. Welch's letter, Roosevelt was now firmly convinced by his other friend's seriously spoken, logical words. Before his visitor left the President assured him that Gorgas not only would be retained but would also have ample support.

That promise was completely fulfilled. Shonts was summoned to the White House, informed that his recommendation for Gorgas's removal had been rejected, and told that the President wanted an immediate and complete end to the halfhearted co-operation which Gorgas and the Sanitary Department had been receiving. From then on Shonts was a different man. Neither the chief sanitary officer nor the Sanitary Department as a whole had occasion to complain of non-co-operation as long as he remained at the head of the Canal Commission.

Meanwhile, Gorgas's fortunes had received a mighty lift from an entirely different quarter. As unfortunate as Chief Engineer Wallace's resignation had been in its effect upon Canal Zone morale, subsequent events had revealed it as a veritable boon for the Alabamian. For in Wallace's successor, John F. Stevens, he had found an ardent believer in the mosquito theory and a stout and fearless defender of himself and his work—exactly the reverse of Stevens's Gorgas-hating, sanitation-scorning predecessor. For this of course Gorgas was properly grateful. He called the period ushered in by Shonts's presidentially inspired change of heart and Stevens's arrival "the high-water mark of sanitary efficiency on the Isthmus" and averred that more sanitation work was done at that time than during any other period of comparable length in the entire history of the canal.

Delighted with these changes, Gorgas did what he often did when he had good news, he wrote to his mother. "Everything seems to be coming my way now," he told her and enclosed a clipping from the Boston *Transcript* containing a letter from "someone down here, I don't know who." It spoke in the highest terms not only of his sanitary work but also of the manner in which he had won the affection of the men working under him. He called it "one of the prettiest compliments I ever had paid me." This letter which gave him and Amelia Gayle Gorgas so much satisfaction was as follows:

Every man who has been in the fever ward swears by Colonel Gorgas. Although at the head of one of the largest and busiest departments and obliged to be at his office in the city most of the day, he visits personally everyone in the fever ward morning and evening and prescribes for their treatment. Not a man among them who does not feel 100 per cent better after his visits. He has a wonderfully attractive personality, is equally kind and courteous to the humblest, and, above all, inspires an implicit confidence in his treatment which removes all worry from the patient's mind and makes very strongly for his recovery. He listens patiently to every request for a change of diet or other privileges, and, unless it is manifestly unwise to grant it, arranges matters so the patient is satisfied. Many a man has been heard to say that it was worth having the yellow fever to have been under the care of Colonel Gorgas.

Some of the measures which he was able to put into operation as a result of the turn of events in his favor were largely duplications of those that had worked so well in Havana. Others had to be devised to suit the peculiarities of the new job to be done, particularly the need for affording health protection to workers hacking and digging their way through the jungle.

The Canal Zone was divided into twenty-five sanitary districts, varying in size from fifteen to thirty-five square miles, with a sanitary inspector in charge of each. Some districts contained only a few hundred residents and others as many as ten thousand. As most of the workers' quarters were situated within a mile of the canal right-of-way, the sanitary work was concentrated in that narrow area.

Chief reliance in the anti-mosquito campaign was placed of course in large-scale drainage projects to convert swampy mosquito-breeding areas into dry land. In a country where rain fell daily during eight months of the year and the weather was so warm that vegetation growth was continuous, the famed Gorgas resourcefulness was put to a severe test to prevent the drainage ditches from becoming clogged and breeding more mosquitoes than the swamps they eliminated. He solved the problem by lining many of them with cement, while others were kept open by partly filling them with rocks, which did not interfere with the flow of water but prevented the growth of bushes. In some cases no ditches were dug at all, drainage being accomplished by tiling, which not only could not become clogged but had the additional advantage of being inaccessible to mosquitoes and of not interfering with the cultivation of the land.

As the work of canal-digging went forward, these operations themselves constantly created shallow indentations in the land surface, which quickly filled with water and, if neglected, would have created important mosquito-breeding areas. As any effort to drain these puddles would have interfered seriously with the construction work, other measures had to be devised to prevent them from becoming veritable pest-holes. The same was true of any number of other water areas unsuited to drainage. The device resorted to was oiling. Plain kerosene was used in most cases.

Sanitary Department workmen made frequent rounds of these places, each carrying on his back a large oil can containing a hand-operated pump, which forced the kerosene through a nozzle to any spot requiring attention. As had been demonstrated in Havana, this formed a thin film on the top of the water, which clogged up the baby mosquitoes' breathing passages and killed them whenever they would rise to the surface—as they had to do from time to time—to breathe.

The warfare against mosquito larvae was by no means limited to the operations of this army of kerosene shooters, however. In more inaccessible places and at the headwaters of streams, Gorgas placed ash cans containing a solution of crude carbolic acid, resin, and caustic soda, and from the hole near the bottom of each one there protruded another household appliance of another day—a lampwick. Through that the liquid would pass slowly and fall, drop by drop, upon the water directly below, to be carried downstream by the slowly moving current. After being dissolved in the water, it killed the larvae whenever they came into contact with it. A New York *Times* writer once called these homely ash cans, equipped with their equally homely lampwicks, "the outposts of the sanitation army" in Panama.

Still another example of the Gorgas way of not giving the mosquito any of the "breaks" was described by Congressman J. Warren Keifer, of Ohio, in an address in the House of Representatives:

It seemed to me at one time as if Col. Gorgas and his force down there were a little over-particular, but I guess I was mistaken. I believe it is one of the rules to prohibit people who live in the lowlands or on level lands along the line of this canal from keeping cows, because when the rainy season is on they might walk around in the damp places and with their hoofs make holes in the ground that would hold water and later constitute breeding places for mosquitoes.

In spite of all Gorgas and his staff could do, a certain number—fortunately, a greatly reduced number—of mosquitoes escaped the well-laid plans to kill them in infancy. Even after they reached adulthood, however, they faced a ruthless campaign of extermination. Most of those that were not destroyed were prevented, in one way or another, from transmitting disease germs.

Putting much faith in screening, notwithstanding the sneers it had received from members of the Canal Commission staff, Gorgas instructed his inspectors to see that all houses were properly screened and that the screens, once installed, were kept in proper condition. Men were employed for the single purpose of promptly repairing any that might be damaged.

In order to reduce as much as possible the load carried by the Sanitary Department hospitals, which provided free treatment to canal workers and treatment at nominal cost to their families, Gorgas established a system of dispensaries, where those who did not require hospital treatment obtained free medical advice and those unable to pay for medicines also received them without cost. Quinine, the medicinal backbone of every anti-malaria campaign, was free to all, and all were encouraged to take it regularly.

Negroes have an inherent and often violent distaste for medicine of any kind, and that is particularly true of quinine. So great was that distaste in the case of colored canal workers that it required considerably more than free treatment and the usual powers of persuasion, aided by their natural fear of sickness, to induce them to avail themselves of its malaria-preventing protection. However, this problem, like many others, was solved in

typical Gorgas fashion. Gorgas's eye was as alert as his
brain. Coached no doubt by the memory of good-natured darkies at work and play in the Brierfield of his
childhood, Gorgas quickly observed the great enjoyment
the Negro workmen derived from liquids pleasingly
pink in appearance and temptingly sweet in taste. So
from the Gorgas office went orders to manufacture and
keep freely available a soft drink containing a sufficient
quantity of quinine but strongly resembling, in taste and
color, the ever-popular pink lemonade of circus fame.
From then on this masquerading dose of medicine was
served regularly at meals and could be had at other
times, too. As the refreshing drink slid down dusky
throats, their owners thought gratefully of a generous
Uncle Sam who was going to so much trouble and expense to provide this reminder of circus days back home.

A Gorgas admirer, Judge John Bassett Moore of
the Permanent Court of International Justice, described
a personal experience with Gorgas's thoroughness while
on a visit to Panama. Writing in the *American Review
of Reviews,* he told of arriving at the Tivoli Hotel after
a long journey, thoroughly tired out and "fed up" on
the many brands of mineral water which he had felt it
necessary to drink in lieu of ordinary drinking water of
questionable purity. He seated himself at a table and,
moved by that longing for fresh, uncarbonated water
which he had known back in his native country, seized a
carafe and started pouring. As he watched the unspar-
kling liquid rise in the glass before him, his natural cau-
tion reasserted itself, and he turned to the waiter to
inquire whether he would be endangering his health if
he should drink it. Thereupon, the waiter, "with proud
assurance," replied: "Sir, that water is certified by Dr.
Gorgas."

Meanwhile, the success of the Gorgas anti-mosquito
campaign was becoming more and more evident to anyone who had been in Panama long enough to be able to

look around and make comparisons with the past. One who did so was Lindsay Denison, a writer for *Everybody's Magazine,* who took a long look, remembered what he had seen some time before, and wrote:

There are mighty few mosquitoes left on the Isthmus. In seven days I was approached, so far as I know, by only two, and these were met at night. Mr. Harrison* was bitten by six or seven. Time was when one walked the streets of Panama in a cloud of mosquitoes by day as well as by night. The British consul, Mr. Mallet, showed me that he had taken all the screens out of his office windows. "Two years ago," he assured me, "at this time of the year, we should not have been able to sit in this room with the window open. The mosquitoes would have driven us mad."

Gorgas had mathematical proof that Mr. Denison was right. For the fumigation of houses was showing a steadily diminishing harvest of mosquitoes. The piles of them that were swept up when the liberally used pyrethrum would put them to sleep and cause them to drop from ceilings, curtains, and any number of other places grew smaller and smaller. Finally they became so few as to be all but nonexistent.

Fortunately, the chief sanitarian had even better proof than this that he was winning his war against yellow fever. From the record high of sixty-two yellow fever cases and nineteen yellow fever deaths reported in June—which gave Shonts, Magoon, and the others such powerful ammunition when they went after his official scalp in the summer of 1905—both cases and deaths had been dropping sharply during the past several months. Only forty-two cases had been reported in July, and only thirteen of them had proved fatal. In August cases had declined to twenty-seven and deaths to only nine. The downward swing of the yellow fever curve had continued without interruption during the rest of the year, the last month of which had brought only a single case and that not fatal.

* Presumably a fellow-journalist.

Delighted though he was, Gorgas did not realize then how complete his victory had been. For it was then too early for him to know what is now a part of the Canal Zone health records—that only a single case, believed to have originated elsewhere, was reported during all of 1906 and that, since that time, this natural breeding place of yellow fever has been all but literally free of it.

CHAPTER IX

Gorgas and Goethals

BREAKING WITH a tradition as old as the nation itself, President Theodore Roosevelt made a personal visit to the Canal Zone in November, 1906, to see at firsthand just how well the work was progressing. Naturally, his trip, made with an impressive entourage of officials, secret service men, and representatives of the press, was an event of great importance to residents of the Isthmus. A tropical storm began just before his arrival at Panama, but it had no appreciable effect either upon the size of the crowd which jammed that section of the city or upon its enthusiasm. An effort was made by the local police force, augmented by law-enforcement officials from other parts of the Zone, to maintain a semblance of order and decorum, but utterly without success. Restraint was thrown to the winds, and everybody seemed moved by a single impulse to crowd as close to the Chief Executive as possible. He entered into the spirit of the occasion as heartily as anyone and appeared to be having the time of his life.

At the conclusion of the noisy demonstration at the station, the President entered a carriage, and the rain-soaked but jubilant procession got under way, headed for the Tivoli Hotel at Ancon, which had been chosen as the Roosevelt headquarters. Arrived there, the crowd waited for him to show himself again. It waited and waited. But it waited in vain, for there was no presidential appearance. The President of the United States, center of all eyes as he was, had disappeared as completely as the humblest citizen could have done.

A dramatic manhunt then got under way. The Canal Zone's chief of police, a former Rough Rider and close personal friend of the distinguished visitor, hurried back to the station, where the President's train was still standing in the yards, and scanned hundreds of faces, hoping to recognize the familiar Roosevelt features. From there he made an unceremonious horseback ride to the American residential section on Ancon Hill. He called every telephone number that might possibly help him out of his predicament. But his efforts were altogether fruitless. Meanwhile, others had been searching other parts of the city without success. The President's dropping out of sight could not have been more expertly executed had it been planned in every detail months in advance.

At last they found him at Ancon Hospital engaged in earnest discussion of health and sanitation problems with Gorgas. The latter was not in any way to blame for his disappearance but had become a party to it. Just before the procession got under way at the station, the President had told the chief sanitarian that he wished to see the hospital at once, and they had driven there in Gorgas's carriage.

The visit appeared to be altogether satisfactory to both men. The President made a typically Rooseveltian inspection of the institution, talking to the patients and staff members and taking a look here and there to see the work being done by the various departments. As his inspection progressed, he expressed himself as more than well pleased with what he saw, and that favorable impression flavored his comments when the inspection ended.

This was the beginning of a general tour of the Canal Zone which continued almost up to the hour of his departure a few days later. Hardly a steam shovel or medicine cabinet seemed to escape his alert, interested gaze. At Roosevelt's request, Gorgas was a member of the presidential party during all of these inspections.

One unfortunate incident occurred. At Colon Hospital, reached on the last day of the Roosevelt visit, a careless minor employee had failed to correct the unsatisfactory sanitary condition of one of the camps and attempted to cover up his dereliction by lying about it. A much less observant visitor than the President would have seen this condition in an instant, and of course it immediately caught his eye, to the painful embarrassment of Gorgas, who had been highly pleased with the favorable impression made upon the President by what he had seen at Sanitary Department institutions previously visited. The hearty cordiality of the Roosevelt manner departed. A stern rebuke fell from his lips, and he took no pains to soften its effect. Gorgas made the best he could of the situation, but that rebuke cut him to the quick and brought fears of permanent official displeasure and the ending of his career in Panama.

"I have failed," he said later to Mrs. Gorgas, sadness in his voice. "President Roosevelt has criticized my work. No doubt I shall soon be relieved and someone else placed in charge of this work."

In that, fortunately, he was mistaken.

Convinced that he was no longer the welcome companion he had formerly been, Gorgas was not with the President when the latter spoke briefly to the crowd assembled to bid him *bon voyage* at the end of his visit. Noting his absence, the Chief Executive inquired about him and let it be known that he wanted to talk to him. Gorgas was found and joined the presidential party, walking with the President to his ship. Farewells were as cordial as ever, and there was no suggestion of the displeasure which had been so unmistakable a short time before. Neither the rebuke nor the sanitary shortcoming which had occasioned it was mentioned either then or later, as far as is known.

That presidential visit brought welcome results to

Gorgas. Before his departure Roosevelt issued an order
putting into effect a general reorganization of the Canal
Zone administration and making the Sanitary Department an independent unit responsible to no one on
the Isthmus except the chairman of the Canal Commission. Only one thing better, from the Gorgas point
of view, could have been done: making him a member
of the Commission. This indeed had been asked for,
not by Gorgas himself, but by the now chastened and
fully co-operative Shonts. But the President was not
then willing to go that far. Needless to say, Gorgas was
well pleased with the new arrangement.

"While this would have been an honor," he wrote
of his suggested membership on the Commission, "it
would not have added to the efficiency of my department. The department organization was all I asked for
and is what I have been trying for for the last two years.
So I am happy."

Shortly after his return President Roosevelt sent a
special message to Congress in which he described his
trip and gave the country's law-makers the benefit of his
impressions of what he had seen on the Isthmus. All
phases of the canal construction work, from sanitation
to complaints about food served in the government
hotels, came in for attention.

"I chose the month of November for my visit partly
because it is the rainiest month of the year, the month
in which the work goes forward at the greatest disadvantage, and one of the two months which the medical
department of the French Canal Company found most
unhealthy," he wrote, adding that, since the weather
encountered during his stay ashore had fully lived up
to its reputation, "it would have been impossible to see
the work going on under more unfavorable weather
conditions."

Characterizing the protection of canal workers' health
as "the first great problem to be solved," the President

told Congress what his visit had shown him concerning
the measures taken by Gorgas and his assistants to solve
that "first great problem."

"The results have been astounding," he declared.

The Isthmus had been a by-word for deadly unhealthfulness.
Now, after two years of our occupation, the conditions as regards sickness and the death rate compare favorably with reasonably healthy localities in the United States. Especial care
has been devoted to minimizing the risk due to the presence
of those species of mosquitoes which have been found to propa-
gate malarial and yellow fevers. In all the settlements, the little
temporary towns or cities composed of the white and black
employees, which grow up here and there in the tropic jungle
as the needs of the work dictate, the utmost care is exercised
to keep the conditions healthy. Everywhere are to be seen the
drainage ditches which, in removing the water, have removed the
breeding places of the mosquitoes, while the whole jungle is
cut away for a considerable space around the habitations, thus
destroying the places in which the mosquitoes take shelter.
These drainage ditches and clearings are in evidence in every
settlement, and, together with the invariable presence of mosquito screens around the piazzas and of mosquito doors to the
houses, not to speak of the careful fumigation that has gone on
in all infected houses, doubtless explain the extraordinary absence of mosquitoes. As a matter of fact, but a single mosquito,
and this not of the dangerous species, was seen by any member
of our party during my three days on the Isthmus.

Declaring that he had personally inspected more than
twenty water closets, including those used by colored
workmen, Roosevelt reported that "in almost every case
I found the conditions perfect," while "in but one case
did I find them really bad." This, presumably the one
which had brought Gorgas such great heartache, he
called "very bad indeed" but minimized blame for its
condition by explaining that the building containing it
was one of those used by the French, that its use by the
American workmen had been on a temporary basis, and
that the installation of a modern water closet to replace
the defective one had been almost completed at the time

of his visit. He did not withhold his blame entirely, however. The message continued:

"Nevertheless, this did not excuse the fact that the bad condition had been allowed to prevail. Temporary accommodation, even if only such as soldiers use when camped in the field, should have been provided."

From this mild criticism, the President returned to praise of the Gorgas method of handling even small details like defective water closets.

I was struck, however, by the fact that in this instance, as in almost every other where a complaint was made which proved to have any justification whatever, it appeared that steps had already been taken to remedy the evil complained of, and that the trouble was mainly due to the extreme difficulty, and often impossibility, of providing in every place for the constant increase in the numbers of employees. Generally the provision is made in advance, but it is not possible that this should always be the case; when it is not, there ensues a period of time during which the conditions are unsatisfactory until a remedy can be provided; but I never found a case where the remedy was not being provided as speedily as possible.

The large hospitals maintained by Gorgas's Sanitary Department at Ancon and Colon he called "excellent examples of what tropical hospitals should be," while in the smaller district hospitals he found the patients, both white and black, receiving treatment "as good as that which could be obtained in our first-class hospitals at home."

So much for the measures taken to protect the health of the canal workers. What did Gorgas and his assistants have to show for their labors? The presidential report was impressive on that score:

Just at present the health showing on the Isthmus is remarkably good—so much better than in most sections of the United States that I do not believe that it can possibly continue at quite its present average. Thus, early in the present year a band of several hundred Spaniards were brought to the Isthmus as laborers, and additions to their number have been made from time to time; yet since their arrival in February last but one of those Spaniards thus brought over to work on the canal has died of disease, and he of typhoid fever. Two others were killed, one in a railroad accident and one by a dynamite explosion. There had been for the last six months a well-nigh steady decline in the death rate for the population of the Zone, this being largely due to the decrease in the deaths from pneumonia, which has been the most fatal disease on the Isthmus. In October there were ninety-nine deaths of every kind among the employees of the Isthmus. There were then on the rolls 5,500 whites, seven-eighths of them being Americans. Of these whites but two died of disease, and, as it happened, neither man was an American. Of the 6,000 white Americans,* including some 1,200 women and children, not a single death has occurred in the past three months, whereas in an average city in the United States the number of deaths for a similar number of people in that time would have been about thirty from disease. This very remarkable showing cannot of course permanently obtain, but it certainly goes to prove that, if good care is taken, the Isthmus is not a particularly unhealthy place.

Notwithstanding its criticism of some aspects of the sanitary work, the message was regarded as a complete vindication of Gorgas and his program. No wonder he called it "a corker."

"I had not expected anything of the kind," he wrote shortly afterward. "I do not think that an army medical officer ever had such recognition in a Presidential message. It probably marks the acme of my career. I have had greater recognition and success than I ever expected." Gorgas's jubilation appeared entirely justified. But there was still stormy weather ahead.

Chief Engineer John F. Stevens gave up his post early in 1907, bringing to the administration an acute recurrence of the "resignation trouble" which had plagued it when the coffin-conscious Mr. Wallace gave up the job and transferred his activities to regions which he considered healthier than the Isthmus of Panama during a yellow fever epidemic. Prodded by widespread criticism of the canal management and by charges that

* Canal workers and their families.

the frequent changes of chief engineers and commission
members indicated at least partial failure of the entire
canal-digging enterprise, President Roosevelt and Secretary Taft decided to place responsibility for completion
of the work upon a group of men who would be virtually
resignation-proof. To that end, they appointed a new
Canal Commission, consisting largely of Army officers,
who were considered much less likely than civilians to be
lured from their task before its completion.

Gorgas was made a member of that new Commission,
along with Major D. D. Gaillard, whose name was soon
to be immortalized in the renaming of Culebra Cut in
his honor; Major William L. Sibert, who had been in
charge of lock work on several rivers; Rear Admiral H.
H. Rousseau, who had recently served as chief of the
Navy's Bureau of Yards and Docks; Senator J. C. S.
Blackburn, of Kentucky; Jackson Smith, who had been
in charge of labor recruiting and housing and feeding
of employees at the Canal Zone; Joseph Bucklin Bishop,
a New York newspaper man; Lieutenant Colonel H. F.
Hodges, who had won considerable renown as designer
of canal locks; and Lieutenant Colonel George Washington Goethals. Bishop was made secretary, and, in the
interest of increased efficiency and better administration,
the President combined the positions of chief engineer
and chairman, appointing Goethals to the dual post. As
an additional move for centralized authority and responsibility, Roosevelt gave him the veto power over all acts
of the Commission as a whole. In brief, the President
made it plain to Goethals and to the world that it was
his job to see that the canal was completed. He was tired
of divided responsibility, indecision, and disunity of
purpose.

Goethals officially succeeded Chief Engineer Stevens
on April 11, 1907, and that day brought a complete
change in the *esprit de corps* of the canal workers. He
made it plain at the outset that he expected to make full

use of the great power given him and as time went on missed no opportunity to let everybody, from high official to humblest workman, know who was boss. The abolition of the commission form of government was only the first step in his assumption of virtually supreme authority over even the smallest detail of the lives and habits of those at work on the canal.

However wise from an administrative and engineering point of view President Roosevelt's action may have been in placing so much power in the hands of Colonel Goethals, it was extremely unfortunate for Gorgas and the sanitary program. Commission member though he was, he found himself back where he had been during the chairmanship of Admiral Walker. Once more he was virtually powerless to do anything without first obtaining the approval of a man who was militantly opposed to his way of carrying on his work. Moreover, Goethals in time developed a bitter personal hostility to him which was reflected in practically every relationship between them as long as they lived.

This is not at all difficult to understand when one understands Goethals. Conflict was inevitable between him and a man like Gorgas. It cannot be explained by saying that Goethals was a typical product of a long and honorable army career, a glorified drill sergeant armed with virtually dictatorial power. Nor can it be explained by saying that he became an autocrat because nobody but an autocrat could do the job that had been entrusted to him. For Gorgas was an army officer too. He too had been placed in positions of great responsibility in which he could have become a glorified drill sergeant had he wished. But how vastly different the two men were!

They had much in common, it is true. Both were products of many generations of culture, were well educated, and knew and meticulously observed the social amenities. Both were characterized by a strong sense of duty and were determined to perform as successfully as possible the tasks upon which they were engaged. And, once convinced that they were right, both stubbornly refused to give ground to those who had different ideas as to how a job should be performed. But Gorgas believed in padding and even concealing the iron fist, winning co-operation by friendliness and a high type of salesmanship, while Goethals was first and always the boss, the man who gave orders and tolerated no back-talk or lack of enthusiasm in their execution. Those who disagreed with him, as Gorgas often did, were considered disloyal. Whereas Gorgas was loved, Goethals was merely admired, respected, and feared. He could be, and often was, a benevolent czar, but he was a czar nevertheless.

Albert Edwards summed up this clash of personalities in an article in the *Outlook*. Said he:

> Before a visitor has been long in the Zone he is sure to discover that there is a conflict of ideals between Gorgas and Goethals. The whole controversy—for that is what it amounts to—is, I think, one of temperament. Goethals, the practical, scrupulous administrator, makes a fetish of economy. Low costs are his hobby. Gorgas is imaginative and enthusiastic. He would like to kill every mosquito on the Isthmus, and then begin on the rest of the world.

Even the Goethals name stands for stiff-necked resistance, if a Goethals family tradition can be believed. In 860, according to this tradition, a ninth-century forebear of the Canal Zone's big boss named Honorius enlisted under the Duke of Burgundy and went with him from Italy to France. On the way the Duke and his followers had an encounter with Saracens, in the course of which the Goethals ancestor was struck across the neck with such force that the blow might well have proved fatal. It did not, however, thanks to his armor and especially to his remarkable physical strength. Indeed he escaped entirely uninjured. This feat made him something of a hero, and he became known as *Bon Coli*, meaning "good neck," or, the virtues of necks being what they are, "stiff neck." Settling in what was then northern France but is now a part of Belgium and Holland on land generously given him as a reward for his military prowess, he took his title with him to his extensive estate. But there it underwent a linguistic metamorphosis. Keeping the same meaning but obtaining a different spelling and pronunciation, it became *Goet Hals.* As time went on, the two words became one, and *Goethals* resulted. With an eye to the future, the family separated into two branches, one occupying the property situated in Belgium and the other assuming possession of that in Holland. Goethals was a descendant of the latter branch, as both his parents were Dutch-born. He himself was a native of Brooklyn, where he was born in 1858.

Even before he went to the Canal Zone he showed more than once that, in a figurative sense at least, he had inherited his full share of the "stiff neck" which had brought a change of name to his fighting ancestor. A certain admiral remembered one of those demonstrations as long as he lived. It occurred while Goethals, then a major, was in charge of the building of facilities for landing supplies in Puerto Rico. Spotting some barges in the harbor, he decided it would be a good idea to sink two of them to use as the foundation for his landing stage. But the admiral, who happened to be in command of all warships in those waters, violently objected and forbade him to use those two barges or any others for that purpose, under threat of court martial. Nevertheless, the stiff-necked Goethals went ahead with his plan, and first one and then the second barge dropped to the harbor bottom. The affronted naval officer blustered and promised dire punishment, but the threatened court martial failed to materialize, although the admiral became so incensed over this challenge to his authority that for several years he refused to speak when the two met socially or officially.

The same sort of Dutch stubbornness was much in evidence when, some time after Goethals took over his new duties, the Secretary of War visited the Isthmus and observed that, though he was an army officer, he had not been seen in uniform during the entire period of the cabinet member's visit. Upon receiving the reply that he had chosen to wear civilian attire, the Secretary of War threatened to order him to wear a uniform, whereupon Goethals countered: "That wouldn't do any good. I have none on the Isthmus."

Equally characteristic of the man was his manner toward a certain superintendent who called at his office.

"I received your letter, Colonel," the man began.

"My letter?" Goethals asked. "I have written you no letter."

"Yes, a letter about that work down there," the superintendent insisted.

"Oh, you mean your orders."

"Well, yes. I thought I would come in and talk it over with you." Goethals gave him a cold, belittling stare. "I'll be glad to hear your views," he informed the discomfited superintendent, "but bear in mind you have only to carry out my orders. I take responsibility for the work itself."

Fortunately, Goethals's appointment came after Gorgas had in a large measure accomplished the task for which he was sent to the Canal Zone. With yellow fever relegated to the status of a nonexistent disease, as far as that narrow strip of tropical land was concerned, and with malaria loosening its grip under the steady pounding of the Gorgas sanitary program, his main problem was merely to keep in operation the preventive measures he had already set up and be prepared to deal with such emergencies as might arise. Therefore the hostility to which he was condemned for the rest of his stay on the Isthmus did not offer such a serious threat to the health-protection program as it would have done two or three years earlier.

Nevertheless, the danger was a serious one, and Gorgas was kept in a state of pained anxiety lest Panama again experience health conditions like those it knew before he and his corporal's guard of faithful walked ashore from the S. S. *Allianca* that day in June, 1904. In a more personal sense he deeply resented the assumption by the new Commission chairman of complete administrative authority, including the right to veto whatever parts of the sanitary program the other man did not like, which appeared to be just about all of it. He found it particularly galling to hear from the lips of his friends the sneering comments they had heard Goethals make about his work. The man who had conceived this program of wholesale health protection, had carried it through to success in spite of stupid officialdom, and, thanks to that success, was winning world fame could hardly be expected to maintain his equanimity and good nature while his work was being so consistently belittled by one who knew next to nothing about sanitation, able though he might be in his own particular field. In the face of this extreme provocation, however, Gorgas remained outwardly calm as he continued to plug away at the job to which he had dedicated himself. Nevertheless, his letters and his conversations with close friends clearly showed how unhappy and at times bitter he really was.

However, all was not discouragement, disappointment, and frustration. This gentle Alabamian, whose hair had turned a snowy white and who still spoke in a soft voice after the manner of most Southerners, received recognition from a source that gave him great satisfaction and made even more puerile the petty antagonism of Goethals. At its 1908 meeting in Chicago the American Medical Association made up for its failure to have him made a member of the original Canal Commission by electing him as its president. As soon as he could get away from his well-wishers he hurried to his room in the Congress Hotel and sent the news to his mother, whose pleasure over this honor he knew would even exceed his own.

"You have a son who now is president of the American Medical Association," he told her. "Congratulations on my election are pouring in from every side." Needless to say, that flood of congratulatory messages did not include one from Colonel Goethals. A message expressing his true feelings would have been very much out of place among those from Gorgas's sincere admirers.

Gorgas did receive many messages from Goethals from time to time, of course, both oral and written. Most of them had to do with money. More specifically, they had to do with money which Gorgas wanted to spend in carrying out his sanitary program. In an exasperatingly large number of cases they were refusals to approve requested outlays. Like his economy-minded predecessor, Admiral Walker, Goethals used his control of expenditures as a weapon against Gorgas. It was his constant plaint that sanitation was too expensive, that Gorgas was wasting money. The two men failed to agree on almost anything, but this matter of expenditures proved a particularly vexing bone of contention between them during the entire period of their official association.

Gorgas never missed an opportunity to answer the charge of high costs with facts and figures. From the lecture platform and through the press he repeated his contention that, instead of being excessive, the cost of protecting the health of the canal workers and their families was, and always had been, quite modest indeed.

"Reports have gone out from the Isthmus, both from those in authority and from newspaper writers, to the effect that sanitation has been very expensive, that when the work shall have been finished, sanitation will have cost five per cent of the total expense," he said in a Commencement address at Johns Hopkins University in 1912.

This comes from getting the expenses of the Sanitary Department confounded with those of sanitation. The Sanitary Department spends a great deal of money that has no relation whatever to sanitation. For instance, more than half the revenues of the Sanitary Department are spent upon hospitals, dispensaries, etc., things which have no relation whatever to sanitation. It is just as misleading to call such things on the Isthmus sanitation as it would be here in Baltimore to charge to the Health Department the expenses of all hospitals and dispensaries and the incomes of all the doctors and nurses. If this were done, the expenses of the Health Department of Baltimore would amount to a very large per cent of the total expense of the city government. As a matter of fact, sanitation on the Isthmus has cost us about three hundred and sixty-five thousand dollars per annum. This is about one cent per day per capita for the total population; and, when we get through, we will have spent on sanitation considerably less than four million dollars, instead of twenty million dollars, as has been stated; less than one per cent of the total cost of the canal, instead of five per cent.

In his book, *Sanitation in Panama,* Gorgas gives some examples of the bookkeeping inconsistencies of which he complained. He mentions, for instance, the promise made by the Canal Commission to workers from the United States that, should they die on the Isthmus, their bodies would be prepared for burial and returned to their homes without cost to their survivors—truly a generous and laudable arrangement. But the fulfilment of that promise was made a responsibility of the Sanitary Department, which was obliged to establish and maintain a free undertaking business. This service, which had nothing to do with sanitation and should have been paid for from a general fund, naturally increased the expenses of that department and gave an unfair impression of the cost of protecting workmen's health.

Nor was the Sanitary Department's venture into the undertaking field limited to the embalming and transportation of the bodies of deceased canal workers. As time went on and the non-employee population increased, its undertaking facilities were made available to the sorrowing friends and relatives of those who had no connection whatsoever with canal construction. These people, having no claim upon the Canal Commission for free undertaking service, paid for it. Sums thus received, however, were not credited to the Sanitary Department but to other agencies. This unusual way of keeping books was emphasized when death overtook the President of the Republic of Panama. The undertaking staff of the Sanitary Department embalmed the body at a cost estimated at one hundred dollars or more, but when the bill for this service was presented and paid by the former Chief Executive's family, not a cent of it was made available to that department, the entire amount being credited to engineering and construction accounts.

Even the excellent medical and surgical care provided at Ancon Hospital was turned to the disadvantage of the Sanitary Department, and its very excellence increased that disadvantage. Not only did it attract paying patients from the Canal Zone and the Republic of Panama, but it also began receiving many sick persons from as far away as Mexico on the north and Chile on the south, cutting heavily into the patronage formerly enjoyed by the leading hospitals of the United States and Europe. As these patients were able to pay, and pay well, every admission meant a nice profit to the Canal Commission. However, although the full expense of maintaining the hospital was charged to the Sanitary Department, the sums received in payment for this service were credited, like the other payments that have been mentioned, to construction and engineering and not to sanitation. In similar fashion, the cost of providing institutional care for more than 125 insane persons sent to Ancon Hospital on a contract basis by the government of Panama was entered on the books as a sanitation expense, but the seventy-five cents per patient per day which the Panamanian government paid for their care was added to the general fund for the construction of the canal. Little wonder that Gorgas, sensitive over the charge of excessive costs of sanitation, complained: "It seems as though the laws were framed with the idea of making sanitation appear to have cost as much as possible and the construction of the canal as little as possible."

He voiced that complaint in his address as president of the American Society of Tropical Medicine at its 1910 meeting:

The ordinary man in speaking of the Sanitary Department has in mind a department such as the Health Department of New York. Besides performing such functions as the Health Department of New York performs, the Sanitary Department on the Isthmus cares for all the sick, both in the hospitals and in dispensaries, administers the national quarantine, does the street cleaning and garbage collecting, reclaims waste lands, pays the salaries of some fifteen ministers of the gospel, cares for all the cemeteries, does a general undertaking and embalming business for some eighty thousand people, and, besides all this, pays directly to the Engineering Department about two hundred thousand dollars per year. . . . Considering our average population for the past five years as one hundred thousand, we have an appropriation for sanitation during the same period averaging $3.88 per capita per year.

Even this modest expenditure, he insisted, was more than should be charged to sanitation:

But these figures could be still further reduced if we were an independent sanitary department there on the Isthmus with the object simply of doing the work we are at present doing. But sanitation is not our [the Canal Commission's] primary object. We [the Sanitary Department] are there as part of a great organization for building a canal. And we have to fit into this organization, irrespective of whether it is advantageous for the Sanitary Department or not. For instance, we find a piece of swamp land belonging to the Panama Railroad. As the Panama Railroad is owned by the government, we cannot make it abate this nuisance. So, in order to preserve health conditions, we have to ask Congress for one hundred thousand dollars with which to fill it in. We do this, and the day after the work

is finished the Panama Railroad rents the land on a rental basis
of two hundred thousand dollars. Of course this is excellent
business for the United States. It spends one hundred thousand
dollars and immediately clears one hundred per cent. But it
calls the work sanitation [and] makes the Sanitary Department
pay for it, but pockets all the profits that arise therefrom. If
the Sanitary Department on the Isthmus were the ordinary
health department of one of our home cities, there would be
no expense involved in abating the above nuisance. A trans-
action in just about the circumstances and figures as described
above has occurred to the Sanitary Department on the Isthmus.

Or again we have a telephone system in our general hospital
costing one hundred and fifty dollars per month. A general
order is issued by the chairman directing that all telephones
be consolidated into one department and a flat rate charged.
At the end of the month the Sanitary Department gets a bill
for two hundred dollars for these same phones that the month
before the Sanitary Department ran for one hundred and fifty
dollars. I am not speaking in criticism. I do not doubt that
the sum total of running all the telephones was less than it
had been before. But to the hospital it was more expensive and
not so efficient. These instances could be multiplied into the
thousands in all directions.

In return for the modest outlay made for sanitation,
Gorgas was fond of pointing out, the canal workers
enjoyed such a great improvement in health conditions
that days of absence from their jobs attributable to illness were 39,420,000 fewer than they would have been
had the former morbidity rates prevailed. He never
tired of telling what this meant in terms of dollars-and-
cents savings to the taxpayers.

It cost us about one dollar a day to care for a sick man on
the Isthmus [he wrote in *Sanitation in Panama*]. The Commission cared for the sick free of charge. Therefore every day
of sickness prevented on the Isthmus lessened the expense which
the Commission had to bear by one dollar. The Commission
was therefore saved by this sanitary work, if we consider the
whole ten years of construction, $39,420,000.

But this was only a part of the saving he credited to
sanitation:

If three hundred men out of every one thousand of our employees had been sick every day, the efficiency of the other seven hundred would have been correspondingly decreased. The other seven hundred would have been more or less debilitated and more or less depressed, and the amount of work turned out daily by each man would have been considerably less than it actually was for the employee enjoying good health and cheerful surroundings. We should have had to pay considerably higher wages if the Isthmus had continued to bear the reputation during our period of construction which it had always borne during the years preceding 1904—if, for instance, it had been known that three out of every ten men going to work on the canal would be sick all the time, that two out of every ten would die each year, and that the whole ten would be dead at the end of five years. . . . I do not think that anyone familiar with the conditions would question the statement that a larger sum in dollars and cents was saved to the Commission in these ways than was saved by the direct decrease in the number of sick.

The subject was a touchy one to Gorgas. He had effectively silenced those who had been saying that he could never make Panama a healthy place in which to live and work. The record was there for all to see. However, his other critics who hid behind hypocritical claims to devotion to economy were more persistent and more difficult to deal with. But he was strong in the faith that they too would eventually be put to shame, as eventually they were.

CHAPTER X

The Reclaiming of the Tropics

NOTWITHSTANDING his position of official subordination to a man who had no faith in his sanitary program and a bitter antagonism for him personally,
Gorgas kept up his enthusiasm for that program and
never for a moment relaxed in his determination to preserve all the gains it had made. Generally speaking, that
determination was realized, for at no time between the
arrival of Colonel Goethals and the opening of the canal
to the water-borne traffic of the world was the progress
of its construction jeopardized or seriously interfered
with by disease.

Gorgas's increasing stature as a world figure was
bringing, and would continue to bring, its inevitable
honors. One of the greatest of these, his election in
June, 1908, as president of the powerful American Medical Association, has already been mentioned. In 1907 the
Liverpool School of Tropical Medicine chose him from
among the medical men of his time as recipient of its
coveted Mary Kingsley medal. Honorary degrees
descended upon him in a pleasant shower, coming from,
among others, the University of Pennsylvania, Harvard,
Brown University, the Jefferson Medical College, the
University of Alabama, Tulane University, and his alma
mater, the University of the South.

No less gratifying than these symbols of his fame
were the tributes paid him and his work by newspaper
and magazine writers who visited the Isthmus and by
those in high and humble positions among whom he
lived and labored.

Owen Wilson, writing in the *World's Work,* called him "one of the most popular officers of the United States Army." Another visitor described him as "a Southern gentleman of the old school." A canal employee referred to him as "the most thorough man I ever knew." He impressed another canal worker as one "absolutely unmoved by slights, praise, success, defeat —anything except sickness and suffering." A third said: "Folks would rather go to his house than anywhere else on the Isthmus." A fourth, throwing all restraint to the winds, called him "the best loved man on earth today." A fifth said he possessed "the same dry wit that Mark Twain had." Still another averred: "If you are in trouble—jail trouble, hospital trouble, homesick trouble, heart trouble, or money trouble—send for Gorgas." A newspaper man wrote of him: "He has inspired fifty thousand laborers to live cheerfully for several years in a fever swamp, simply because he was with them."

Those who knew how genuine was Gorgas's interest in the canal workers and their families and how real was his desire to keep them contented as well as healthy readily understood why he had won such a firm and lasting grip upon their affections. They knew, for instance, how he would make visits to the hospitals as often as he could and how he would appear never too busy, even on his busiest days, to stop and chat with the sick and injured. They knew of his practice of showing up without ceremony or warning early in the morning, before starting out on the day's regular labors. And they knew with what eager anticipation the patients, rough manual laborers for the most part, would look forward to those early-morning visits.

The Gorgas genius for soothing disturbed feelings and shielding people's sensibilities was constantly in evidence. That yellow jack victim who said "it was worth having yellow fever to have been under the care of Colonel Gorgas" was one of a numerous body.

A typhoid fever patient was admitted to the hospital and assigned to bed number thirteen. The association in most people's minds of thirteen and bad luck, superstitious as it is, does not improve the morale of a person combating a fatal disease. The alert Gorgas eyes took this in when he stopped at that patient's bedside the next time he made rounds. Rising to the occasion, he instructed the attendant to assign the bed another number—twelve and one-half.

But sick people were by no means the only beneficiaries of the Gorgas gentleness and thoughtfulness of others. A doctor on the Sanitary Department staff would not make any important decisions himself, but, instead, passed his problems on to Gorgas in long and frequent letters asking what should be done in this and that situation. These tedious letters were referred to other members of the staff, and several of them fell into the hands of a physician not as long-suffering as Gorgas. Finally his patience became strained to the breaking point, and he prepared, for Gorgas's signature, a letter to the trouble-bringer suggesting in ungentle language that in future he refrain from troubling his superiors with anything but important matters. This doctor subsequently found, however, that his impetuous letter had gone no farther than Gorgas's desk; the chief sanitary officer had dictated one of an entirely different kind to take its place. Apologizing later for having done so, Gorgas told the author of the rejected missive that he did not wish to hurt the other's feelings.

His interest in things of the spirit, which had received such great impetus in the little Sunday school his mother had started many years before at Brierfield, found an outlet in the work of the Protestant church at Ancon. One of its most faithful attendants, he often took charge of its services when there was no minister present. His congregation on these occasions included representatives of practically every stratum of life on the Isthmus, from officials of high rank to convalescent manual laborers, who attended in bathrobes and bedroom slippers.

This religious leadership was by no means the only indication he has given of his interest in things of the spirit. Shortly after his birthday in 1909, he received from his mother a letter expressing her love and best wishes for that occasion. In his reply, he thanked her for it and added:

At fifty-five a man can feel a perceptible decline in his physical vigor. I can still stand more than most men I come in contact with but not what I could fifteen years ago. I can see very plainly that I have begun a decline in life that at some time must end in death.

This idea of death is not the bugbear to me that it used to be. I think that I have done a man's share of work in this life and look forward with pleasure to a period of rest, when I can enjoy myself reading, etc. But as soon as, through physical incapacity, I cease to be able to enjoy life, I am ready and anxious to begin my next existence. And the subject of my next existence now interests me more than any other subject. If I do not retain the relation that I have at present to those who are near and dear to me, I do not care for any further state. But it seems to me that all the probabilities are that we go on existing with the relations we have in this life. And I expect to die in that strong hope.

About two years later—Christmas-time in 1911, the last but one before his mother's death—he received from her a simple but exceedingly appropriate gift, which he acknowledged in the following letter:

Your Christmas present, *Why We May Believe in Life after Death,* has just been received in the mail today. It might generally appear rather a heavy subject for Christmas, but it is one that I am very much interested in.

I doubt if man will ever have positive knowledge on this subject. It certainly cannot be proved through the physical senses at present. Still I am convinced that we have a future life and, at my present stage of mental development, am probably more interested in this question than in any other. I always like to read what men of ability think on this question.

The presidency of the University of Alabama became vacant in 1911, and the trustees invited him to return to Tuscaloosa and become the head of the institution which his father had served in the same capacity and which his mother was then serving as librarian. Even had his relations with Colonel Goethals been less trying, the temptation to go back to the scenes of his childhood, to be with his mother during the brief time she would have before her death, and to spend the remainder of his life among those whom he had known in that delightful center of learning would have been strong indeed. With his official relations as they were, it must have been especially so. But he was not to be swerved from the completion of the task he had begun. The urgings that prompted his decision were delineated in a letter to Dr. J. H. Johnson, chairman of the University's Board of Trustees. He wrote:

DEAR DR. JOHNSON:

After consultation with the Secretary of War, General Wood and other friends, I have concluded that, till the canal was completed, my duty lay here and that I should decline your very flattering offer. I cabled you to that effect.

Nothing that could be offered me would be more attractive than the position tendered by the Board.

The University was established while my grandfather—Governor Gayle—occupied the chair of Governor of the State. Forty years afterward my father was President. And now, thirty years after my father, the chair is offered to me.

My mother has been librarian of the University for thirty years and still lives there.

During all this time the courtesy and consideration shown to my family have been unfailing, both by the trustees and the authorities of the University.

My great-grandfather, grandfather and father were citizens of Alabama and lived and died in the state. And my ancestry has been associated with the public affairs of Alabama from the time it became a territory. I was born in Alabama and expect to spend my declining days there.

The position you offer me would have allowed me to renew the association that an absence from the state of thirty years has more or less severed.

Every consideration of sentiment and affection binds me to both Alabama and the University with the strongest sort of ties.

If I had consulted alone my own feelings and wishes, I would have accepted without hesitation. But, on the other hand, comes into consideration my work here on the Isthmus of Panama. This so far is my life work, and it seems to me to be my duty to remain with the work till the canal is finished.

Will you be kind enough to express to the Board of Trustees my deep appreciation of the honor conferred upon me and my acute regret that I am unable to take up the very attractive work which they lay before me?

With kindest regards, I remain

Very sincerely yours,

W. C. GORGAS.

About two years later the governing board of the other distinguished institution of higher learning which his father had served as its chief administrative official tried to induce him to become its president. But to his alma mater, the University of the South, his answer was essentially the same as to the University of Alabama.

Notwithstanding offers like these and the many other honors that were being showered upon him, this was one of the saddest periods of Gorgas's life. For even all these things could not begin to heal the deep hurt which came with the death of his mother.

Maurice H. Thatcher was governor of the Canal Zone at the time and, knowing nothing of it, called upon Gorgas soon after the death message arrived. The latter welcomed him "in his usual gentle and cordial way" and told him of the news he had just received. Then, "with serene and smiling face," he began telling about his mother and her rare qualities of mind and heart, illustrating his description with incidents from the long, useful life of this "good angel"—incidents deeply etched upon the narrator's memory by the realization that, firm as was his faith in a reunion in the future life, he would never see her again this side the grave.

"In speaking of her in terms of idealization, rever-

ence and love," his visitor said later, "he seemed very
happy. Whatever pain may have tugged at his heart
seemed to yield, so far as visible evidence or expression
was concerned, to the proud satisfaction and memory
which were his because of the fact that he had been
blessed with such a mother. To him she was not dead,
and could never be. He thought of her only in terms of
life and loveliness."

Some years later, while Gorgas was traveling in
Europe, he visited the tomb of Mark Twain's wife, on
which he read these words:

> Warm summer sun, shine brightly here.
> Warm southern wind, blow softly here.
> Green sod above, lie light, lie light.
> Good night, dear heart, good night.

The simple inscription touched him deeply. In-
stantly his thoughts were back in a small cemetery on
a quiet Alabama hillside. He turned to his companion.

"That ought to be on Mother's grave," he observed
solemnly. "It fits her so well."

Time, which is supposed to be a cure for the sharp
pain of bereavement, only partly healed the hurt caused
by her death. The anniversary of every important event
of her life—her birth, her marriage, and especially her
death—brought a rush of tender, sad memories. And
how he missed the inspiration of her love as an antidote
for Goethals' animosity.

Although officially the status of Goethals and that of
Gorgas were unaffected by changes in administration in
Washington, Gorgas found his position less onerous after
Woodrow Wilson became President in 1913. This was
due to Wilson's appointment of William Jennings Bryan
as his Secretary of State and the subsequent appointment
of Bryan's close personal friend, Richard L. Metcalfe,
as governor of the Canal Zone. Thanks to the Bryan-
Metcalfe friendship, the new governor's position was
much stronger than his predecessor's had been, and its

DR. GORGAS AND HIS MOTHER, TUSCALOOSA, ABOUT 1908

added strength was won at the expense of Goethals, an appointee of a Republican administration which had been rejected by the electorate.

"Goethals is as mild as a lamb," Gorgas wrote in a letter to a member of his family. "He does not feel quite as certain of this good Democratic administration as he did of the former."

Then he went on to explain this lion-to-lamb metamorphosis:

> We see a good deal of our new Governor, Metcalfe, former editor of the *Commoner,* and like him and his family. He has a much stronger position than any former governor. We are all making love to him for Billie Bryan's sake. It does me good to see old Goethals bend the knee and look sweet when Metcalfe is around. I did not think he had it in him. Such a difference in the way he treats Metcalfe and the way he treated Thatcher, though Thatcher came here as a Taft appointee under a Republican administration and with the personal backing of his senator. But Goethals knew that he had Taft. About Wilson he is uncertain. And Bryan has shown so much determination that Goethals does not want to come in conflict with Metcalfe.

Gorgas also had other reasons to be highly pleased with his situation, in spite of all Goethals could do. For one thing, the country's leading newspaper and magazine writers and many of its prominent men in other fields were full of praise of him and his achievements. All this was not enough to silence his critics of course. But it made much of their yapping ridiculous.

One of his greatest admirers was Sir William Osler, who paid him and his work this tribute in an address at the University of Edinburgh while serving as Regius Professor of Medicine at the University of Oxford:

> There is nothing to match it [the sanitation of the Canal Zone] in the history of human achievement. Before our eyes today the most striking experiment ever made in sanitation is in progress. The digging of the Panama Canal was acknowledged to be a question of the health of the workers. For four centuries the Isthmus has been the white man's grave. . . .

Here is a chapter in human achievement for which it would be hard to find a parallel.

"From a practical point of view the work accomplished by Dr. Gorgas and his 'five hundred brave young Americans' in opening the tropics to safe residence by the white races takes rank with the achievements of the great explorers," averred the New York *Sun* in a laudatory editorial.

It may not have the same appeal to the imagination; the quest after microbes, the chase of the mosquito and the fly, the draining of marshes and the disinfection of stagnant pools are not so romantic in their seeming as the ranging of the seas, the penetration of the jungle, wrestling with the elements or taming the wild races of mankind. But in beneficent effect upon coming generations the quiet man of science may prove to tower above the navigator and pioneer, and his name may be written larger in the books of the future.

Sir Frederick Trevos, sergeant surgeon to King George V of England, a member of the Advisory Board of the British Army Medical Service, and president of the London Radium Institute, was equally generous in his praise of Gorgas's achievements in Panama upon returning to New York after making a visit there.

"I think," he said, "that Colonel Gorgas' work may be accepted as a standard of what preventive medicine should be in the tropics. What has been done on the Isthmus in the way of sanitation and the prevention of disease is as good as anything could possibly be in that line. . . . I may say that I found at Panama a world exhibit."

Surprisingly enough, in view of his earlier willingness to ally himself with Gorgas's enemies, William Howard Taft made a visit to the Alabamian's alma mater to tell a younger generation of students and a host of educational and political dignitaries that Gorgas's sanitary work had made the Panama Canal possible.

"You have in the Isthmus a gentleman named Gorgas

to whose teachings and to whose practices we owe the structure of the Panama Canal," he said.

I say that with care. The French attempted to build the canal, as you know. There were a number of obstructions, but the chief obstruction was malaria and yellow fever. During the Spanish War, through the enterprise, the self-sacrifice and proficient enthusiasm of the Army Medical Corps, of which Colonel Gorgas was most prominent, we learned a good deal about malignant malaria and all about yellow fever, and we found that both were communicated by mosquitoes. Having found the mosquito, we had the secret, and through the actual direction of Colonel Gorgas on the Isthmus, in two years malignant malaria was reduced to a kind not serious in its obstruction to work, and yellow fever disappeared entirely. Therefore the construction of the Panama Canal would have been impossible without Colonel Gorgas.

From an eminent member of Gorgas's own profession came still another glowing tribute to his work in the Canal Zone. Sir Patrick Manson, famed English specialist in tropical diseases, felt that his name should head the list of all the heroes of Panama, because "without what Gorgas has accomplished, the canal could not have been completed without a loss of life from disease that would have been appalling."

Exactly what was this achievement in health protection which evoked such enthusiasm? How did the health conditions that prevailed during the early period of canal construction compare with those prevailing as the great army of workmen neared the completion of their monumental task?

The dramatic conquest of yellow fever has already been described. The reader is familiar with the sharp decline in the killing and disabling power of this dread disease between June, 1905, when there were sixty-two new cases and nineteen yellow fever deaths, and December of that year, when the official reports listed the last case of yellow fever ever to originate in the Canal Zone and the second to the last case ever to originate on the entire Isthmus of Panama.* However, the story of other aspects of the Gorgas conquest of disease remains to be told.

"Yellow fever is frightful, because it kills and does it quickly," Gorgas once told a newspaper writer.

Aside from its physical effect, therefore, it seizes upon the imagination and by the terror of its name increases its power to work death and demoralization. On the other hand, malaria, being not so surely and speedily fatal, occasions less fear, yet, as a matter of fact, causes more incapacity than all other tropical diseases combined. If there were no way to control yellow fever and malaria, the hot countries would be left to the inertia of the ages and the blacks who inhabit them.

In order that the white man might rescue the Canal Zone and the tropics generally from "the inertia of the ages," Gorgas made as determined an effort to stamp out malaria as he did to free the area from yellow fever. Unfortunately, this effort fell considerably short of the complete success that rewarded the other one.

Any consideration of the malaria situation in Panama cannot properly go back as far as 1904, when Gorgas arrived to begin his work, or even to 1905, for malaria records for those two years are not considered trustworthy. However, in 1906 there were 821 malaria cases for every 1,000 employees, and the malaria death rate was 8.79 per 1,000 employees. The next year the morbidity rate dropped nearly 50 per cent, to 424 per 1,000 employees, while the malaria mortality rate took an even greater drop, to 3.92 per 1,000 employees. By 1913 the malaria morbidity rate had declined to only 76 per 1,000 employees—less than one-tenth the 1906 rate— and the malaria death rate had dropped to only .37 per 1,000 employees, or only slightly more than one-twenty- fourth the 1906 rate. However, it was not until 1921, seven years after the first ship used the new waterway,

* This refers only to cases of urban yellow fever. Cases of jungle yellow fever have recently been discovered in Panama. This type, somewhat different from the type Gorgas battled so valiantly, is described in the Epilogue.

that the records show a single year in which no canal employee died of malaria, while every year except two has brought at least 144 cases of this disease among canal employees.

His inability to eliminate malaria at Panama as completely as he had eliminated it at Havana was a source of much chagrin to Gorgas, all the greater because he was convinced that he would have succeeded in doing so had he received the proper support from his superiors. He expressed that conviction many times in frank talks with his intimates and in at least one public address. The occasion of that address was the dedication on April 30, 1915, of the Washington University Medical School in St. Louis.

Although he carefully refrained from mentioning Colonel Goethals by name, he made it so plain that he had him in mind that the newspaper men reporting the ceremonies identified Goethals unequivocably as the object of the speaker's criticism.

"He [Gorgas] indicated his belief that, if Colonel Goethals had been in full control in the four years before 1908, as he was after that time, the sanitary authorities might not have succeeded in doing away with yellow fever," the *Post-Dispatch* story declared.

Colonel Goethals was not mentioned by name in Dr. Gorgas' address, but the reference to his office was explicit. Dr. Gorgas told of his own success in Havana in abolishing first yellow fever and then malaria, and said that, in May, 1904, he began use of the same methods in Panama. In the Fall of 1905, he said, the last case of yellow fever occurred in Panama, and from 1906 to 1907 the reduction of the malaria death rate began. It continued to decrease, he said, but the disease did not disappear, as it had done in Havana. Then he stated his reasons for blaming Colonel Goethals for the partial failure in regard to malaria.

Gorgas was quoted directly by the newspaper as follows:

I was much disappointed that we did not get rid of malaria

on the Isthmus of Panama, as we did at Havana. I had fully expected to do so, and when we went to the Isthmus we put into effect the same anti-malaria measures that had been so successful at Havana. The measures were vigorously pushed for the first four years. At the end of our four years of work in May, 1908, small towns, such as Ancon, had been completely freed of malaria, as had Havana. The malaria rate had been reduced from 821 per thousand [in 1906] to 282 in 1908.

In 1907 a new Commission was placed by the President in control of the Isthmus, and in 1908 all power on the Isthmus was concentrated in the hands of a single man, the chairman of the Commission. This officer thought it advisable to make radical changes in the methods of sanitation. These changes, ordered by the chairman, took execution of the anti-malaria work out of the hands of the sanitary authorities and placed it in the hands of men who had no special knowledge of anti-malaria work.

I argued against these changes as forcibly as I could, but to no avail.

Looking back over my fifteen years of experience in tropical sanitation, I believe that, if I could have continued at Panama the same methods that I had used previous to 1908, the results would have been the same as at Havana, and the canal workers would have been as entirely free from malaria as were the citizens of Havana. And I feel equally convinced that, if our chairman of 1908 had been able to put into effect in 1904 the methods he forced upon me in 1908, we would not have accomplished the sanitary success at Panama which we accomplished prior to the year 1908.

Gorgas's reference to Goethals could hardly have been more specific of course had he called him by name over and over. His plain speaking at that particular time was undoubtedly due in large measure, if not entirely, to the publication just a few days before of *Government of the Canal Zone,* the Goethals story of the digging of the canal, in which its author went to a great deal of trouble to avoid giving any credit at all to Gorgas and attributed the improvement in health conditions solely to the discoveries of Sir Ronald Ross, Walter Reed, and the other members of the Reed Board. His thesis was that these men had shown how the Canal

Zone or any other region could be made healthful and
that it required no particular ability to make use of the
knowledge which they had made available.

"With Sir Ronald Ross' discovery of the cause of
malaria which had led him to adopt means for its reduction and eradication in Egypt and India, and with Reed,
Lazear, and Carroll proving the theory that yellow fever
is transmitted by the mosquito and formulating rules
which freed Cuba from the ravages of that dread disease,
there remained but the application of the methods followed elsewhere to secure similar results on the Isthmus
with respect to these two diseases," he wrote. "The work
in Panama developed nothing new."

Goethals also showed how little he thought of Gorgas's work and how much credit he accorded Reed, Ross,
and the others in an article published in *Scribner's Magazine* for June, 1915, which reached its readers shortly
after Gorgas spoke at St. Louis. In that article, the
fourth in a series he wrote for that publication on "The
Building of the Panama Canal," he dismissed the subject
of sanitation in the following brief paragraphs, conspicuously lacking in any mention of the chief sanitarian:

Much that was of inestimable value had been learned from
the French and from their experience, and that they builded
well so far as they went is the consensus of opinion of all those
who know. Their failure was due not to faulty engineering,
for their engineering was above criticism, nor to the lack of
proper sanitation, which appears to be the popular belief—for
they worked on through the various epidemics that occurred,
new men undauntedly taking the places of those who fell—but
purely and simply to poor and maladministration. They were
handicapped also in that they constituted merely a private cor-
poration working under a concession, without absolute control
over the territory—a situation which brought difficulties and
delays. These were removed entirely when the United States
acquired its rights through treaty provisions.

The forces of the United States were fortunate in other
respects, for before the transfer of the work to them preventive
medicine had made such advances as to make possible the con-

version of the pest hole into a habitat where most white men could live and work. The diseases which sapped the energy and vitality of the men and struck terror to their souls were malaria and yellow fever. The cause of the former had been discovered by Sir Ronald Ross, of the British Army, who formulated rules by which an infected locality could be rid of its influences. Not only were his theory and practices known, but we had the benefit of his advice and experience, for he visited the Isthmus on invitation of the Commission at the instigation of the health authorities in order that we might have his assistance. After Sir Ronald Ross' discovery, Doctors Reed, Lazear and Carroll, in Cuba, with Aristedes Agramonte, a Cuban immune, proved the correctness of the theory advanced by Dr. Carlos Finlay, of Havana, that yellow fever was transmitted only by the mosquito, and prescribed the methods that resulted in ridding Cuba of that dread disease. It naturally followed that the Isthmus could be freed in the same way.

Not a word of praise for Gorgas. Just an indirect but sweeping dismissal of any suggestion that he had played even a fairly important part in this transformation of a pesthole into a place where men could live and work in good health. Plainly, in Goethals's prejudiced eyes, the problem of saving human life at Panama had been solved once and for all by Ross, Agramonte, Carroll, Lazear, Finlay, and Reed. Any amateur sanitarian could have memorized their simple rules and gone forth into Panama's steaming jungles slaying the disease dragons right and left! The killing of mosquitoes in astronomical quantities and the prevention of billions of others from coming into existence were nothing at all. Not sanitation but administration—the Goethals part of the canal-digging enterprise—was the secret of success in Panama. How wrong all the others had been in saying all these years that disease was responsible for the failure of the French as canal-builders. Had Ross, Agramonte, and the others been born half a century earlier, the French would hardly have been troubled by yellow fever while working on the canal, assuming of course that they would have had a George Washington Goethals to prevent them from falling into the errors of "poor and maladministration."

Nobody was more ready than Gorgas himself to admit his debt to Ross, Lazear, Agramonte, Walter Reed, and the others. That he proved any number of times. One of them has already been mentioned—the time when a friend called him "one of our great men," whereupon Gorgas expostulated that he was not a great man but was merely doing his best to follow in the footsteps of a great man, Walter Reed. About a decade and a half later Gorgas addressed the Royal Society of Medicine in London, and in that speech he declared: "During the intervening twenty-four years [between 1880, when the French began work on the Canal, and 1904, when the Americans took charge] it had been discovered that malaria and yellow fever were transmitted from one human being to another by the mosquito—malaria by the *Anopheles* and yellow fever by the *Stegomyia*." Had the Americans known no more about these two diseases in 1904 than the French had known in 1880, he freely admitted, he did not believe they could have done any better than the French had done in the way of controlling them. These discoveries were credited by the speaker with having had an effect "as far-reaching as those of any discoveries ever made in medicine." Here certainly was no braggart claiming credit for the work of others.

He did quite properly claim credit for having reaped for humanity's enjoyment the rich fruits of these men's labors. He knew, as we know, that all the knowledge regarding the relationship between the mosquito and disease which a million Ronald Rosses and Walter Reeds could unearth would never save a single human life unless it could be applied to the actual saving of life. He knew that many communities had been visited by yellow fever outbreaks after the Walter Reed discoveries had been given to the world, simply because these places had had no one on the job capable of making use of those discoveries in a practical way. He knew that very little progress had been made in the curbing of malaria throughout the tropical world years after Ronald Ross had told how it could be done. And, for that matter, we know that for decades after Goethals wrote that astonishing article, malaria continued to afflict more Southerners and imposed a heavier economic burden upon the people of the South than any other single disease known to medical science. How utterly absurd it was to pretend that the complete conquest of yellow fever and the effective curbing of malaria at Panama were due virtually altogether to the work of these truth-bringers, great though their contributions were and powerless though Gorgas might have been without them! Gorgas claimed for himself, and his supporters have claimed for him, only the credit due him as the person who translated these men's knowledge into the language of the morbidity and mortality figures. And that indeed was an epochal accomplishment.

Goethals had not the slightest reason to believe that the work of Walter Reed, Ronald Ross, and the others had been sufficient of itself to solve the disease problem at the Isthmus, for the official records told an undeniable story of death and invalidism during the 1905 yellow fever epidemic which, competent health workers are certain, would have raged indefinitely, in spite of the great knowledge these men gave the world, had not Gorgas or some other genius of sanitation made good use of that knowledge. Nor indeed did Goethals make any effort to minimize the seriousness of that epidemic. On the contrary, he referred to it more than once. One occasion when he did so was during an interview with John O. Collins, of the *Manufacturers' Record,* who quoted him as follows:

The black shadow of pestilence was hovering over the Isthmus [in 1905]. There were in hospitals, stricken with yellow

fever, more than one hundred Americans, a third of whom
were gathered to the final harvest of death. Those who had
escaped were in no mood for jubilation of any sort, and their
one desire was to flee as quickly as possible from what they believed to be an accursed land. Their fright-dimmed eyes could
not see so far into the near future as to catch the first glimmer
of the coming dawn of a veritable day of freedom for the Isthmus—a day that was to mark its lasting deliverance from the
scourge of centuries and convert it from a valley of death into a
land of health and comfort.

Again no mention of Gorgas. No reference to his
part in converting the Isthmus of Panama "from a valley
of death into a land of health and comfort."

Government of the Canal Zone reached the book-
stores just before Princeton University conferred an
honorary degree upon its author, and the eulogistic citation that accompanied the bestowal of this honor indicated that President John Grier Hibben had both read
and been greatly impressed by it. At any rate, the citation was as completely lacking in credit to Gorgas as the
Goethals opus. Calling Goethals "a Hercules who has
put health in the abode of pestilence," the eminent edu-
cator praised him for his "labors in colossal construction, tropical sanitation and arduous administration"
and characterized the Goethals attainments as "too vast
and complex to recount or describe."

This was too much for a certain Gorgas admirer, one
Douglas Broan, who, speaking for himself and others
who shared his admiration, wrote a letter of protest to
the New York *Tribune* in which he insisted that the
"health in the abode of pestilence" should not be
credited to Goethals but "was put there by Colonel
William C. Gorgas and his aides." Instead of contributing to improved health conditions on the Isthmus,
the letter-writer insisted, Goethals had seriously handicapped Gorgas and the other health workers at every
opportunity both by interfering with their work and by
curtailing Gorgas's authority, and only the fact that

Gorgas had laid the solid foundation for his sanitary program before Goethals's arrival prevented a major health
crisis which might easily have made completion of the
canal impossible.

Panama had become a clean city, well paved and with proper
sewerage disposal and water supply. The good work was progressing in Colon. The methods of protecting the water supply
of the government cantonments across the Isthmus from any
possible contamination were firmly established. The work done
by the medical men of the Army in Cuba had proved that the
digging of the canal would depend more on protection from
and destruction of the mosquitoes than on the number and
size of steam shovels.

Mr. Broan, unlike many others, based his appraisal
of Gorgas's work upon the latter's sanitary program as
a whole, rather than solely upon his complete conquest
of yellow fever and his less than complete but effective
curbing of malaria. In that he had the support of the
mortality records of the canal-digging period, which also
emphasize the success of other aspects of the Gorgas
campaign of health protection. They show, for instance,
that the general death rate for employees dropped from
41.73 per 1,000 in 1906 to only 9.18 per 1,000 in 1912.
By 1915 the rate had dropped another 37 per cent to
only 5.77 per 1,000, the lowest general death rate among
canal employees for more than a quarter of a century.

In 1906 an average of 28.48 employees out of every
1,000 were constantly kept from their ordinary duties
by sickness or injury. This rate dropped to only 21.11
per 1,000 in 1912 and only 10.28 per 1,000 in 1915.
Marked reductions were also achieved in the rates for
the non-employee population of the Canal Zone and
for the residents of Panama and Colon, which, while outside the Canal Zone, were under the sanitary control of
the United States Government.

When we consider that the Isthmus of Panama long
had the reputation—and few questioned its right to it—

of being "the worst pest-hole in the Americas," and that its ill fame was once so great that sea captains had to shanghai sailors to handle ships putting into its ports, it is an eloquent tribute to the work of Gorgas and his fellow-sanitarians that in 1914, when the general death rate for Canal Zone employees was only 7.04 per 1,000 and that for the entire Canal Zone population (employees and non-employees combined) was only 15.31 per 1,000, the general death rate for the United States Registration Area was 13.65 per 1,000.

As early as 1910 the general death rate for the entire area under American sanitary control was 29 per cent lower than that for Charleston, 21 per cent lower than that for Savannah, 8 per cent lower than the rate for Mobile, Gorgas's birthplace, 7 per cent lower than that for Richmond, 6 per cent lower than that for Key West, slightly lower than those for Memphis and New Orleans, and only 8 per cent higher than that for the nation's capital. Even when proper allowance is made for the relatively small number of women and children on the Isthmus, which undoubtedly affected the death rates, this showing cannot fail to reflect great credit upon Gorgas and those associated with him in his work of life-saving.

Gorgas reviewed the fruits of his labors up to that time in an address to the students and faculty of the University of the South, in June, 1912. The French, with an average of 10,000 employees, lost through death during their period of construction 22,000 workers, while the Americans, with an average force of 33,000 men, lost during approximately the same length of time only 4,000, he said, and continued:

The French, with an average of 1,600 white employes, lost during their construction period from yellow fever 2,000 men. We, with an average of 5,000 white employes, during the same length of time have lost from yellow fever only 17. Our maximum of sickness from malaria was in 1906, when we had in hospital from that disease 821 men out of every 1,000 of our employes. This number has been steadily reduced till the year 1911, when we had only 184 out of every 1,000 sick in hospital from malaria.

The general health conditions of the whole community are about those of a healthy community in the United States. . . . I think a still better way of satisfying oneself with regard to health conditions is direct observation of the American employes. They as a class are rugged and healthy-looking, of good color and energetic and active in movement. They look more like the farmer and his family of the Northwest than like people who have lived in the tropics for four or five years.

A certain grizzled canal worker undoubtedly was guilty of considerable exaggeration when he pointed to a piece of castoff machinery and opined that the French, who had left it there to rust, had failed to dig the waterway because "they didn't know the difference between a bumblebee and a mosquito." He was striking at the truth, however, and when the mortality and morbidity reports kept emphasizing from month to month the success of the sanitary program, it became evident to those in charge of actual construction and to the American people generally that the failure of the French need not be followed by failure of the Americans, who, fortunately, had learned that important difference. Thus, with the disease curse of the centuries forever removed, lingering doubts as to the success of the great enterprise vanished, and the work of construction went ahead rapidly.

It went ahead so rapidly indeed that, on August 15, 1914, when vast armies were meeting in mortal combat in the opening battles of the First World War, the dream of the ages—the dream of Christopher Columbus and of Ferdinand and Isabella, of Charles V and of Balboa, of De Lesseps and of Goethe—came true. The symbol of its coming true was the S. S. *Ancon,* which on that day moved slowly away from her pier near the canal's Atlantic entrance, eased into the narrow waterway, and took her position in one of the newly completed locks, where she was taken in tow by small electric locomotives. Moving without a hitch from lock to lock in this fashion, her superstructure rose higher and higher until at last her bow was eighty-five feet above sea level. From that peak, as it were, she began the rapid descent through Gatun Lake and the remaining locks to the Pacific entrance, not far from where Balboa, several centuries before, had come to a halt with his tired Indians and his dismantled boats and completed his preparations to explore this new ocean.

It was only in an official sense, however, that the *Ancon* was the first craft to transit the canal. Actually, a rival had covered that same distance many months earlier, going in the opposite direction. It was not a rival in size, for in that respect it was hardly comparable with the luxurious steamship which made the first transit that August day. It was indeed one of the humblest of all the instruments of navigation—a simple canoe. Its passengers, who also of course constituted its crew, were Gorgas, LePrince, and Colonel Charles Mason. Work of construction was still under way at that time, and once or twice they narrowly escaped serious injury by failing to understand frantic signals warning them that a dynamite blast was about to be set off. They survived the hail of dirt and rock and the other dangers, however, and in time arrived at Colon, to the surprised delight of their friends, who knew nothing of their plans for the adventure.

The official transit of the S. S. *Ancon* and the holiday-spirit transit of the canoe symbolized more than appeared on the surface. It was far more than the mastery of the troublesome landslides and mountains that kept moving into the pathway of the diggers. It was even much more than the sanitary clean-up of one of the world's most ill-famed disease areas and the turning of approximately 550 square miles of such a place into a virtual health resort. That vastly more important accomplishment, in Gorgas's eyes, was the lifting of the barrier which had largely kept civilized man from the tropics and the opening of that vast belt of the earth's surface—much of it among the world's richest and otherwise most desirable areas—to development. The curse of disease, having been removed from Panama, could also be removed from other parts—all other parts, if desired—of those regions lying near the equator, provided civilization was willing to pay the modest cost of its removal. The mosquito-killers and other health workers on the Isthmus had demonstrated that languor, inefficiency, disease, and death are not the inevitable concomitants of hot weather and tropical conditions generally.

Soon after Columbus made his epochal voyages, Gorgas remembered, the great European nations began huge colonization schemes in the tropics. But their efforts were largely futile. Those sent forth with high hopes fell prey to the miasmas and fevers they encountered. Those fortunate enough to escape death paid a fearful price for their adventure in lost health, reduced efficiency, and general disability. As time went on, the conviction gradually took shape in the European massmind that there was something mysterious in the climate of those tropical regions which marked them as cursed to all those who had not been hardened to them by generations of living there. Gradually there grew the belief that, as long as civilization might last, that curse of the tropics would remain to slay and incapacitate those from the temperate zones. This conviction had taken a particularly firm hold among the great colonizing nations like the Dutch, the English, the French, and the Portuguese.

But in withdrawing from the tropics, Gorgas reasoned, the white man must have evacuated a region that had cradled the human race in its infancy. For, in all the uncounted aeons lost in the black night of the past, when man knew neither clothing nor fire, where could he have lived and survived save in the tropics? Who, however hardy, could have reached adulthood, to say nothing of old age, north of the Potomac, the Rhine, or the Volga without these two to keep him warm? The tropics alone of all the earth's surface could have been capable of supporting life during those cradle days of civilization.

In Gorgas's mind, tropical diseases were a complete answer to the question that had long been asked by students of population movements—why civilized man had evacuated regions where nature had made life easier, where the problem of food and shelter had been no problem at all, and where happy living should have been the normal lot of everyone, and had gone to other parts of the earth that were plagued with harsh climate and unproductive soil. Tropical diseases, and they alone, he was convinced, had made the tropics uninhabitable, as far as the white man was concerned. After he had enjoyed these blessings for a long time, disease germs, finally introduced from nobody knew where, found the warm tropical climate as favorable to their growth and propagation as he had found it for his own. And so yellow fever, malaria, the plague, and any number of other diseases had obtained a firm foothold and begun their devastating assaults upon the human population. Epidemic after epidemic had swept upon these people with devastating fury. Their numbers had been heavily reduced by these periodic onslaughts, and always there had been left behind a state of fear, lest the next one be even more frightful and deadly. And so it was that the white man had been driven to those colder climates, where life was much harder and physical comfort could be had only by troublesome artificial means like fire and clothing.

But now Gorgas and his faithful aides had demonstrated that the tropics could be made healthful too, that the white man could return to this land where nature had bestowed her gifts so generously without having to pay for their enjoyment with his health or with life itself. Was it too much to expect that, as a result of that demonstration, the stream of population would again turn toward the tropics, leaving behind forever the cold, harsh climate of the temperate zones, with their unnatural ways of life and the great difficulty of satisfying physical needs? Gorgas was sure that it was not.

"The advances in tropical sanitation in the last fifteen years have shown that the white man can live in the tropics with as good health as he can in the temperate zones," he said in his address as president of the American Medical Association at a time when his sanitary program still faced several years of tough going.

This has been demonstrated both by our military occupation of Cuba and by our occupation of Panama. He can protect himself against disease in the tropics at no greater expense than he would have to undergo to protect himself against cold in the temperate zones. I think, therefore, the tendency in the next few centuries will be for the white man to drift to the tropics, and I dare predict that, by the time the year 1909 is as old as is at the present day the Norman conquest of England, localities in the tropics will be the centers of as powerful and as cultured a white civilization as any that will exist in temperate zones. I believe that our work in Cuba and Panama will then be looked upon as the earliest demonstration that the white man could flourish in the tropics and as the starting point of the settlement of these regions by the Caucasian. I am inclined to think that at that time the Panama Canal will be known less as a great commercial route or engineering feat than as a first demonstration that the white man can flourish in the tropics under most trying conditions.

Nor was Gorgas alone in that view. Newspaper editors, students of world affairs, and any number of others placed exactly the same interpretation upon his achievements.

"The conquest of tropical disease, when fully

achieved, promises to open the most luxuriant part of the earth's surface to the uses of civilized man," declared the New York *Sun* editorially.

Vast tracts of Asia, Africa, and South America, wherein until lately residence was almost the synonym of death, will become the field of busy colonization and fruitful cultivation. A new figure must be set on the earth's capacity to support mankind, and this means an expansion of the race in the course of a century or two, exceeding any that has taken place within historic times.

CHAPTER XI

The Battle of South Africa

A S GORGAS'S sanitary triumphs rose to new heights and his fame rapidly extended to the farthest corners of the earth, there came within the widening circle of admirers a certain South African mining man whose interest and admiration grew with his knowledge of those triumphs. But Samuel Evans, of the Transvaal Chamber of Mines, cared comparatively little about the Alabamian's conquest of yellow fever and malaria, upon which his fame largely rested. What interested him much more was Gorgas's achievement in a relatively unpublicized field—the protection of West Indian Negro laborers from pneumonia.

It is not generally known but it is true that pneumonia was far more fatal to Canal workers, especially Negroes, than either yellow fever or malaria, or even the two of them combined. In 1906, for instance, when malaria killed only 224 employees of the Canal Commission and the Panama Railroad Company and yellow fever was not even included in the mortality tables, there were 413 deaths from pneumonia, or more than half as many as those from all other causes combined, including accidents. In 1913, when there were more than twice as many employees as in 1906, there were only 47 pneumonia deaths. This reduction of more than 88 per cent in the face of an increase of more than 100 per cent in the number of prospective pneumonia victims was a triumph in lifesaving altogether worthy of the conqueror of malaria and yellow fever.

Gorgas's success in pneumonia control is attributable

to the same careful planning and attention to little things which brought such sweeping triumphs in other fields. Determined as he was to fight every form of illness that menaced the lives and impaired the working efficiency of canal employees, from the beginning he naturally devoted particular attention to this one. His searching, sympathetic eyes quickly discerned that the crowding of imported black laborers from the West Indies in the miserable huts which the Americans had taken over from the French created living conditions which made high sickness and mortality rates for this disease all but inevitable. He saw how they perspired from their arduous labors under the tropic sun and particularly how they had to work in the rains that fell in heavy downpours during two thirds of the year.

As he studied them and their disease problems more, he found out something else about them, something which appealed even more strongly to his pity than to his medical mind: the wages they received were so low that, even at the end of the day, they could not change to dry clothing for the simple but tragic reason that they had none. Whenever they would become drenched from rain or perspiration, therefore, they had no choice but to keep on wearing their wet garments. Many indeed could not even remove them at night. Wet or dry, what they had on during the day they also wore while asleep.

Gorgas could do nothing about the wage scales, and he had no control over the habits of tropical rainstorms either. But he could, and did, give those Negroes some wholesome advice about keeping as dry as their limited clothing would permit, sleeping in warm garments whenever they had any to sleep in and reporting any signs of illness. More important, he could do something about overcrowding. And he did.

There was considerable unused land belonging to the government, and he began using some of it. The long tiers of bunks that rose from the floor and reached

almost to the ceiling, each occupied by a workman who
could hardly cough or indeed breathe without exposing
others to whatever contagious disease he might have,
went the way of many another pre-Gorgas way of doing
things, and the men began enjoying the luxury of small
cabins, each close enough to its neighbors and to the
day's work for convenience but sufficiently removed
to insure an ample supply of health-giving, germ-free
air. The sharp reduction in pneumonia among this
group of workers followed as a matter of course.

Mr. Evans and his South African mining confreres
had the best of reasons for watching with growing interest this phase of the Gorgas sanitary triumph. For
they had been for some time wrestling with a grave
pneumonia problem among the Negro laborers employed
in their own mines, who were falling victims to this
disease literally in droves.

Nor was it altogether a high spirit of humanitari-
anism which inspired that interest and the desire to do
something about pneumonia. These men were under
heavy fire, being accused of coining tainted profits from
the blood and sweat of hordes of poorly paid, ill-treated,
and overworked natives lacking the intelligence and
leadership to protect themselves from a state of virtual
slavery. From press, platform, and pulpit had come ring-
ing denunciations of this form of human exploitation
and demands, in humanity's name, that it end. A strike
of Rand gold miners, who emphasized the prevailing
health conditions among their grievances and insisted
that something be done to reduce the appalling death
and morbidity rates, threw the pneumonia situation into
dramatic focus and fanned the flames of popular
resentment.

Had health conditions among those Africans brought
no more serious repercussions than wholesale denunciations, it is questionable whether it would have been
considered necessary to do anything drastic about im-

proving them. The mine moguls had run into storms
of public indignation before and had ridden them out,
one after the other. In spite of the outbursts, they had
continued the recruiting and transportation of these
half-civilized laborers and their assignment to the shovels, picks, and machinery that had been left idle by those
who had already fallen victims to the deadly pneu-
mococcus germs. But this time they could not merely
ride out the storm. As the mounting deaths from pneumonia sent the general death rate up to three hundred
and fifty per thousand—more than one out of three—the
British government took official cognizance of the situation by announcing that the recruiting of these laborers
would have to end unless they could be assured better
health protection. The Bureau of Native Affairs went
even further. It actually prohibited the employment
in the mines of workers from tropical Africa, who had
proved particularly easy prey to the disease. Thus the
harassed mine operators found themselves confronting
the threat of a complete shut-down of their properties,
normally employing in excess of two hundred thousand
workers. Either something drastic would have to be
done about the pneumonia situation or one of the greatest industries under the British flag would be forced into
bankruptcy.

That is why Mr. Evans became so interested in pneumonia control at Panama. Here, he was convinced, was
a man whose work was all cut out for him in Africa.
Here was an achievement that was crying to be repeated
in another part of the world.

To find out more about the Gorgas methods and
sanitary triumphs, Mr. Evans made a visit to Panama,
spending several weeks there. He and Gorgas became
warm personal friends. The Alabamian opened his
records, modestly described his procedures, and answered
the Britisher's questions. Then, even more fully convinced than before that the conquest of pneumonia on

the Isthmus of Panama could be duplicated in the diamond and gold mines of the Transvaal, the visitor sailed
for home to report to his business associates. His report
consisted in the main of a strongly worded recommendation that Gorgas be urged to visit South Africa and
devote his sanitary genius to their problem. The Chamber of Mines promptly approved the recommendation,
and the invitation was extended.

Some of Gorgas's friends strongly advised him to
decline it. His sixtieth birthday was not far away, and
he had complained more than once that he had lost
much of the strength and physical energy which had
been his in such abundant measure as a young man.
His reputation apparently was now at its peak, as great
as he could wish it to be, and he would risk its serious
impairment should he fail to repeat in South Africa the
success that had rewarded his labors at Havana and
Panama. All these considerations and many others were
called to his attention with a warning that he ought to
let well enough alone. But to his friends' urging he
turned an unhearing ear. He had dedicated his life to
the relief of suffering and the conquest of disease, and
here was an opportunity to perform still another service
for the human race. Should the task prove too great
for his physical powers, he would give up the effort or,
more likely, die in action. Should he be instrumental
in saving the lives of thousands of dark-skinned miners,
he would have another accomplishment in lifesaving to
give him satisfaction in his old age. As for the danger
that his reputation might be imperiled by failure—well,
he never worried much about his reputation anyhow.

So he persisted in his decision to accept the invitation. But before he could give Mr. Evans and the
others a definite answer, he had to obtain permission
from Colonel Goethals. In view of the strained relations
between the two men, there was considerable doubt in
his mind whether this permission would be forthcoming.
But it was, and quite readily. Surprised and not a little

puzzled, Gorgas began packing for the long trip, convinced, as he wrote a member of his family, that the tsar of the Canal Zone "has some reason for wanting me out of the way." Far from increasing his regard for Goethals, this supposed act of generosity made him "all the more suspicious."

"I went out to see him a few days before I left to arrange several things, but particularly to arrange so that Marie* could keep our house," he wrote on board the S. S. *Ancon* a few hours after sailing. "He asked me to say to Mrs. Gorgas that he would gladly do anything he could for her and that she had no better friend than he was. You see, the old villain is up to something. He is like the other villains in that he has a most winning way with him."

Fortunately, Gorgas's fear that Goethals was "up to something" proved unfounded, as nothing unusual happened in Canal Zone sanitation during his absence. Nevertheless, his suspicion is understandable.

Gorgas's new work naturally attracted much attention and newspaper comment. The New York *Evening Post* declared editorially that his departure for another field of activity symbolized "the virtual completion of our task at Panama" and demonstrated that "for the good as for the wicked in this world, there is no rest."

The summons has come from South Africa, where the miners of the Rand, numbering an army of workers greater than that assembled at Panama, have been the victims of the pneumonia scourge and other endemic diseases. The authorities at Johannesburg found it natural to turn to Col. Gorgas in his capacity as consulting specialist to sick regions of the earth. Yellow fever has now become an "historic disease" at Panama, no epidemic case having occurred since 1906. Malaria fever has been reduced from twelve hundred cases per thousand of the population in 1906—an average of more than one case for each person—to eighty-one per thousand in 1912.† The attention of the world will now be fixed upon Johannesburg.

* Mrs. Gorgas.
† It will be noted that the rates quoted here are somewhat at variance with those shown in official reports.

En route to South Africa, Gorgas spent some time in London preparing himself for his mission. He made the most of that stopover by talking to medical men, mine officials, and many others, obtaining from them as much information as he could about the pneumonia situation, and acquainting himself with the measures that had already been taken to cope with it. He took occasion also to renew his acquaintance with a number of persons who were not primarily interested in pneumonia. Among them was Sir Ronald Ross, whose identification of the mosquito as the chief vector of malaria had made possible the success of his malaria-control work at Havana and Panama and whose visit to the Canal Zone has already been mentioned.

In company with Major Robert E. Noble, one of his most capable medical officers at Panama, and Dr. Samuel Taylor Darling, who had been serving as chief of laboratory at the Canal Zone since 1906, Gorgas sailed on the final leg of his long sea journey on November 15, 1913, and arrived at Capetown on December 2. From there the trio took train almost immediately for Johannesburg, some 950 miles away. There they were greeted at the station by Mr. Evans and several of his associates of the Chamber of Mines. Headquarters were established at a local hotel, and the group lost no time in settling down to the job at hand. The first task, naturally, was to visit the mines, see the men at work, inspect their living quarters, and become acquainted with the methods employed in caring for the sick.

Gorgas soon became convinced that the pneumonia problem could not be solved without devoting considerably more time to it than had appeared necessary at first. As his studies got under way he began to realize that many factors, some of them only indirectly medical, entered into the situation and contributed to the heavy mortality. In time, therefore, he found himself deep in investigations of such matters as labor recruiting, living

conditions among the miners prior to leaving their semi-
civilized home communities, methods of transportation,
etc. These investigations he found almost as illuminat-
ing as his more orthodox studies of housing, the preparation and consumption of food, and the measures taken
to protect the workmen's health.

In all, more than fifty hospitals situated in all parts
of the Rand were inspected with characteristic Gorgas
thoroughness, with eyes directed especially at possible
opportunities to effectuate improvements in the treatment of pneumonia. The living quarters were studied
with particular care and the number of cubic feet of
air space per workman looked into. He got all the information he could as to where the food came from and
particularly the sanitary conditions under which it was
produced. Was it properly prepared? Was it served in
sufficient quantity to build and maintain strong bodies
capable of doing the heavy physical labor which these
two hundred thousand or more Negroes were doing?
These and any number of other questions were constantly in his mind as he made his patient rounds, looking here, asking questions there, and tasting a kitchen
concoction yonder.

Acting upon his conviction that recruiting conditions and the conditions prevailing in the mine workers'
primitive native villages were important factors in their
health, Gorgas sent Major Noble and Dr. Darling to
Ishambane, in Portuguese East Africa, which was regarded as typical of the communities from which the
Negroes came to become miners. Upon their return
these investigators told him about the arrangement by
which laborers recruited there were sent by ship and
train to Rosanna Garcia, where they were kept until
they totaled about twelve hundred. Then they were
herded onto trains for the rest of the trip to the mines,
during which they were taken from sea level to a height
of somewhat more than a mile. Starting out with only

the scantiest of clothing, which was all they needed at that temperature, they found it difficult to adjust themselves to the rapidly increasing cold, even with the help of the blanket with which each man was provided. Infections received before leaving home, while they were waiting at Rosanna Garcia, and after they began the last leg of the journey to the mines naturally developed rapidly, and, as a result, nearly every train-load included several suffering from pneumonia. Conditions in the mining communities being as they were, particularly with regard to crowding and lack of sufficient air space, these cases became highly contagious, and the infection quickly spread to others. The sudden change from the warmth underground to the mile-high mountain tops upon which they emerged upon quitting work was found to be especially productive of this form of illness.

Gorgas's devotion to his professional labors did not absorb all his time and attention by any means. His letters tell of such nonmedical adventures as a breakfast at the Y.M.C.A., at which he addressed some two hundred, comparisons of South African and Oklahoma dust storms, visits to diamond mines, a visit to the National Observatory, an examination of war records, luncheons with fellow-Americans, music from a great organ, a motor trip to Victoria, and the emotions stirred by seeing half a million dollars' worth of diamonds piled upon a single table.

He also had sorrowful memories during those weeks in which he labored with such assiduity to solve the problem that had brought him here. When the new year arrived, he thought much of his mother, whose death had occurred on the third day of the year which had just ended, and of her final illness.

"This must be a sad time for you all at home," he wrote to one of his sisters on January 1.

It was just a year ago today that dear Mother was so ill. I had just landed at Panama on my return from Canada. Generally

I do not appreciate that Mother has gone. But, when I do, it gives me such a pang to think that I cannot return the love she so liberally showered on me. I can think of so many ways that I might have shown my love for her and so many occasions.

His letter ended with this tribute straight from the heart:

She, more than anyone I ever knew, acted upon the belief that "love is the principle of existence and its only end." She felt sympathy for everyone with whom she came in contact and roused the same feeling. Taking it all in all, she had the greatest intellect that I have ever personally known.

Early in that new year which brought such poignant reminders of his mother's death, his pneumonia studies were brought to a temporary halt by a strike of miners and railway workers. Enemy to idleness that he was, he again turned his attention to malaria, accepting an invitation from the government of Rhodesia to visit the capital city and suggest procedures for the curbing of that disease, which had been giving the authorities considerable worry.

He and his party were entertained in grand style during their stay and lionized at a number of social events, for which he managed to find time in spite of his preoccupation with malaria. Among those they met during that visit was Sir Leander Starr Jameson, hero of the famed "Jameson raid" which had launched the Boer War. Jameson had a rich store of reminiscences, to which the visitors from the United States listened with great pleasure.

It was only natural that this famous conqueror of yellow fever and malaria should be called upon to tell about his work at Panama. Speaking to a large audience at a meeting in the Palace Theatre at which he was officially welcomed and warmly praised by the mayor, he modestly described the successful efforts of the Sanitary Department to curb these two diseases and other forms of illness—a story familiar to many Americans but known only fragmentarily to these residents of a distant continent.

Shortly after his arrival in Rhodesia, Gorgas paid a courtesy call upon Sir William Milton, the governor. The latter, to his considerable surprise, presented him to Lady Milton as "General Gorgas," giving him an official rank somewhat higher than the colonelcy to which he had been promoted some time before. Somewhat embarrassed by what he considered his host's lapse of memory, he attempted to set him right, with that engaging courtesy for which he was so well known. Thereupon Sir William smiled broadly as though enjoying his confusion, and insisted that "General Gorgas" was correct. Some friendly expostulation and counterexpostulation followed, ending with Sir William's reaching into his pocket and producing a news bulletin which had just arrived. It revealed that President Wilson had appointed Gorgas Surgeon General of the United States Army, succeeding Surgeon General George H. Torney, whose death had occurred just a short time before. Gorgas was delighted.

The President's choice was greeted with enthusiasm in military and medical circles and among the rank and file of the country's population. The *Journal of the American Medical Association* voiced virtually unanimous approval when it declared editorially: "Probably not since the days of the Civil War has it been possible for a President to make an appointment that will cause so much general satisfaction."

Looking forward with the eagerness of a schoolboy to beginning his new work, Gorgas began planning his return home. February 28, eighty-eight days after his arrival in South Africa, was the date decided upon for his departure.

A few hours before he left he turned over to the Transvaal Chamber of Mines a complete report covering his study of the pneumonia problem, together with certain recommendations for its solution. Having become convinced that this problem was essentially the same in South Africa that it had been in Panama and would therefore yield to the same remedies, he urged the Transvaal mine operators to do what had been done, upon his insistent urging, on the Isthmus. He laid particular stress upon the elimination of overcrowding by the use of small cottages to replace the large barracks in which the men were then being herded like animals.

When he boarded ship for the Capetown-to-London leg of his return journey, he carried in his pocket an invitation to address the Royal Society of Medicine at a reception then being arranged in his honor in the British capital. He found after his arrival that this was only one of many honors awaiting him. Leaders of the medical profession, high-ranking officers of His Majesty's Army and Navy, scientists in many fields, journalists, and innumerable other outstanding men of his time greeted him warmly at informal conferences and at the numerous formal affairs which crowded his calendar during his brief stay. His reception was described by the admiring Sir William Osler as "the greatest ever accorded a medical man in England." The London *Daily Mail* voiced the praise of the entire nation when it declared editorially:

"Perhaps of all living Americans he has conferred the greatest benefits on the human race. The whole world, particularly the British Empire, with its large tropical possessions, owes him a debt which Britons are proud to acknowledge."

A particularly high honor that came his way was the conferring upon him by venerable Oxford University of the honorary degree of Doctor of Science at a special convocation inspired by the enthusiastic Sir William Osler. This most impressive ceremony, to which the American Ambassador and a number of other dignitaries were invited, was held on March 23. Neither

Gorgas nor the others knew that in less than five months Oxford's and England's sons would be called upon to offer their lives to their country in a kind of war which mankind has known since time immemorial, but all of them must have been conscious of its inevitability, even then. Perhaps it was because of that consciousness that the public orator of Magdalen College found such lofty words in which to praise this hero of another kind of war, a war, not of life-taking but of lifesaving.

"Those are most honored by us who have increased knowledge and thereby promoted the welfare of the world," he said.

Such are many students of medicine. It is a fine thing to have the scientific knowledge which can cure disease; but theirs is a still finer, if more dangerous, task who can extirpate the causes from which disease springs. It is such men who destroy the seeds of death which breed in swamps, risking their health and even their lives to save their fellows. These heroes are a modern realization of the legend of Heracles, the cleanser of foul places and the enemy of evil beasts.

Gorgas, in the orator's view, had given the world a shining example of that kind of soldiership of medicine:

The eminent American whom you see today has, like so many of his countrymen, fought in the forefront of the battle. His achievements are too numerous for me to relate in detail. Suffice it to say that it is he who cleansed Havana; it is he who put fever and pestilence to flight in the Isthmus of Panama and made possible the long-thwarted construction of the great interoceanic waterway; it is he who has recently improved the sanitary conditions in the South African mines. He purified foul air; he waged war on the myriad swarms of death-disseminating mosquitoes. The result has been an amelioration of the conditions of human life in plague-haunted districts, where once "in silent fear the helpless healer stood," and where it is now possible to live in comfort and work with advantage. There can be no better example to those

"Whose skill hath served the human lot to raise
And won a name that endless ages praise."

The following citation was delivered by Oxford's acting Vice-Chancellor, Dr. T. H. Warren, as Gorgas bowed his head to receive the symbol of this new honor:

Preeminently distinguished, sagacious, health-bringing, the modern Machaon of the American Army, whom indeed I wish to salute not only in Latin prose but also in Greek verse thus:
   "Hail, router of the plague of flies.
   Hail, Isthmian conquerer true!
   Gorgas, to that wise goddess dear,
   The Gorgon death who slew!"

The eloquent public orator of Oxford's Magdalen College was somewhat premature in his praise of Gorgas as the person "who has recently improved the sanitary conditions in the South African mines," as it was then, less than a month after he completed his study, too early for the fruits of his labors to become apparent. They did become apparent in time, however, conspicuously so.

Acting upon the Gorgas dictum that "the success of any system of sanitation which is more or less new to any locality will depend a great deal upon the choice of the man who has charge of carrying it into execution," one of the larger Transvaal firms, the Central Mining Company, employed as chief sanitation adviser a man who had served under Gorgas at Panama, giving him the job of obtaining for its workers the greatest possible benefits from the Gorgas report and recommendations. That real progress could be made in the conquest of pneumonia and other diseases by such a man, guided by the advice of a master sanitarian and health enthusiast, was amply demonstrated by the mortality figures. By the middle of 1918 the pneumonia death rate among those black-skinned workers had dropped to approximately three per thousand population, or less than the 1918 Negro pneumonia death rate in Gorgas's home state. During the same period the death rate for all other diseases dropped more than 50 per cent—from thirteen to six per thousand population. Such rates were indeed remarkable in view of the already mentioned fact that shortly before Gorgas went to South Africa these miners, or their predecessors, were dying at the rate of more than one out of every three a year.

CHAPTER XII

Medical Mobilization

GORGAS ASSUMED his new duties as Surgeon General of the Army, with the military rank of Brigadier General, on April 6, 1914, just about four months before the outbreak of the First World War and three years to the day before this country entered the conflict. On March 4, 1915, in recognition of his achievements in sanitation, he was advanced to Major General by special act of Congress. This gave him a higher rank than his immediate predecessor had enjoyed and one which indeed was without precedent in the long history of the Medical Corps. Thus, at the age of sixty, this lover of the Army, who had become a doctor in order to become a soldier, found himself occupying a post of conspicuous brilliance in both professions. Had he been alive, Josiah Gorgas would have found great satisfaction in the knowledge that his son was the only son of a general officer in the Army of the Confederacy who ever became a general officer in the Army of the United States.

The new Surgeon General had hardly had time to learn the routine of his job when American bluejackets landed in Vera Cruz and held the city until relieved by troops put ashore under the protection of American battleships. Once again Gorgas returned to his favorite role of sanitarian and issued carefully prepared instructions for the sanitary protection of the residents of the conquered city, the natives as well as the men from the transports.

A clean-up campaign marked by typical Gorgas thoroughness got under way at once. Three thousand men, working continuously in relays, pushed it through to completion in seventeen hours. Streets were flushed and scrubbed to glossiness. Houses were fumigated and forced into unaccustomed cleanliness, often over the angry protests of their owners. Mosquito-breeding puddles were filled. Rotting things, both animal and vegetable, were removed from sight and smell. Rigid sanitary regulations were adopted, publicized, and enforced. War correspondents saw what was going on and were pleased. One of them wrote: "The city's cleanliness is assured as long as it is occupied by American troops and its health laws are made and administered by army sanitarians."

About the time that writer was calling Vera Cruz "the cleanest place in the tropics" and other visitors were expressing equal enthusiasm over the Army's campaign of cleanliness, Gorgas predicted that, for the first time in history, a real war with Mexico or any other nation would find American soldiers in a state of "hygienic competence." This meant, he explained, that, thanks to the advances made by sanitary science, major loss of life in this nation's wars of the future would be limited to that caused by enemy soldiers and enemy machines of destruction. He was convinced that the old ratio of several times as many deaths from disease as from battles had no place in modern warfare.

Fortunately, the conflict with this country's back-door neighbor did not last long enough to furnish a test of Gorgas's powers of prophecy, and three or four years were to pass before they could be proved or disproved under the cruel test of a prolonged military campaign. Meanwhile there were to be insistent pleas that at least some of the victims of the war then in progress across the Atlantic be permitted to enjoy the benefit of his healing touch.

A few months after the outbreak of war Serbia found

herself in the grip of a devastating typhus epidemic. In an effort to care for its victims and prevent its possible spread to other parts of Europe and eventually even to the United States, the American Red Cross sent a sanitary commission, consisting of six physicians and twelve nurses, to the stricken country. Soon after their arrival all but one of those eighteen health workers had contracted the disease, and two of the six doctors had succumbed. At one time a single American physician, aided by six untrained volunteer nurses and lacking beds, blankets, and drugs, was doing his best to care for one thousand patients, all of them lying on the floor of a dirty tobacco factory. Doctors were rushed from England and France, and additional sanitary workers were sent from this country to strengthen the American contingent trying to stem this murderous tide of infection.

The situation was made infinitely worse by war conditions. The rapidly shifting battle lines carried the conflict to many parts of the embattled country, leaving behind little but disease, poverty, hunger, and devastation. Often bodies would remain unburied for a long time, and, even when there were enough able-bodied soldiers and civilians to dig the long trenches used in burying them, many of those makeshift graves, dug with little knowledge of the disease, were so shallow that the dead continued to constitute a serious threat to the health of those who had not yet succumbed. And of course the vicissitudes of war completely disarranged the normal life of the entire nation, forcing city dwellers, accustomed to a measure of sanitary protection, into the most insanitary camps and huts. There they were subjected to conditions of extreme crowding and to exposure to each other's diseases—typhus along with many others. Small wonder that Serbia became known as a national morgue.

It was natural if not inevitable that, with such a staggering problem of sanitation crying piteously for

solution, there should be demands that the sanitary conqueror of Havana, Panama, and the mining regions of
South Africa be placed in charge of still another campaign of lifesaving. Of all the sanitarians and physicians
of the world, he alone appeared to be properly equipped
to rid Serbia of her cruel burden of sickness and death.

Early in April, 1915, Gorgas received from the
Rockefeller Foundation, then in the early stages of its
world-wide health improvement program, a flattering
offer of a position as general adviser on matters having
to do with sanitation and the control of epidemics.
Although the proffered post was of such a nature as to
involve permanent association with the Foundation, it
was made plain at the time that the immediate purpose
of the proffer was to obtain the Surgeon General's services for a campaign against the Serbian typhus epidemic.
Newspaper stories stating that the position carried a
salary of $50,000 a year, with a generous pension for
Mrs. Gorgas in the event that he should succumb to
the disease, were promptly denied by officials of the
Foundation, who pointed out that the compensation
offered was much less than that reported, although considerably greater than his salary as Surgeon General.

Like other tasks of wholesale lifesaving, this one
appealed to him strongly. Though past sixty now, he
was in good health and had no doubt of his ability to
endure the physical strain which the work would involve. This old war horse of medicine was eager to return to the kind of battle he most loved.

But there were serious difficulties in the way. He
was a high-ranking officer in the military establishment
of the United States, a neutral. Serbia, the theater of his
proposed labors, was at war. And, while the work in
which he would be engaged was primarily among civilians, the typhus epidemic was doing the little country
more military damage than many divisions of Austrian
troops and thus was proving a formidable ally of Serbia's

enemies. How those enemies would react to an American general's leadership of a campaign to combat that epidemic was easy to predict. Plainly, delicate questions of neutrality were involved.

It was hoped by officials of the Rockefeller Foundation and by Gorgas himself that his acceptance would not necessitate his resignation from the Army but only his retirement from the active list. This would not involve any loss of rank or jeopardize his future usefulness to his country in his official capacity in the event of war or other national emergency. His decision as to acceptance or rejection of the offer had to await an official ruling on this point by Secretary of War Garrison.

Meanwhile, the offer and its possible consequences received considerable editorial attention in newspapers in all parts of the country.

"The tender is highly creditable both to General Gorgas and to the Foundation," averred the New Orleans *Times-Picayune*.

The former's preeminent qualification for leadership of the sanitary fight in Serbia will be acknowledged, we have no doubt, the world over. Typhus is fearfully well fortified in the little Balkan country now fighting the third war in which it has been engaged during a period of something like forty months. If General Gorgas feels that his services are needed, we may be sure that he will accept the appointment and make the sacrifices involved, cheerfully and without hesitation.

But there were others who wanted Gorgas kept at home. They insisted that he was too valuable to his own country to be sent to another part of the world on a hazardous mission like that, however great might be the need for him there.

"In times of such dire distress," declared a newspaper spokesman for this group, "the first instinct of those who can render aid is to reach out a helping hand. General Gorgas himself is no doubt willing to go to the scenes of infection and set his scientific mind and his

tremendous energies to work to solve the sad problem."
However, this paper went on:

Gorgas is one of the most valuable assets of this government.
We need him to fight the evils of disease for his own people.
Suppose we went to war this year or next year with some other
nation, on whom would we depend for the protection of our
own camps and fighting forces against the inroads of disease,
except upon Gorgas? We have other surgeons and sanitation
authorities, but he is our greatest. Are we called upon to give
our very best to the people of a foreign country, sorry as we
may be for them? We would not give Serbia or any other nation
our best general or our biggest warship, and, with equal self-
protection, we should keep our best sanitation scientist.

Serbia can give us no guarantee that she will return Gorgas
to us. He might contract the very disease he went to combat and
be sent back to us only for the honors of a national funeral.
The risk is too great. We need Gorgas for our own work, our
own possible protection.

The Rockefeller Foundation pays him a great and merited
compliment in wishing to secure his services, that he may be
at the beck and call of the world. But a bit of individualized
Monroe Doctrine that reads "America's greatest men belong first
to America" would not be a bad idea, in spite of the thread of
selfishness that runs through it.

We need Gorgas, and we do not know at what hour we shall
have even more vital need for him; and so it is to be hoped that
he will not be sent as a possible sacrifice to the Serbian typhus.

The neutrality-conscious Secretary of War virtually
took the decision out of Gorgas's hands by ruling, with
the approval of President Wilson, that he could not go
to Serbia under any circumstances as long as he was an
officer, active or inactive, of the United States Army.
Faced with a hard choice between turning down the
offer and resigning permanently from the Army, he
wisely did the former and left to others the task of leading Serbia's campaign against typhus fever.

Gorgas, of course, was greatly disappointed. He expressed his disappointment in a letter to his sister Jessie:

Has Dick written you about the sanitary work in Serbia?
They asked me to go in charge. But the President does not wish
Army officers to take an active part, fearing our neutrality might
be affected. I would like to have tried so big and so useful a
work. . . . My working days are now drawing to a close, and I
would like to pass on to the next existence while at the head
of some big and successful work like this Serbian work. I feel
the desire of the old soldier to die with my boots on.

Gorgas was thinking more about death and "the next
existence" during those early months of the war than
ever before. Always deeply religious, he mentioned them
frequently in his letters to his family and others as the
swiftly passing years carried him close to the age at
which his father had died.

One of those letters, not to his family, or indeed to
anyone he had ever seen, but to a humble private suffering in a distant state from an incurable disease was
found among Gorgas's papers after he died.

Presumably, this sick person, a patient in an army
hospital, had acted upon an impulse to write to someone he didn't know and preferably someone with the
glitter of official importance about him. The soldier's
letter was not found among the Gorgas papers. Its con-
tents, therefore, can only be conjectured. But, judging
from Gorgas's reply, he must have written at some length
about another sick person known to both of them and
also about death, the hereafter, and the writer's hope of
immortality.

Most major generals, burdened with official duties,
would have turned such a letter over to a subordinate
to answer or, more likely, would have ignored it entirely.
But Gorgas, busy as he was, took time to answer it
personally.

WAR DEPARTMENT
OFFICE OF THE SURGEON GENERAL
WASHINGTON,
April 21, 1916.

MR. F. G. HENNESSY,
U. S. ARMY GENERAL HOSPITAL,
FORT BAYARD, NEW MEXICO.

DEAR MR. HENNESSY:

Yours of April 10th is acknowledged. I was very glad to get your letter, though we have never met. I am very glad to know that you feel toward me as you do.

Since I have received your letter poor Frances O'Reilly has died; you have no doubt heard of her death. Poor lady. I think from all I know of the circumstances that her death is not to be too much deplored.

I had hoped that you might grow better but, if it is true, as you say, that you have only a few weeks to live, I think it probable that we will never meet in this world. If you have only a few weeks to live, I have only a few years. I am now sixty-one, and, in the nature of mankind, my course is nearly run. I hope, however, to meet you in that future life toward which we are all marching and in which I believe both you and I will again take up our work to do our mite toward helping to finish out the great scheme the Almighty has established. I like to think that we will have the same free will for making or marring which we have had in this world, and that there we may be employed to correct some of the faults that we have made down here.

With friendship and good will, I remain

Yours very sincerely,

W. C. GORGAS.

That letter was never read by the person to whom it was addressed. It was returned to Gorgas undelivered. A postal clerk had written "Dead" across the envelope.

The Surgeon General's disappointment over his inability to lead the fight against typhus in Serbia was short-lived. For a few months only was he to be deprived of an opportunity to carry on the kind of warfare that appealed to him most strongly. This time, as before, it was the Rockefeller Foundation that sought his services in a campaign of lifesaving. And this time no neutrality-conscious Secretary of War or President could tell him: "You mustn't."

Spurred to enthusiasm by Gorgas's conquest of yellow fever in Havana and Panama, the officials of that great philanthropic organization conceived an ambitious but apparently feasible plan to drive this disease forever from the face of the earth by rooting it out of the few remaining areas—small in extent as well as in number—where it was still entrenched. With those remaining reservoirs of the yellow fever germ erased, they reasoned with excellent logic, it would be as dead as one of its own victims as far as being a menace to the health and happiness of the human race was concerned. On the contrary, as long as these yellow fever areas were allowed to remain undisturbed, sparks from those relatively small fires might alight almost anywhere in the world and start a flame of disease and devastation that would rival the great epidemics of history.

Thus it was that the Rockefeller Foundation turned again to Gorgas, who, on any number of occasions, had spoken of his conviction that these remaining strongholds of yellow fever could be stormed as successfully as its other citadels had been and who had also voiced a hope that he would be privileged to have a part in that final engagement of this war of extermination.

The matter was discussed at several conferences participated in by the ever-enthusiastic Gorgas, the equally enthusiastic Dr. Henry R. Carter, whose yellow fever studies in 1898 had given new emphasis to the role played by the mosquito in the transmission of the disease, and the increasingly enthusiastic Dr. Wickliffe Rose, president of the Rockefeller Foundation's International Health Board. The immediate fruit of those discussions was an invitation to Gorgas and two or three other enthusiasts to meet with the Board's executive committee and tell them what they had already told Dr. Rose.

These gentlemen caught at least some of the others'

enthusiasm and decided to undertake, with Rockefeller
Foundation funds, a vigorous yellow fever campaign in
Central and South America. As a preliminary step, it
was decided to send a group of scientists to those countries where endemic yellow fever areas were believed to
exist. It would be their task to obtain, for the guidance
of those who would be in charge of the major effort, as
much information as possible regarding the status of
yellow fever in those areas. Gorgas was invited to assume
the leadership of that group.

He of course eagerly seized this opportunity, which
appealed to him even more than the opportunity to aid
stricken Serbia. Receiving a four months' leave of absence from his official duties, he left with the other six
members of his party on June 14, 1916. Finding it impossible to complete his study within the time originally
set, he made a second trip in the fall.

On that second voyage he came perilously close to the
realization of his expressed wish to "die with my boots
on." A day or two after sailing from New York he happened to be visiting the captain of his ship, the S. S.
Vasari, when the subject of German submarines came
up. Observant as he was, he had noticed that the ship
was being darkened at night and that numerous other
measures had been taken to avoid attack. These precautions, some three thousand miles from Europe's
troubled waters, struck him as altogether unnecessary.
So, with engaging good humor, he teased the captain
about them. Thereupon the latter "got very confiden-
tial," and told him that he had the very best of reasons
for taking no chances. For, the captain explained, just
after leaving New York, he had received a wireless message revealing that a German submarine had put in at
Norfolk and after leaving there had sunk six ships—
four British, like the *Vasari,* one Swedish, and one flying
the flag of another Scandinavian country—off Nantucket.
The *Vasari* had intercepted the SOS from one of the

British ships, which had many passengers on board, but, in accordance with an admiralty order never to go to the assistance of other ships attacked by submarines, had continued on its course. When the *Vasari* arrived at Bahia, Brazil, and the American consul went aboard to welcome the members of the party, he confirmed what the ship's commander had told Gorgas.

"The submarine left Norfolk at 5 o'clock Saturday afternoon going north," Gorgas wrote that night in his journal. "We left New York about the same time coming south, so that we must have passed each other Saturday night at no very great distance. Our precautions as to keeping the lights darkened at night possibly saved us from being torpedoed."

Notwithstanding that close brush with death and the other dangers to which he was exposed, he appeared to enjoy every minute of those two voyages. Everywhere he went—in Ecuador, Peru, Colombia, Brazil, Mexico, and several other countries—he was greeted like a homecoming hero and found officials enthusiastic over the proposed sanitary campaign. His charming personal qualities, no less than his reputation as the world's greatest sanitarian, reflected much credit upon the Rockefeller Foundation in selecting him for this work.

After completing his survey Gorgas gave the Rockefeller Foundation the benefit of the knowledge he had gained and worked out a plan of procedure which, he was confident, would destroy the last surviving yellow fever reservoir in the New World. But that was not all he and they had in mind. After removing that danger spot they planned a quick transfer of operations to the Old World for a clean-up of those regions in West Africa where the disease was known to be still prevalent. Gorgas was made director of the comprehensive, longrange program, and steps were taken to get it under way as soon as possible.

But those ambitious plans had to be put on the shelf.

There was much more pressing work for Gorgas to do. Less than four months after his return from the second of those visits to Latin America the United States entered World War I, and he plunged into the task of making good his prophecy of nearly three years earlier that this country at last could participate in a large-scale conflict in which disease would not kill more men than bullets and high explosives.

Gorgas's preparations for that conflict began long before the United States actually entered the war. Realizing the probability of eventual American participation, he started preparing for it as soon as the war began. As early as January, 1916, he was greatly concerned over a threatened shortage of vital drugs—notably opium and quinine—and appealed to Congress for authority and funds to build up a war reserve.

Even more important to the work of preparing the nation for effective participation in the conflict were his efforts in behalf of medical preparedness. During those years of neutrality he carried on among the nation's practicing physicians a campaign to break down the widespread prejudice against the kind of career he had found so full of satisfaction—that of the army doctor. Thanks to that effort, more than two thousand officers were added to the rolls of the Medical Reserve Corps prior to the fateful April 6 which brought neutrality to an end.

More important still was the part he played in the drafting and passage of the National Defense Act of 1916, which increased the authorized enlisted strength of the Regular Army to 175,000 men and provided corresponding increases in other branches of the service, including of course the Medical Department. During Congressional consideration of that measure the Surgeon General was to be seen almost daily in the committee rooms of the Senate and House of Representatives. He was also in frequent consultation with Congressional leaders when other preparedness legislation was under consideration, including measures not primarily concerned with his department.

Among the most important sections of the National Defense Act was that creating a Council of National Defense, consisting of Secretary of War Newton D. Baker, chairman, Secretary of the Navy Josephus Daniels, Secretary of the Interior Franklin K. Lane, Secretary of Agriculture David F. Houston, Secretary of Commerce William C. Redfield, and Secretary of Labor William B. Wilson. Also brought into being by the National Defense Act was the Advisory Commission, consisting of seven members, each having specialized knowledge in some field allied with the country's defense. Dr. Franklin H. Martin, director general of the American College of Surgeons, was nominated by the Council and appointed by President Wilson as medicine's representative and spokesman on this distinguished body. The other six members were Daniel Willard, president of the Baltimore & Ohio, who became chairman; Howard E. Coffin, vice-president of the Hudson Motor Company; Julius Rosenwald, president of Sears, Roebuck & Company; Bernard M. Baruch, the banker; Dr. Hollis Godfrey, president of Drexel Institute; and Samuel Gompers, president of the American Federation of Labor.

Like the other members of the Advisory Commission, Dr. Martin was authorized to appoint as his personal advisors a group of outstanding men in the field he represented. It was natural, in view of Gorgas's fame and official position, that he should be included in this group, which became known as the Medical Committee of the Council of National Defense. The other six topflight medical men chosen to serve with him were Surgeon General William C. Braisted of the Navy; Surgeon General Rupert Blue of the U. S. Public Health Service; Col. Jefferson R. Kean, director general of military relief of the American Red Cross; Dr. William H. Welch, a member of the National Research Council; Dr. William J. Mayo, chairman of the Committee of American Physicians for Medical Preparedness; and Dr. Frank F. Simpson, chief of the Medical Section of the Council of National Defense and secretary of the Committee of American Physicians for Medical Preparedness.

Although the Medical Committee had a number of duties, its greatest single contribution to the nation's war effort was to do as a group what Gorgas had been doing as an individual for some time—lining up the medical profession and getting physicians and surgeons interested in Medical Reserve Corps commissions. Thanks to its work, there was rapidly built up a large body of medical men whose qualifications and specialties were known and classified and whose services were available when needed in the creation and training of a large army for war service.

Thus, even before the United States became a belligerent, Gorgas found himself surrounded by a group of outstanding medical men. Their assistance proved invaluable in the rapid change-over of the Medical Department from peace to war. His work with that group, however, was only one of many examples of the close interlinking of the Surgeon General's office with the country's medical profession.

As the need for medical officers kept pace with the rapid expansion of the Army, Gorgas leaned more and more heavily upon his fellow-physicians. His personal popularity made them even more eager than they otherwise would have been to perform their full patriotic duty in the crisis. Especially helpful were the American Medical Association and its co-ordinated bodies, the state medical societies. Every issue of the Association's *Journal* contained detailed information about the medical phases of the nation's war effort, and, when the need arose for more and still more medical officers, its col-

umns, going directly to those whom Gorgas particularly
wished to reach, were open to his appeals. A new department, "Medical Mobilization and the War," introduced
in the first issue of the *Journal* to appear after this
country's entrance into the conflict and continuing until
after the Armistice, contained a wide variety of medico-
military articles. Lists of physicians who had accepted
Medical Reserve Corps commissions were published regularly and served as an incentive to others to do the
same. In addition to relieving the Surgeon General's
staff of a vast amount of letter-writing by disseminating
information which otherwise could have been obtained
only through correspondence, the A. M. A. *Journal* also
conducted an information bureau of its own and encouraged doctors interested in military service to send
their inquiries to its Chicago editorial offices, rather than
to Washington.

One of the American Medical Association's most
valuable contributions to the winning of the war, a
product of the cordial relations existing between Gorgas
and that organization, was the sending by the latter of
a personal appeal by mail to every physician under fifty-
five years of age, urging him to offer his professional
skill to his country. Although prepared by and at the
expense of the Association, each letter was signed by
Gorgas's personal representative assisting in this work.
Every one that went unanswered was followed by a second. In addition to the printing required for this mail
appeal, which included a circular letter, a return card,
an application blank, and a list of examining boards, the
American Medical Association also did a great deal of
other printing for which it made no charge whatsoever.

What that organization did on a national scale state
and county medical societies did in their own more
limited way. Indeed practically every physician's group,
large or small, became an active recruiting agency for
Gorgas's rapidly expanding Medical Reserve Corps.

By virtue of his official position, the Surgeon General became a member of the General Medical Board, composed of carefully picked military and civilian doctors who had been called together to serve as a link of understanding and co-operation between the Medical Departments of the Army, the Navy, and the Public Health Service on the one hand and the civilian physicians and surgeons whom these services were anxious to enlist for war duty on the other. At its initial meeting, held just three days after war was declared, he was made a member of this Board's Executive Committee. His associates on that committee consisted of six of his associates on the Medical Committee of the Council of National Defense —Dr. Martin; Dr. Simpson; Surgeons General Braisted and Blue; Col. Keen; and Dr. William J. Mayo—and also Rear Admiral Cary T. Grayson, personal physician to the President; Dr. Charles H. Mayo, the second of the famous medical brothers; Dr. Victor C. Vaughan, like Gorgas a former president of the American Medical Association, and Dr. Frederick A. Beasley, professor of surgery at the Northwestern University Medical School.

All matters brought before the General Medical Board were passed upon by the Executive Committee, which thus became, in effect, the larger body's alter ego, acting for it and, generally speaking, exercising its normal functions. Since this committee's chairman, Dr. Martin, occupied an influential position in the administration as an official adviser to six members of the President's cabinet, this ten-man body played an important role in the conduct of the war, exerting an influence by no means limited to medical affairs.

Gorgas was untiring in his praise of his fellow doctors' contribution to the nation's war effort and gave them a large share of the credit for the Medical Department's success in discharging its vastly increased responsibilities. In his annual report for 1918 he told the Secretary of War that their assistance had made possible "the organization of a medical service which, for completeness of detail, from the first-aid station on the firing line to the reconstruction hospitals at the base, has rarely, if ever, been excelled."

He was by no means alone in his praise of the men and women who served under him. American officers returning from France told a writer for *Collier's Weekly* that military experts there regarded the Medical Department of the United States Army as the best in the field.

To meet the needs of a rapidly expanding fighting machine, Gorgas's major tasks were to enlist, train, and equip a huge personnel of capable medical officers, nurses, sanitarians, etc., and to provide and equip the buildings they would need to carry on their work. Of the two duties, that of increasing the Medical Department personnel was perhaps the more formidable.

In April, 1917, there were less than one thousand trained commissioned officers in the Army Medical Corps. With the help of the Medical Reserve Corps, the total increased between then and the following June 30 to 4,125. On June 30 of the following year they numbered 23,274, and at the time of the Armistice the total had swollen to 30,591, or more than thirty times as many as were on duty when the United States entered the war. Between June 30, 1917, and November 11, 1918, the Dental Corps, including the Dental Reserve Corps, increased from 86 to 4,620, the Veterinary Corps from 57 to 2,234, the Sanitary Corps from none to 2,919, and the Army Nurse Corps from 1,176 to 21,480.

The figures for those other corps, like those for the Medical Corps, include only officers and nurses, of course —no enlisted men. Add to them the 281,341 non-commissioned officers and privates on the Medical Department's rolls at the time of the Armistice, and you have a health-protection army of staggering size. Quite properly did Gorgas's successor say that he had been in charge of a force larger than the entire army with which this

country entered the war. Indeed probably no other
United States major general ever commanded such a
large force as he did.

Devoted though it was to the saving of human life,
rather than its destruction, that huge force nevertheless
endured most of the perils to which those in the combatant units were exposed. A later Surgeon General of
the Army has written of its men and women that they
"braved the risks of contagion as well as those from the
missiles of the enemy" and "shared the dangers of their
brothers of the line." The official records show that
3,047 of them—540 officers of the Medical Corps, 250
nurses and 2,257 enlisted men of the Medical Department—made the supreme sacrifice.

No less impressive was the growth under Gorgas's
guidance of physical facilities to care for the sick and
wounded among America's fighting men. Prior to this
country's entry into the war the Army's four general
hospitals and five base hospitals contained a total of only
4,150 beds—all that were available for the care of officers
and enlisted men except those in the small hospitals attached to army posts. When the war ended, the Surgeon
General's Hospital Division had under its supervision
in the United States no less than 92 large hospitals containing a total of 120,916 beds. These were exclusive,
of course, of those in small post and camp hospitals.
Moreover, the Army then had under construction and
authorized a number of hospital enlargements aimed at
increasing the available beds to more than 147,500, while
plans were being made for the leasing and construction
of still more buildings to be used for hospital purposes,
increasing by still another 60,000 or more the number
of beds which those in charge of the hospital-construc-
tion program were preparing to make available on the
home front. Thus, had the war lasted much longer, the
Army's total hospital capacity in the United States would
have exceeded the total officer and enlisted personnel
provided by the National Defense Act of 1916.

No less ambitious was the hospital-building program overseas. Looking ahead to and preparing for the needs of a long war, with increasing American participation in a military sense, Gorgas issued instructions that there must be fifteen hospital beds in France for every hundred American soldiers serving in that country, and this ratio was consistently maintained, except when urgent pleas from General Pershing for all available combat troops gave priority in shipping to combatant units at the expense of those not intended for front-line fighting duty. This situation, of course, was one over which Gorgas had no control. There was nothing he could do but bow to the authority of a superior officer. In spite of these inevitable upsets, however, the overseas hospitals were able, and more than able, to meet the demands made upon them.

The supervision of these mushrooming activities at home and abroad necessitated a tremendous expansion in Gorgas's staff, and this in turn created an insistent need for more and more office space. Prior to this country's entry into the war his staff consisted of himself, six medical officers, and one hundred and forty-seven civilian employees, all housed in modest quarters in the State, War and Navy Building. The duties of the Surgeon General's office were then performed by only four administrative units, known as divisions. By April, 1918, they had grown to thirty or more; the Surgeon General's staff had expanded to 181 medical officers and 1,534 civilian employees, and those modest quarters in the State, War and Navy Building had been vacated in favor of six entire floors in the Mills Building across the street. Continuing personnel increases made even these quarters altogether inadequate, and Gorgas and his assistants moved again, this time to one of the temporary structures hastily erected to meet the housing emergency created by the war.

Soon after the War Department announced that it

was going to launch a record-breaking cantonment construction program there came a pledge from Gorgas
that the Medical Department would make those military
communities as safe, from a sanitary standpoint, as modern science could possibly make them.

"When a recruit has passed his examinations, which
will be rigid, he may rest assured that the government
will put him into as nearly an ideal sanitary environment as will be found anywhere," he promised. "We
are putting the best brains in the country to work on
the problem and have commissioned as majors in the
Medical Reserve Corps specialists in the medical and
surgical branches we wish to cover."

To bulwark this promise, he made public a list of
eminent physicians and surgeons who were helping him
safeguard the health of the American doughboy—men
like Dr. William H. Welch, famous pathologist at Johns
Hopkins University; Dr. Victor C. Vaughan, dean of the
University of Michigan Medical School and nationally
known authority on sanitation; the famous Mayo brothers; Dr. Theodore C. Janeway, a confrere of Dr. Welch
at Johns Hopkins and secretary of the Russell Sage Institute of Pathology, Dr. J. E. Goldthwait, one of the
outstanding orthopedic surgeons of his time, and Dr.
Pearce Bailey, top-ranking neurologist and psychiatrist.

"These specialists I have mentioned are of course
only a few," Gorgas went on.

No ten hospitals in the country could get together such an
advisory staff as we have. It encourages me, as I look around
and see the sort of men who are working with me, to know that
the 24,000 physicians we are going to call into service within
a year will come forward as earnestly and eagerly as have these
leaders of their profession. The rule of our medical force in
each cantonment will be "Watch! Watch! Watch!" Just as we
are keeping liquor and vice as far as possible away from our
new troops, so too must we declare "No Admittance" to all the
germs which of old wrought havoc with armies. . . . We spent
five million dollars for supplies last week, and that money

bought material which is going toward saving what the Germans wreck. We have increased our assistants nine-fold and are calling for more.

The lax sanitary practices which had permitted disease to run rampant in previous wars passed out of the picture. Cleanliness standards much higher than those maintained by any but the most health-conscious families were put into force at all troop concentration centers. Gorgas ordered that no water be used for beverage or dishwashing purposes, or for any other purpose that might affect soldiers' health, without first being analyzed and pronounced safe. With regard to drinking water, the regulations went even farther, requiring that it be sterilized in the forty-gallon canvas bag furnished each military company. Every soldier was required to have an individual drinking cup and, moreover, to keep it clean. Kitchens and mess halls had to be properly screened. Water used to wash dishes and tableware had to be kept at sufficiently high temperature to prevent them from serving as mediums for the transmission of disease, and no towels of doubtful cleanliness could be used to dry them. Iceboxes had to be elevated and the drip pans emptied and cleaned every day. Sanitary officers were required to inspect all food before it could be served. Canned goods opened today could not be served tomorrow.

The hand of the master sanitarian was also plainly evident in other regulations that poured from the Surgeon General's office. The food peddler was banned from the cantonments, lest soldiers be made sick by food prepared or distributed in an unsanitary manner. No water was allowed to collect in pools in or around the camps. Whenever natural drainage was not provided, camp sites had to be equipped with artificial drainage. Land where horses were kept had to be burned over with oil once a week to prevent it from becoming a breeding place for flies. Showers comparable to those in use in the best men's clubs were provided, and the men were required to use them at least twice a week. Inspectors working under division surgeons made their rounds regularly to see that there was no carelessness in the observance of these and other sanitary regulations.

Nor did Gorgas leave these matters altogether to the division surgeons and their inspectors. He personally visited every camp, often without warning, and sometime during each visit he would eat a meal with the troops, also without warning. In that way he was able to find out exactly how the men were being protected against diseases due to eating impure food.

It was not the purity of the food alone that interested him, however. He was also determined to give the trainees the kinds of food they needed for health, strength, and soldiership and, to that end, organized a special division—one of that large crop of new administrative units which grew up in his office during the war. Working in close co-operation with the Quartermaster Department, this division kept a close watch upon food products purchased for soldiers' mess halls and planned improvements in their handling and cooking. The fifty or more commissioned officers who were placed in charge of this work, as well as the enlisted men assigned as their assistants, received special training for their new tasks at the army schools for cooks and bakers and also at the Bureau of Chemistry of the United States Department of Agriculture.

Finding that an unusually large percentage of the men wounded in the war—one third or more—were in need of orthopedic treatment and that from 70 to 75 per cent of such cases could be restored to military usefulness after receiving this treatment, Gorgas formed a Division of Military Orthopedic Surgery. In this field of rehabilitation he enjoyed the same co-operation from the American Orthopedic Association that was accorded him in his broad medical program by the American Medical Association.

In addition to providing orthopedic care in the United States, the new division maintained well-equipped and well-staffed hospitals overseas for the treatment of cases of this kind as soon as possible after the injuries were received. The two orthopedic hospitals in this country—in Washington and Boston—were intended to provide complete facilities for the physical rebuilding of the war-wounded and their training for a return to civilian life under as slight a handicap as possible. To that end, specially trained masseurs were added to the staffs to treat every joint, muscle, and deformity condition likely to be met with. Artificial limbs were furnished those needing them.

Gorgas pledged every soldier seriously wounded in battle to stand loyally by his side, doing everything he and his corps could to prevent deformity and sparing no expense to refit him for a useful and, if possible, economically self-supporting place in society. That, in his view, was the least the nation could do in behalf of its war-wounded.

"The whole conception of governmental and national responsibility in caring for the wounded has undergone a radical change," he said.

Instead of the old idea that responsibility ended with the return of the soldier to private life with his wounds healed and such pension as he might be given, it is now considered that it is the duty of the government to equip and re-educate the wounded man, after healing his wounds, and to return him to civil life ready to be as useful to himself and his country as possible.

Nineteen "reconstruction hospitals" occupied an important place in the Gorgas rehabilitation program. Other phases of his plan for the restoration of the war-wounded included industrial training for these hospitals' former patients, tie-ups with industrial establishments for additional training, and the establishment of full-time employment bureaus to be devoted to the all-important business of finding jobs for these wounded men that would be suited to their handicapped condition.

Gorgas told about his broad program of health protection and rehabilitation in an address at the 1917 meeting of the Clinical Congress of Surgeons of North America.

"The life of every boy who falls upon the fields of France while fighting under the Stars and Stripes will be saved if medical science and human care can do it," he promised. "Every known expedient is being provided to give the men the best care possible."

CHAPTER XIII

A Prophet with Honor

NOTWITHSTANDING Gorgas's determination to keep death, disease, and disabling injury as far as possible from the American soldier and the carefully planned measures he took to translate that determination into reality, there came a time in the fall and winter of 1917 when it seemed certain that he would have to leave to some later Surgeon General the realization of his fond dream of an army virtually free from preventable diseases.

As members of the National Guard, draftees, and other men fresh from civilian life poured into the hastily constructed training camps to be whipped by drill and military discipline into America's great new armies for overseas service, alarming reports began reaching Washington regarding outbreaks of epidemic diseases, especially pneumonia, meningitis, and measles. By the middle of December 60 pneumonia deaths had occurred at Camp Sevier, 11 at Camp Doniphan, 43 at Camp Funston, and 41 at Camp Bowie. At Camp Bowie 2,900 measles cases were reported in a single month, and at Camp Sevier there were 2,000 during a similar period. Fifteen cases of meningitis and 175 cases of pneumonia occurred at Camp Sevier between November 15 and December 15. Newspaper writers, exercising one of the sacred privileges enjoyed even in wartime by those living in a democracy, unleashed a storm of criticism.

Gorgas was worried. So were his superiors. Something, obviously, was wrong. He determined to find out what it was. In order to get at the truth, he dropped everything else and made a thoroughgoing inspection of the four camps that have been mentioned, where conditions appeared to be worse than anywhere else. He found plenty that was wrong, much more than could be excused on the plea of military necessity, and his report to the Chief of Staff made the front pages all over the country. It also received much attention from editorial writers.

From it the people of the United States learned that newly mobilized soldiers were wearing summer uniforms in December, that there were insufficient overcoats to go around, that overcrowding at the camps had reached disgraceful proportions, that hospital facilities were totally inadequate, that the authorities had failed to segregate freshly recruited troops from others, exposing all to the diseases from which the recruits had happened to be suffering when they left civilian life, and that those in charge had been guilty of any number of other offenses against sanitation, good health, and military wisdom.

Of the four camps visited, he had found only one (Funston) with a base hospital completely ready to receive and treat the sick. Of Camp Sevier he wrote:

> Sanitary conditions here are serious. Sixty men have died of pneumonia in the last month. The camp has been exposed to a general epidemic of measles, about 2,000 cases having occurred within the last month. During the same period they have had 175 cases of pneumonia and fifteen cases of meningitis. The new conscripts of this command are men who are non-immune to measles. They come from the neighboring Southern states, where population is sparse, and therefore have not had measles in childhood. Always with measles a certain number of cases of pneumonia occur. The mortality of pneumonia from any cause is always high.
>
> The basic sanitary condition, however, in my opinion, is overcrowding. In the past, in this camp, the division commander has had to put eleven or twelve men in a tent, due to a shortage of tentage. At present he has to put nine men in a tent, which gives about twenty-eight square feet to the man.

I urge that the division commander be directed to furnish at
least fifty square feet of floor space to the man, which would
give about five men to the tent.

I also recommend that an observation camp be established,
where fresh men can be isolated and kept under observation for
at least two weeks or until the camp itself shows evidence of
being free from infection.

Inasmuch as it was the duty of the Medical Department—Gorgas's department—to provide hospitals, the
Surgeon General might appear to have been casting
stones from a glass house. However, he could do little
upon his own initiative, since it was the responsibility
of his official superiors, with or without advice or suggestions from him, to determine whether men should
be mobilized before hospital facilities could be completed. Indeed, had his superiors chosen to provide no
hospitals at all for the troops, he could have done nothing but protest. None of them did that of course, but it
soon became evident that many were willing to send
the men to camp as soon as their basic needs—food and
shelter—had been taken care of, trusting to Providence
or pure luck to keep them reasonably well until proper
treatment facilities could be provided. As events were
rapidly proving, this was a risky gamble, with the lives
of thousands of men at stake.

His inability to sway the higher-ups and their determination, in spite of his urging, to construct and equip
practically every other type of building ahead of hospitals were brought to the attention of the important
Senate Military Affairs Committee at a hearing in January, 1918. Appearing as a witness, Gorgas told the committee members quite frankly that Secretary of War
Baker had been among those disregarding his warning
against overcrowding.

At some camps, he testified, the hospitals were still
—nine months after the declaration of war—not ready to
receive patients. In almost none had steam heat been
provided. Because of a lack of adequate hospital per-

sonnel, newly drafted men who knew a great deal less
about the care of the sick than about farming, clerking,
and doing the other work they were doing when they
were drafted were entrusted with the care of those whose
condition called loudly for expert hospital treatment.

The Surgeon General had still another complaint
against the War Department—the failure to provide hospital ships, which he had recommended months earlier.
Instead of following his recommendation that the Army
provide its own ships in which to bring home the sick
and wounded, it had reached an agreement with the
Navy to do so. But the Navy was unable to carry out
its part of the agreement because it had only three hospital ships of its own, and these it needed badly for
its own purposes. Under the circumstances, Gorgas told
the committee, the Army would probably have to return
its sick and wounded in transports, which, under the
Geneva Convention, enjoyed no immunity whatsoever
to submarine attack.

But this was a relatively minor difficulty. Before any
American troops could be wounded or incapacitated by
illness overseas, they had to be trained and equipped at
home. And now their training and equipment were
being gravely interfered with by epidemics of measles,
pneumonia, and other diseases in South Carolina, Kansas, Texas, and many other places. It was to this more
immediate problem that he and the committee devoted
their greatest attention.

Asked by the chairman whether he personally, as
head of the Medical Department, had ever been consulted in regard to the selection of cantonment sites,
the Surgeon General promptly replied: "No, Sir. I was
not." In reply to another question, he said that in the
early stages of the war effort the United States had been
divided into military districts and that the general officer
in charge of a district had been accorded full responsibility for the selection of camp sites within that district.

While he undoubtedly felt that his advice should have been sought, he made it plain that he did not resent this assumption of authority or question these officers' right, under the military regulations, to make their own selections.

The question then switched to a matter more directly within Gorgas's special field. The chairman wanted to know what he, as a physician, considered the maximum number of men who could be placed in a regulation army tent without overcrowding and danger to health. Gorgas's reply was that he had always recommended at least sixty square feet of floor space per man.

"I say 'always,' " he continued. "That was the original recommendation when the question of construction first came up in May. I have modified that at various times. Afterward I recommended to the Secretary (of War) fifty feet. We finally came down in some of our recommendations to forty-five. I would always like to have as much as possible of floor space."

The chairman then asked: "You had some reason for reducing that from sixty square feet to forty-five square feet, thus bringing it to what you consider an irreducible minimum for health and sanitary purposes?"

"Yes, Sir," Gorgas told him. "We were endeavoring to meet the question of expenses and the feasibility in various ways."

"You believe a floor space of less than forty-five square feet does not provide good sanitary conditions?" the chairman wanted to know next.

"I believe that anything less than that would be extreme overcrowding," Gorgas answered.

Replying to another question, he told the committee that the army tents used by the troops measured sixteen by sixteen feet, or 256 square feet, each. Tents of this size should contain not more than five men, he added, but some had contained as many as twelve, giving an average of about twenty-one square feet to a man—less than half the space he a few minutes before had called "an irreducible minimum."

The chairman called attention to the testimony of an earlier witness at the hearing, a general officer, who had expressed the opinion that to assign as many as twelve men to a tent—a practice which he described as commonplace at Camp Bowie—necessarily exposed them to constant danger from epidemic disease. Gorgas of course expressed full agreement with that view.

The committee and its witness then returned to the subject of hospital facilities at army camps.

Gorgas readily agreed with a member who asked him if, in building the cantonments, hospitals had not been left to the last.

"In general," he said, "the cantonments have been pretty well completed before the hospitals were commenced."

"Was that in accordance with your advice?"

"No, Sir. I thought just the contrary, that the hospitals ought to have been commenced and completed first."

Gorgas said it was "my own knowledge," as well as "general knowledge," that the men had been rushed to cantonments before the latter were properly prepared to receive them and care for their health. Arriving draftees found them "very incomplete," he added.

The question was raised whether "the clamor from certain parts of the country" for haste in getting the men into training and the urgent pleas from the British and French for more and more American troops as rapidly as possible had not caused Secretary Baker to order the men to camp before adequate hospital facilities could be provided. Referring to his recommendation that hospital building at least keep apace of cantonment construction, the Surgeon General went on:

I presume that he [Secretary Baker] said "No, build the cantonments first," because he had some military reason for it.

I presume he has been pressed by our allies to get troops over
to Europe as rapidly as possible, and, if he delayed the cantonments until the hospitals were finished, or put hospitals in first,
it would delay for a longer or shorter time getting those troops
into the cantonments. . . . It certainly would have been better
for their [the soldiers'] physical health to go more slowly."

The impression gained by those who crowded the
committee room and the vastly larger number who read
Gorgas's testimony in the newspapers the next day was
that, while blunders and mistakes undoubtedly had been
made, his official conduct deserved no censure.

"Every member of the Senate committee was a friend
of General Gorgas at the close of this all-day grilling,"
Gorgas's associate and warm admirer, Dr. Martin, wrote
in his memoirs. "Every newspaper man present became
his friend. This gentleman, at the head of the most
important corps of the Army, in whom every father
and mother who had sons in the service was interested
vitally, was pronounced a safe executive."

Unfortunately, there were some who did not share
Dr. Martin's and the others' enthusiasm. Among the dis-
approving minority were a number of Gorgas's official
associates in the War Department, who made no efforts
to conceal their resentment.

"Just at present I am having a pretty hard time," he
wrote to one of his sisters. "All my friends seem to have
deserted me and everybody is giving me a kick as I
pass by."

But that letter also told with obvious satisfaction
about "a pretty good, friendly pat" he had received a few
days before in the form of a commendatory editorial in
the New York *Times*. "General Gorgas Unheeded" was
its title.

"In his testimony before the Senate Military Affairs
Committee, Surgeon General Gorgas was, as a man of
his profession and fame should be, a thoughtful, deliberate and responsible witness," the *Times* editorial

writer had declared. "At the same time, he had the courage of his convictions, which is characteristic of him. No man of his attainments had previously spoken, through the Senate committee, to the American people about the management of the Army by the War Department since the United States entered the world conflict."

That "pretty good, friendly pat" went on:

If General Gorgas could have commended the hygienic conditions and the hospital facilities of the camps and cantonments, or even found excuses (not reasons) for omissions and shortcomings, he would have done so with great satisfaction. He is not a destructive critic, and as a scientist he is far-seeing and fair-minded. General Gorgas, weighing his words and calculating their effect upon his standing and reputation, was compelled by a high sense of duty to make statements that reflected upon the efficiency of his superior, the Secretary of War. There is no escape from that conclusion. . . .

It seems astonishing, in fact inexplicable, that the advice of the surgeon who combatted and by scientific discoveries triumphed over yellow fever at Havana, and who made the Panama Zone a sanatorium for the canal builders, should have been disregarded. The result was an unnecessary increase in the death rate of soldiers committed to makeshifts of hospitals without heat, proper equipment or trained attendants. It is a shameful argument that, after all, the death rate per thousand is not high. It proves nothing but indecent partisanship. Can there be a doubt that if the cantonments had to be built over again the construction of hospitals would not keep pace with them?

But the waste of life, which was so unnecessary and is such a reproach to the War Department, had another salient cause than the lack of adequate hospital facilities, and that was overcrowding in the camps. General Gorgas urged as the minimum of floor space forty-five square feet—his preference was sixty feet as a sanitary precaution. "We were endeavoring," he told the committee to account for the compromise, "to meet the question of expenses and the feasibility in various ways."

What happened? When General Gorgas made his inspections he found nine men crowded into floor spaces large enough for five only. He had heard that as many as twelve men were compressed into space intended for five. Such was the condition last September at Camp Bowie, according to the testimony of General Greble, the commander who called for sufficient clothing for the men and waited an unconscionable time for it. The overcrowded camps became breeding places for epidemics.

Judging from what now appears in the record of performance, what reason is there to believe that he [Secretary Baker] will make the best Secretary of War obtainable, that, at any rate, if his commission is indefinitely continued, he will not pile Ossa on Pelion?

Less than two months after he emerged from that Senatorial inquiry which had proved so embarrassing to him, Gorgas found himself in another bitter conflict that made headlines all over the country. Like the earlier controversies in which he had been engaged, this one could have been avoided had he been willing to pay the price of peace—acquiescence in a matter in which he held strong convictions. As on those earlier occasions in which he had faced this choice of sacrificing strongly held convictions or fighting for them, he fought, and he fought hard.

It all grew out of his belief, and that of many other medical men, that officers of the Medical Reserve Corps —the physicians who had been called from the private practice of medicine to safeguard the health and treat the wounds of the fighting men in the trenches and behind the lines—were being unfairly discriminated against by service regulations which provided that members of that corps, whatever their attainments and reputations in civilian life or the responsibilities imposed upon them after entering the Army, could never attain higher military rank than that of major. Transportation executives, college administrators, psychologists, chemists, and experts in numerous other fields—even medical officers in the United States Navy—entered their country's service with the knowledge that there was no bar to their advancement to the highest ranks open to anyone serving his country. But the most famous surgeon, earning an income of $100,000 or more a year, entered the Army knowing that throughout the war he would have to salute relatively unknown engineering school professors

and receive correspondingly smaller compensation. The
Surgeon General, jealous of the dignity of his own profession, also feared that this arbitrary discrimination
would cause many badly needed physicians and surgeons
to turn down Medical Reserve Corps commissions. So
he determined to correct this obvious injustice.

He and those of a like mind—Dr. Martin, Dr. Welch,
the Mayos, Dr. Victor Vaughan, and a number of others
—naturally turned to Congress for a remedy, since it
could be provided only by that body. Finding considerable sentiment there in favor of the legislation they
had in mind, they requested Senator Robert L. Owen,
of Oklahoma, and Representative Leonidas C. Dyer, of
Missouri, to introduce simultaneously in their respec-
tive bodies identical bills providing that officers in the
Medical Reserve Corps be eligible to all ranks corresponding to those open to medical officers in the United
States Navy. It was estimated that passage of the measure would result in the creation of 70 new generals, 800
new colonels, and 1,700 new lieutenant colonels.

Gorgas and his cohorts received the immediate and
enthusiastic support of President Wilson, who wrote
letters to the chairmen of the House and Senate Committees on Military Affairs urging passage of the measure. In spite of the Surgeon General's recent criticism
of the War Department—certainly not conducive to cordial relations between him and the Secretary of War—
that gentleman also promised it his support, which, however, proved to be somewhat less than enthusiastic.
Lined up in firm array against them were Assistant Secretary of War Benedict Crowell, the General Staff, and
the War College.

To win the support of wavering Congressmen, the
bill's backers sent letters to medical societies, state and
county committees, and other medical groups, telling
of the pending action on the measure and urging them
to exert whatever pressure they could, through personal

letters, telegrams, resolutions, and other means, upon their representatives in Washington.

The need for such pressure became evident when even the lukewarm support which Secretary Baker had accorded the bill was largely nullified by his departure for a visit to France, leaving the militantly hostile Assistant Secretary of War in temporary charge of the War Department.

As the energetic Dr. Martin points out in his memoirs, these efforts to exert pressure in the right places were "very helpful in showing Senators and Representatives that the medical men of the country favored the legislation." In the unsympathetic eyes of the Acting Secretary of War, however, such activity on the part of the Surgeon General of the Army and other officials of the government was just plain lobbying of a kind sternly forbidden to those in their positions. Gorgas and Dr. Martin, therefore, were peremptorily summoned to appear before Crowell and General Peyton C. Marsh, Chief of Staff, to answer charges of "pernicious activity" in behalf of the bill.

The unrepentant Surgeon General, who had refused to kowtow to the dominating Colonel Goethals at Panama and had not hesitated to speak his mind in regard to blunders in the construction and operation of cantonments, showed equal unconcern and aplomb in the presence of the acting head of the War Department. Questioned whether he had done this and that, he replied that he could not remember having performed the specific acts mentioned but freely admitted that he had taken a prominent and active part in the campaign to line up support for the proposed legislation.

"You know, Mr. Secretary," he said, with dignity, "I am in favor of the passage of the Owen-Dyer bill, and I would consider myself disloyal to my corps if I did not do everything in my power to bring about its passage."

This bold admission left his chief antagonist momentarily speechless. Thereupon the matter at issue shifted from a threatened reprimand to the merits of the bill. Crowell charged Gorgas with inconsistency and declared that his advocacy of the proposed legislation indicated a desire to play favorites by creating a preferred status for members of the Medical Reserve Corps. Would not passage of the Owen-Dyer bill, he asked, result in discrimination against other large groups in the Army—men as famous and as deserving of promotion to the higher military ranks as physicians and surgeons?

Gorgas had an answer to that one too.

"I have no definite knowledge of the requirements of the other corps, and I should never think of interfering in their organization," he replied. "I do, however, know the needs of my own corps, and I feel that I must favor such a change in the law as will meet them."

The next question was: How would passage of the Owen-Dyer bill benefit the Medical Reserve Corps and enable it to perform more efficiently its duty to the sick and wounded?

Thereupon Gorgas undertook to give this civilian Army man a concept of the Medical Reserve Corps—the men composing it and their duties and responsibilities—which he had never had before. He told him about the camps and cantonments that dotted the country, each one crowded with the men upon whom the nation depended for victory. In every one of these concentration centers, he pointed out, and in American hospitals in France, there were medical men, some of them undistinguished country physicians but others as outstanding in the field of medicine as an Assistant Secretary of War in the field of public affairs. He told him about Harvey Cushing, Hugh Young, George Crile, Hugh Cabot, Welch, the Mayo brothers, and a host of others—not one of whom, with all his fame and military responsibilities, could ever aspire to a military rank higher than that held by thousands of relative unknowns comparatively fresh from West Point and officers' training camps. And when American doctors were sent overseas, he went on, they found themselves at a humiliating disadvantage working alongside Britishers, Frenchmen, and Italians who wore the insignia of generals, colonels, and lieutenant colonels, although many of these foreigners were much less outstanding in their own countries and in world medicine than they were.

Gorgas's earnestness, simple common sense, and eloquence won the day for him. Although the Acting War Secretary would not admit that the Surgeon General's arguments had brought about any lessening of his opposition to the Owen-Dyer bill—subsequent events proved unqualifiedly that they had not—he did withhold the rebuke which Gorgas had been summoned to receive.

But that conference in Crowell's office was only a side issue. Meanwhile, the fight over the bill went on with undiminished energy. A highlight of that controversy came on March 15, 1918, when Gorgas and other supporters of the measure appeared before the Senate Military Affairs Committee. A letter from Crowell, calling the proposed enactment "undesirable legislation," was also read at that hearing.

Gorgas, who had become the chief actor in this drama of wartime conflict between the Medical Corps and the General Staff, told the committee how medical officers' recommendations had been thrown lightly aside any number of times by line officers. He spoke with particular earnestness of their refusal to accord hospital construction its proper place in the building of cantonments and of their consistent failure to act upon sanitary measures and others recommended by Medical Reserve Corps men. The reason for this, he insisted, was that in the Army authority and respect from one's associates go with rank—that few officers are willing to take suggestions from their official inferiors. His remedy was to

give physicians and surgeons military rank in keeping
with their responsibilities and knowledge.

"Line officers have had no hesitation in ignoring the
sanitary recommendations of medical officers of lower
rank," he complained. "The men of the Medical Corps
should get higher rank, rank commensurate with the
positions they hold. Some of them are administering
great hospitals, yet they hold subordinate rank."

Gorgas was followed in the witness chair by several
others who had accompanied him to the hearing. Dr.
Martin read a number of letters from members of the
Medical Reserve Corps with the A.E.F. All complained
of the embarrassment they were suffering because they
were of lower military rank than medical officers in other
armies. One letter writer was especially bitter.

"I have never endured so many insults in my life
as since I came over here," Dr. Martin read from his
letter. "But I am keeping a stiff upper lip and carrying
on."

Dr. C. H. Mayo, holding the highest rank permitted
a member of the Medical Reserve Corps, also stressed
this side of the picture. America's famous physicians
and surgeons who had volunteered for war service "have
not taken up some new thing, in which they must be
trained like rookies," he told the committee. On the
contrary:

"We are going right ahead with our life work. We
are the only men in the service who are. When the
war is over, those of us who remain will return to our
homes and again take up this work."

He continued:

What we ask from our Government is recognition that will
remove the handicaps under which we are now laboring. While
we are in the United States, working in camps and cantonments, our names, which we have made prominent by our own
efforts, gain us some recognition and respect, but when we go
to France the men over there look at our insignia. They look

to see what our Government has done for us and judge us by
that. They don't know who is inside the clothes. They look
at the clothes.

The fate of the Owen-Dyer bill hung in the balance
for some time. Unexpected and demoralizing opposition
developed. Some of those who were expected to support
it failed to do so. For a while Secretary Baker was listed
among its opponents, and hardly anyone supposedly
favoring it did as little to insure its passage. Even President Wilson, whose endorsement had been obtained as
a trump card, let it be known that, while he favored the
principle of higher rank for doctors, he feared it would
create a top-heavy medical organization containing too
many general officers.

The bill's hard-pressed proponents rose to meet this
new crisis by assuring him that, while such a danger
might have been inherent in the measure as introduced,
it had been entirely eliminated in the rewritten version
then under consideration. Thereupon the President
agreed to give the matter more study.

Badly battered but essentially unchanged, the bill
was approved by both houses of Congress on July 9,
1918. It was particularly gratifying to Gorgas that, in
spite of the severe treatment to which it had been subjected, the measure still recognized the principle for
which he had struggled—that medical officers are entitled
to the same rank accorded to members of other branches
of the Reserve Corps of the Army. With that official
recognition clinched, it was only a minor irritant that
the number of high-ranking officers in the Medical Reserve Corps would not be as large as he had hoped it
would be.

About this time Gorgas's admirers both inside and
outside the Army, and especially his friends among the
nation's doctors, began to realize that the following
October 3, then just a few months off, would be his
sixty-fourth birthday and that, unless something could

be done to prevent it, he would automatically retire from active duty at that time. With all indications pointing to many more months of war and with increasing emphasis being placed upon the maintenance of the highest possible health standards for the country's growing armies, they became more and more convinced that he should be retained at his post at least until the end of the conflict.

This conviction found expression as early as May, when three national medical organizations—the American Laryngological Association, the Laryngological, Rhinological and Otological Society, and the American Otological Society—holding a joint meeting in Atlantic City, drew up memorials to President Wilson urging that Gorgas be retained as Surgeon General as long as he should be physically able to perform the duties of that office. This was followed a short time later by a similar move on the part of the House of Delegates of the American Medical Association, which also adopted resolutions asking the President to intervene to prevent the country from losing his services at such a crucial time.

Newspaper editors appeared as unwilling as doctors to have Gorgas retire. Typical of sentiment in that quarter was the following editorial in the New York *Times:*

The petitions of several national medical associations to President Wilson asking that the service of Surgeon General William C. Gorgas be not lost to the government during the war because he will reach the statutory age of retirement, 64, on October 3, reflect the desire of the American people who know the career of General Gorgas and how brilliant and merited his international reputation is.

At 64 a surgeon or scientist—General Gorgas is both—may be at the meridian of his usefulness. Some of the most eminent medical men in this city are well past that age, and they still practice their profession. In France and England there would be no question of retiring an army officer of the attainments of General Gorgas while the war lasted. It would be considered fatuous, without the shadow of reason. The President has authority to keep the present Surgeon General in active service, notwithstanding the statutory requirement, and it would seem that it was not necessary to memorialize the President to hold fast to our most distinguished army doctor.

But President Wilson, or at least his Secretary of War, had other plans. Although two of Gorgas's friends, Dr. Martin and Dr. W. J. Mayo, urged Secretary Baker to retain the Alabamian as Surgeon General and appoint Major General Merritte W. Ireland and Brigadier General Robert E. Noble as Assistant Surgeons General, their urging was to no avail.

"The Secretary was very sympathetic to our suggestion," Dr. Martin wrote in his memoirs, "and said he would tell us frankly what was in his own mind, namely, to retire Gorgas, giving him the highest rank possible, and retain him for work here, making Ireland Surgeon General to be stationed in Washington, with Noble as Assistant Surgeon General, stationed abroad."

That is exactly what happened. On the eve of Gorgas's sixty-fourth birthday the President named General Ireland as his successor. General Noble was named Assistant Surgeon General.

Gorgas was not able to turn over the affairs of his office personally to General Ireland because he was in Europe at the time. He arrived in France early in September, in company with Secretary Baker, and remained there, watching American troops in action and inspecting military hospitals, until after his successor took charge. Upon returning to the United States, he began writing a complete report of his trip. His recall to active service and assignment to this task had followed immediately upon his retirement as Surgeon General.

Shortly after his retirement Gorgas received the following letter from Secretary Baker, showing that, if any ill-feeling had been created by the then Surgeon General's criticism of the War Department in his testimony before the Senate Military Affairs Committee, it no longer existed:

THE SECRETARY OF WAR
WASHINGTON

October twenty-sixth
Nineteen Hundred Eighteen

MY DEAR GENERAL GORGAS:

Your official term as Surgeon General of the Army having expired, I beg leave to express to you the appreciation of the Army and the country of the distinguished services which you have rendered during your long and brilliant career as a Medical Officer. Even the gracious modesty which is a part of your habit of thought cannot keep you from realizing that your career has been one of brilliant distinction, and that the Medical Department of the Army has profited from your services, as it has been honored by your deservedly high reputation. The operation of law has terminated your period of active service, except for emergency work which you are now doing under my direction, but it will be a source of satisfaction to me and a comfort to the people of the country to realize that your interest will continue in the Army and in the great scientific researches in which your life has been engaged.

If I may add a personal word to this note, I beg you to accept my grateful acknowledgment of the cordial and helpful relations which have existed between us officially, and to thank you for many personal courtesies and kindnesses which I have received from you during our most happy association.

I am placing a copy of this letter in the hands of the Adjutant General in order that it may become a part of your record in the Department, and may there remain as an evidence of the complete success with which you as a soldier and a doctor have through long years and under varying and difficult conditions served your country.

Cordially yours,
NEWTON D. BAKER
Secretary of War.

A few days later Major General Emilio Guglielmotti, military attaché of the Italian Embassy, made Gorgas a grand officer of the Order of the Crown of Italy in recognition of his services to the cause of military sanitation. Many other honors were also bestowed upon him.

And what of the Gorgas prophecy in 1914 that America's next great war would be fought in a state of "hygienic competence"—that at last the centuries-old ratio of several deaths from disease for every death due to enemy action had become a thing of the past as far as this country was concerned?

In his annual report for the fiscal year ending June 30, 1918, which was submitted to Secretary Baker early in December of that year, Gorgas told in modest but convincing fashion of the results of his stewardship. After calling attention to the spectacular increase in the officer and enlisted man personnel of the Medical Department, he proudly wrote that "the health of the Army both at home and overseas has been excellent" and that the death rate was "lower probably than in any similar body of troops in the history of warfare," notwithstanding the much publicized measles and pneumonia epidemics. He appeared especially pleased with the success of the Medical Department's campaign against the intestinal diseases.

The report told about typhoid fever as the men of the Spanish-American War knew it—killing them in droves and striking down ten times as many as it killed —and pointed out that, had no progress been made in its control, there would have been no less than 136,000 cases of the disease and 13,600 typhoid deaths among American soldiers during that year. Actually, however, "there were 297 cases and 23 deaths." Obviously, "the insanitary conditions seen at Camp Alger, at Jacksonville and Chickamauga in 1898 do not exist in the country today."

Another triumph won by the Medical Department while he was Surgeon General, which he might have included in that report but didn't, was the wresting of a coveted distinction from Japan. At last the American Army, and not the army of Nippon, was leading the world in curbing physical disability and the resulting drain upon military efficiency.

The complete story of Gorgas's success in keeping

American soldiers healthy could not be told of course
at the time he yielded his office and official records to his
successor, or for some time afterward. It can now be
told, however, in terms of unemotional, truth-speaking
facts and figures.

That story, in brief, is exactly what Gorgas predicted
it would be—that, for the first time in history, the United
States trained, transported, and sent into battle a huge
army without having a vastly larger number of men lose
their lives from disease than from the bayonets, bullets,
and high explosives of the enemy. Among members of
the American Expeditionary Forces, 50,554 officers and
men were killed in action and died from wounds received in action as compared with only 23,853—considerably less than half as many—who succumbed to disease. Even if we consider the American Army as a whole
—the troops in training in the United States as well as
those exposed to battle casualties—we find that deaths
due to disease outnumbered those due to the enemy by
only 12,064, or less than 24 per cent. This showing,
remarkable as it was, would have been even better had
health conditions and mortality rates in the Army not
been adversely affected by pandemic influenza, which,
with its ally, pneumonia, is estimated to have killed in
just a few months more than half a million persons in
the United States alone. Even the best of medical care
for the men in uniform could not prevent them from
sharing in this huge loss of life.

Contrast this record with the health history of earlier
wars. Summarizing a series of papers on this general
subject by Dr. L. L. Seaman, the *Medical Times* declared editorially in its issue of April, 1908:

The Crimean campaign lost in allied forces 50,000 from disease, as against 20,000 from casualties in battle. In the Russo-
Turkish war of 1877-8 there succumbed to disease 80,000 men,
or four times as many as died in battle or from wounds. In
our Mexican, as also in our Civil, War three men died from

disease to one from wounds. The French sent 14,000 men to Madagascar in 1894. Of these only 29 were killed in action, and more than half the rest died of disease. The last Boer War in South Africa lost the English ten men from disease to one from wounds. In our Spanish war fourteen lives were needlessly sacrificed to ignorance and incompetency for every soldier who died on the firing line or from wounds.

Nor was the American Army of the First World War period merely a fortunate beneficiary, along with the armies of other nations, of the latest advances in military preventive medicine. The fact is that many of the disease conditions which prevailed in those earlier wars were being largely, if not entirely, duplicated in other armies at the time when the United States Army was making such a notable health record.

Take malaria for instance:

In his *Malaria in Europe,* Dr. L. W. Hackett, one of the world's leading malariologists, tells us that in the Macedonian campaign the disability due to this single disease was so heavy that "we had the spectacle of three fine armies [British, French and German], backed by the most powerful nations of Europe and equipped regardless of expense with every modern appointment, virtually paralyzed before they were able to strike a blow."

Thanks to malaria, "in the autumn of that dreadful year of 1916 the French could put no more than 20,000 men in the line out of a force at least six times that number, and General Sarrail had to report to his government that his army was immobilized in the hospital." Moreover, "the British had at least 30,000 men down with malaria in 1916 and 70,000 in 1917, and no one knows what might have happened in 1918 had they not repatriated 25,000 of the worst and most chronic cases."

It will be recalled, from Gorgas's testimony before the Senate Committee on Military Affairs, that the selection of sites for training camps was taken out of his hands and entrusted to area commanders, who might, or might not, be guided by sanitary considerations in making

their decisions. We have it on the word of J. A. Le-
Prince, who had charge of malaria control work in all
camps and contiguous areas during the war, that little
or no thought actually was given to sanitation in the
selection of these sites. In a number of instances sites
chosen for World War I camps were the same that were
used in the Spanish-American War, including several
which had been veritable breeding grounds for malaria
during that earlier war. Regardless of the wisdom or
unwisdom, from a sanitary point of view, of the selection
of individual camp sites, it was the policy of the War
Department, for more effective all-year-round training,
to establish the great majority of these camps in the
South, where malaria has always been much more prevalent than in other parts of the country. Moreover, the
operation of the draft laws and voluntary enlistments
sent to the camps, regardless of where they were situated,
hundreds of thousands of recruits fresh from "the
malaria belt," and actually or potentially suffering from
this disease, as they, their associates, and their ancestors
had been doing for generations.

In spite of all these things, however, malaria never
became a serious problem among America's fighting
men. Of the approximately four million soldiers serving under the American flag in this country and Europe
between April 1, 1917, and December 31, 1919, only
11,460 were admitted to treatment, only twenty-six died,
and only twenty-five were discharged for disability because of it. Malaria was never in all that time included
among the thirty leading Army diseases on the basis of
either admissions, deaths, discharges for disability, or
time lost from ordinary duties. Quite properly did
Lieutenant Colonel Joseph F. Siler write in his report
of the work of the Medical Department during the war:
"It is believed that never before in the history of the
world has so small a number of deaths from the malarial
infections been recorded in any army in time of war."

CHAPTER XIV

And So to Rest

ONE DAY while the nation's energies were still concentrated upon the task of winning the war, Gorgas and his friend Dr. Martin happened to be together in an anteroom of Secretary Baker's office awaiting a summons to a conference with their chief. Dr. Martin remarked upon the cynical turn of fate which had given Gorgas, an apostle of lifesaving, a position of great responsibility in history's greatest mass killing. The irony of the thing impressed both of them.

Gorgas made it plain that, notwithstanding his great love for the Army, he had no stomach for the wholesale slaughter of his fellow-men and expressed a fervent wish that the war were over.

"What is the very first thing you would do, if, tomorrow morning before arising, you should receive a message telling you that the war was ended?" Dr. Martin asked.

Gorgas's eyes had a far-away look in them. But his answer was ready. He would, he said, book passage on the first ship sailing to South America and begin a campaign to eradicate yellow fever from those areas here and there in the world where it was still endemic and thus remove once and forever this menace to the human race. That task accomplished, he would return to the scene of his greatest battle with this old enemy and there, in Panama, "end my days writing an elegy on yellow fever."

In view of this wish, which he had expressed to others as well as Dr. Martin, it is not surprising that his

retirement as Surgeon General was followed within a
few weeks by his acceptance of a proffer from the Rockefeller Foundation to do just that—go back to South
America and take up again the task which he had reluctantly dropped when this country entered the war.

Having decided from his earlier trips that there was
probably more yellow fever in Guayaquil, Ecuador, than
anywhere else, he spent considerable time there. He
also spent a great deal of time at Quito, the capital. The
President was enthusiastic about the project, and the
two men, bending over maps and reports, worked out an
ambitious program for the rapid curbing and eventual
extinction of Gorgas's No. One enemy, the *Stegomyia*
mosquito. The more the former Surgeon General
learned about the yellow fever situation in Ecuador and
the co-operation he was likely to receive, the better
pleased he was with his decision to use that country as
the starting point of his campaign.

His stay was not without its embarrassing situations,
however. Nor did it lack reminders of the heartbreaks
which yellow fever so often caused. Just before Gorgas's
departure from Quito, the President asked if two of his
relatives, a Doctor and Señora Esquerizo, might accompany him and his party in the private car which had
been placed at their disposal for the trip to Guayaquil.
Gorgas replied that, while he personally would be happy
to have the lady and gentleman accompany him, the car
had been furnished his party by railway officials as a
special courtesy and he did not feel at liberty to have
others use it without their permission. A similar request by the Secretary of State in behalf of a member
of his official staff and the latter's sister was declined with
the same explanation. Gorgas confessed later that these
two requests made him feel "a good deal embarrassed."
His embarrassment was due, however, not to his having
to refuse the Chief Executive and Secretary of State of
a country whose good will he was trying to cultivate

but to the subsequent discovery that he had been altogether mistaken about being the guest of the railroad—
that, on the contrary, the private car had been placed
at his party's disposal by the Ecuadorean government.

The trip's most poignant reminder of yellow fever's
tragic potentialities came shortly after his arrival in
Guayaquil. Among the warm personal friends whom
he had made during his 1916 visit were U. S. Consul
General and Mrs. Frederick W. Goding. A native of
Montevideo, Mrs. Goding was a woman of rare charm
and intelligence and had attained a mastery of her husband's and Gorgas's language almost as complete as her
mastery of her own. Both husband and wife had shown
him innumerable courtesies during that earlier trip,
and he had developed a great admiration for them. But
Mrs. Goding was no longer there, having succumbed
to yellow fever a few months before, and the second
member of that once-happy and congenial couple was
now a "changed and broken man."

"Marie asked him to dine with us at a farewell dinner," Gorgas wrote in the journal which he kept during
the trip, "but he asked to be excused, saying that he could
never pass our hotel without a wave of emotion. He
thinks that Mrs. Goding contracted yellow fever at a
dinner which she attended at this hotel. It is pathetic
to hear him speak of her. A year ago she was so charming and full of life, the social center of the American
colony."

Then he thought of Nast, the famous cartoonist, who
had died of yellow fever while serving as American consul at Guayaquil, and of others whom he had known
personally before this disease brought an end to their
labors. Stirred by these memories, he wrote somewhat
bitterly: "What a destroyer yellow fever has been to
American officials at Guayaquil!"

Much more pleasant were the memories aroused by
his arrival at the scene of his greatest sanitary achieve-

ment. Dining with old friends he encountered here and there on the Isthmus, talking over adventures of those trying but stimulating days and revisiting places which he had helped turn from disease incubators into virtual health resorts, he felt, he wrote enthusiastically, that he was "almost back to construction times."

Back in Guayaquil, his main theater of operations, Gorgas was subjected to considerable pressure from governmental officials and others trying to persuade him to assume the general management of the yellow fever campaign which it was planned to get under way in that city soon. Interested though he was in any campaign of this sort, especially here in what he considered the most dangerous yellow fever endemic center in the Western Hemisphere, he nevertheless clung to his decision not to limit his activities, for the present at least, to a single city or country, not even this one. A compromise agreement was reached. He promised to assume the honorary —and presumably payless—post of director, with the understanding that to someone else would be entrusted the actual management of the proposed campaign.

He found himself similarly importuned by the health-conscious officials of Peru shortly after his arrival at Lima about two weeks later. But this time his services were sought, not in behalf of a single city, but as director of sanitation for the entire country, with full authority to reorganize the nation's health machinery and supervise sanitary engineering activities in twenty-five cities and towns. President Leguia, who made the offer personally, promised him a salary of fifteen thousand dollars a year and the services of a medical assistant and sanitary engineer, each of whom would receive twelve thousand dollars annually.

When Gorgas gave the President virtually the same answer he had given the municipal authorities at Guayaquil—that, interested as he was, he did not yet wish to discontinue his association with the Rockefeller Founda-

tion—the President made him essentially the same offer
that had been made him on that earlier occasion. Thereupon, as at Guayaquil, he promised to serve without
compensation as honorary director of the projected program, leaving the actual direction of the sanitary work
in the hands of a personal representative to be appointed
by himself. It was also agreed that the matter of his returning and assuming personal charge would be re-
opened at the end of another year or two, when he hoped
to have completed the particular work in which he was
then engaged.

At the conclusion of his stay in South America,
Gorgas expressed confidence that the sanitary measures
already instituted under his supervision at Guayaquil
would result in the virtual eradication of yellow fever
in that city. With considerable enthusiasm, he reported
that no cases had occurred there during the previous
three months, when normally it would have been unusually prevalent, and predicted that this latest sanitary
triumph would free that part of the world, once and forever, from its grip.

How truly he spoke. For so literally did his prophecy
come true that Dr. Rafael H. Elizalde, Ecuador's minister to the United States, was able to say in 1921:

In some four months after the work began actively the ancient
scourge, which had held Guayaquil captive for several centuries
and made her name a terror to travelers and commerce, had
been exterminated, and now, since May, 1919, this city is as safe
for human life as any on the American continent.

En route home, Gorgas arrived at the Canal Zone
on the eve of an important anniversary, which found
him in both a reminiscent and forward-thinking frame
of mind, as such anniversaries had a habit of doing.
His health appeared unimpaired, and there was every
indication that he would retain not only life itself but
also his physical vigor for a great many years. Nevertheless, as his ship nosed into her pier, he was thinking the

same kind of thoughts that were in his mind when he wrote to that hopelessly sick soldier out in New Mexico.

"Here I am on my sixty-fifth birthday back again at Panama," he wrote to a member of his family just after his arrival.

A year ago today I was under fire of the German batteries in France. Where will I be a year from today? If I am not teaching sanitation in Peru, I hope to be doing something equally useful in Heaven, helping Mother and Father and all our dear ones with their useful tasks there. What will become of the poor mosquitoes?

While Gorgas himself was experiencing a premonition of early death and thinking more and more about the reunion with his father and mother which his strong religious faith assured him would take place, others were planning new tasks for him in this world. Among them were the leaders of a little-heard-of but ambitious political group, the Single Tax party.

He had been interested in that party and espoused its principles for several years. In an address to the Cincinnati Business Men's Club as early as 1915, he had not only publicly proclaimed himself a Single Taxer but had gone so far as to say that the sanitary cleanup of the Canal Zone and the resulting conquest of disease there would have been accomplished much more promptly had the principles of the Single Tax party been translated into law in that country. He revealed, moreover, that he had discussed with the municipal authorities of Panama and Havana a suggested tax levy upon unimproved real estate—one of the strongest planks in the Single Tax platform—as a means of financing sanitation work in those cities.

"I finally got the Panama authorities around to the point of seeing the justice and advisability of such methods," he said, "but the organic law would have to be changed, and this always takes time. I hope that something of this kind may yet come about in Panama."

Because of Gorgas's standing as a world figure and
the resultant weight of his influence, even in a field in
which he had never been active, his adherence to the
Single Tax party was regarded by that party's members
as a notable acquisition indeed. Nor is it surprising that
they looked to him for leadership.

At a meeting of party members held in New York
in June, 1919, there was a pronounced crystallization of
sentiment in favor of nominating him as the Single
Taxers' candidate for President and Mrs. Carrie Chap-
man Catt for Vice-President, both of whom it was
planned to boom in a national campaign the following
year. About eight months later—in February, 1920—
James A. Robinson, a party stalwart, announced that
plans were under way for the organization of local Single
Tax clubs throughout the country and added: "Our
candidate for President has not been selected, but General William Gorgas, the man who cleaned up the
Panama Canal Zone, is a member of the party, and we
have reason to believe he will run."

When, however, the Single Tax party held its convention in Chicago on July 12, it nominated neither
Gorgas nor Mrs. Catt. It had the best of reasons for
leaving the name of the former off the ticket, as we shall
see.

Gorgas, meanwhile, was thinking little about political
honors and much about the work in which he was engaged in South America. On March 4 he was back in
Peru occupying an ultraluxurious suite in one of Lima's
most elegant hotels. He had been taken there immediately upon his arrival and told that his suite had been
reserved for him by none other than the President of
the Republic.

"I was rather startled by all this grandeur," he wrote
in his journal. And he was worried about it too. For
he knew that a palatial suite like this must rent for a high
figure—ample cause for anxiety to a person who, in spite

of all his fame, never reached the fortunate position of not having to keep a watchful eye upon his expenditures.

Determined to find out the worst and, if necessary, to ask that his luggage be moved to a room more in keeping with his financial status, he timidly went to the business office and inquired about the charge being made for his suite. Great was his relief when the manager assured him that he was the guest of the Peruvian Government, which would not permit him to pay for anything.

Just a few hours after being relieved of that worry, he was waited upon by a delegation from the Bricklayers' Association and received from its spokesman a beautifully engraved certificate attesting to his election as an honorary member. This was not an entirely gratuitous honor. The spokesman dropped something stronger than a hint that some gift was expected in return. Taken aback somewhat, Gorgas thanked him and indicated that he would express his appreciation in the desired manner—later. That night, before he could find out what was really expected of him, he confided to his journal his fear that, "as a member of the Rockefeller Foundation, I am expected to give at least as much as a Peruvian President."

The Gorgas journal does not reveal how this little diplomatic crisis was handled, but presumably the gift he decided upon was entirely acceptable to the Bricklayers' Association, and he retained the good will of its officials and his fellow-members.

Those preliminaries over, he got down to the serious business of his trip. At the first opportunity he and President Leguia again discussed the position offered him during his earlier visit. As before, he pointed out his contractual obligations to the Rockefeller Foundation's International Health Board and explained that, while it was the Board's desire that he remain with it until January 1, 1921, it was entirely willing for him in the meantime to be of such assistance as he could to the Peruvian health authorities, with due regard to his other responsibilities of course. After that time he would be free to undertake full-time direction of the project then under consideration. This arrangement was agreed to, and his compensation was set at $15,000, the salary previously offered him. Delighted with the outcome of these negotiations, he wrote his sister of his good fortune in being able "in my old age, to supervise such a great and useful work."

While Gorgas and President Leguia were laying these ambitious plans to bring the people of Peru the blessed gift of better health, three fellow-countrymen of his were struggling in another part of the country with a desperate health problem of a much more personal nature. These three—a young woman, her mother, and her small child, all of San Antonio, Texas—had been visiting one of the smaller cities for some time when the child became ill. Fearing it was developing pneumonia, the mother and grandmother hastened with it to Lima and were assigned a hotel room next to Gorgas's. Before they could get in touch with any of the city's famous physicians, the child became much worse, developing, not the feared pneumonia but another grave illness, dysentery. Nobody in the party could speak Spanish, and they had not a friend in the city. Learning of their plight, Gorgas offered his services and, upon their grateful acceptance, returned to the relatively humble role of the bedside physician. Presumably, the child recovered completely.

There is a brief reference to this incident in the Gorgas journal. "The mother is quite young," it says, "and appeals strongly to our sympathy."

Early in April, 1920, Gorgas was again at sea, en route this time to Panama, New York, Belgium, England, and the yellow fever endemic centers of West Africa. Delighted over the apparent success of his South American campaign and the prospect of crowning his life work with the wiping out of the disease's greatest stronghold in the Eastern Hemisphere, he forgot that his sixty-sixth birthday was just a few months away. Gone apparently were those premonitions of an early death which had come to him so frequently in recent years.

On the brief train ride from Balboa to Colon, he heard some interesting gossip about a young man who, then the world's most sought-after bachelor, has since become a King and an ex-King. He passed it on to the members of his family, for whose information and pleasure he was keeping his journal:

Mr. [Andrew P.] Bennett, the English minister [to Panama], and his family were on the train with us. Mrs. Bennett and her party are going to England . . . . I am told Mr. Bennett is much perturbed about his entertainment of the Prince of Wales, who has just left Panama. There were two extremely pretty girls down there, daughters of one of the canal employes—both good dancers. The younger one is so good that she is asked to dance at all the charity entertainments. A ball was given by the citizens, and the younger sister danced—one of the events of the entertainment. But the Prince was more attracted by the elder sister, who, besides being a good dancer, was remarkably pretty. The Prince asked her to dance, and she was charmed. He asked her for a second, third, fourth and fifth dance. The young girl did not seem to object, but all the authority of the Legation had to be brought to bear to make H. R. H. keep the engagements that had been made for him. The next day the British minister gave an entertainment for the Prince, to which all the notables were invited. The same evening some of the young men connected with the Legation gave the pretty dancer a dinner. The Prince is strongly suspected of having had a finger in this affair. At any rate, his guardians felt very uncertain about him and half an hour before the time for the big dinner sent out scouts to look him up. Sure enough, he was found dining with the pretty dancer and his other young friends and was dragged off just in time to keep his dinner engagement. The pretty dancer is now the heroine of the Isthmus, and the Prince has sworn by his warmest heart's blood that he will return by way of the Isthmus just for one more dance.

Gorgas paused but briefly in the United States. He had been chosen as the 1920 recipient of the Harbin gold medal in recognition of his "services to mankind" and had been asked to be in Brussels by May 20 for the opening session of the International Hygiene Congress, when it was planned to have the medal presented by King Albert. Because of a delay in his arrival in New York, he was unable to obtain passage on a ship sailing from there early enough to assure his reaching the Belgian capital by the time set. However, he found that he could still obtain passage on the S. S. *Victorian,* sailing from Quebec a day or two later and due on the other side before the opening of the Congress. So he and his party—Mrs. Gorgas, General and Mrs. Noble, General Noble's sister, and two private secretaries—left by train for the Canadian port city.

Even this change in their plans did not enable them to reach Brussels by May 20. The ship was slowed by fog and a rough sea, and Gorgas was obliged to send a radiogram to King Albert expressing his regret at the delay and asking that the presentation ceremony be postponed.

Shortly after his arrival King Albert conferred upon him the order of the Star of Belgium, and this brief ritual proved to be the first of numerous ceremonies, meetings, and social affairs given in his honor. He and the other members of his party were received by the King and Queen at the royal palace, were the guests of the prime minister at luncheon, were entertained by Burgomaster Max, and visited Cardinal Mercier at Malines. They were also the guests of Ambassador and Mrs. Brand Whitlock. And, at the banquet which brought the three-day meeting of the International Hygiene Congress to a close, Gorgas received the Harbin medal, not from King Albert, as had been planned, but from Lord Sandhurst.

During his stay in Brussels, where he remained

MARIE DOUGHTY GORGAS, 1926

several days after the International Hygiene Congress ended, Gorgas discussed his plans with King Albert and other officials of the Belgian government, all of whom expressed much interest in the proposed West African yellow fever expedition. In adding his own best wishes to those of his government, the King showed particular enthusiasm over that part of the expedition which was to be devoted to the Belgian Congo and expressed the hope that it would prove a great boon to his subjects there.

Gorgas was a tired man during this trying round of social and official visits. He was also a sick man, a dangerously sick man, although neither he nor his friends realized it. He wrote to his sister Jessie on May 26, just on the eve of his departure from Brussels, and in that letter, presumably the last he ever wrote, he confessed that he was tired. He also hinted at a realization that he was suffering from something more serious than temporary physical fatigue.

He told her about his arrival in England on May 19 and his having been "in a turmoil ever since." Then he went on:

Marie and the Nobles left yesterday for a three-days' trip to Coblenz, Antwerp and neighboring points. We all return to London within a few days. Marie is well, though she tires easily. The fact is, I do the same. We are not as young as we used to be. This Lima position comes at a very good time. It will not be as hard work as traveling under pressure, as I have been doing for the last two years.

Back in London a few days later, he rejoined Mrs. Gorgas and those who had accompanied her to Antwerp and Coblenz and immediately plunged into a round of conferences with British officials whose assistance he needed for the proposed African trip. A dinner was given in his honor on the evening of May 29, permitting him to renew his acquaintance with many of the leading medical men and scientists of the Empire. One who was present wrote later: "He was never more keenly alert mentally and was apparently physically vigorous."

But his great physical vigor was only apparent, and those who were charmed by his courtly manners and ready wit were soon to find how badly mistaken they had been in assuming that all these things indicated good health. For just a few hours later—about two o'clock the following morning—he woke Mrs. Gorgas, telling her he was feeling faint and feared he had suffered a slight paralytic stroke.

Dr. Noble was summoned. Realizing immediately that Gorgas's condition was grave, he called Sir John Goodwin, Surgeon General of the British Army. The latter also quickly comprehended the gravity of the patient's condition and approved Dr. Noble's suggestion that he be removed at once to the Queen Alexandra Military Hospital, Millbank.

It is one of the penalties of being a physician that doctors usually know the whole disturbing truth about their condition when they themselves become sick. So Gorgas could not be lulled into a false sense of optimism by anybody's cheery bedside manner. He never lost his own cheerfulness and good humor. But he knew almost from the first that his illness was likely to prove fatal. And Mrs. Gorgas and the others who waited upon him so faithfully knew that he knew.

Because of this, Mrs. Gorgas did her best to keep his mind away from thoughts of death and also away from something he dreaded much more—the possibility that, while he might not immediately succumb, the wrecking of his health might make it necessary to return home, leaving to others the completion of the task of driving yellow fever from the earth.

"You're not going to give up," she would urge him. "You will do your best to get well!"

Yes, he promised. He would try to get well.

"W. C. is a fighter, you know."

Then:

"I am going to fight to the very last. But this time I do not believe I shall win out."

The best medical minds in all England were at his service, and Dr. Noble, who had developed a warm affection for the sick man from close association with him at Panama, in the office of the Surgeon General during the war, and on several medical expeditions like this one, did not spare himself in his devotion to his task of keeping death at a distance as long as possible. Writing later of his devoted care and thoughtfulness in this dark hour, Mrs. Gorgas called him "a tower of strength to us both."

She also gratefully remembered others, who kept the room filled with flowers and performed countless other medical and nonmedical services for the patient and herself. Among them were Henry S. Wellcome, generous patron of London's Museum of Medicine; Lord Dawson, the King's physician; and the already mentioned Sir John Goodwin, who responded so promptly when Dr. Noble called him on the night of Gorgas's collapse.

The patient was most appreciative of everything. But he clung to his conviction that he was soon to join his father and mother in the warm comradeship of death.

"How fortunate I am to be here," he said to Mrs. Gorgas. "You know, I might have died at sea, or on the way to West Africa, and separated from you."*

That they were together when death threatened a permanent separation was due in part at least to the fact that he had been asked to come to London before beginning the last leg of his long journey and receive from His Majesty the insigne of the Most Distinguished Order of St. Michael and St. George. When he became ill, it was decided to postpone that ritual until after his recovery or at least until he could regain his strength sufficiently to make the trip to Buckingham Palace and go through the physical strain of the ceremony.

* Mrs. Gorgas did not expect to accompany him to West Africa.

But as time went on it became apparent to the King, as it already had become to Gorgas, that the sick man probably would never be well enough to go to Buckingham Palace and, moreover, that he probably would not live long enough to receive it at all unless it should be presented immediately.

"If General Gorgas is too ill to come to the palace to see me, I shall go to the hospital to see him," the King said with determination when he realized how unsubstantial was the hope that the patient would long survive.

So a member of His Majesty's personal staff telephoned the head surgeon at Queen Alexandra Hospital one morning and inquired whether the King might, without too greatly upsetting the patient, slip quietly into the sickroom, present the insigne in a brief and simple ceremony, and quietly depart. No English surgeon will willingly deny his King anything, and anyhow this particular surgeon was convinced that even the excitement of a royal visit would be unlikely to affect the course of his patient's illness. So instructions were given that everything about the place be put in shipshape order, and an air of excited expectancy pervaded the famed institution.

The King, accompanied only by Sir John Goodwin and his Equerry in Waiting, arrived as quietly and unceremoniously as one of his humblest subjects would have done. At the entrance the small party was greeted by staff physicians, the hospital matron, and a nurse. The group proceeded immediately to Gorgas's room. Mrs. Gorgas was already there.

King George was graciousness itself, and his simple manner and expressions of interest in Gorgas's condition warmed the hearts of the patient and the others present. After voicing his sympathy and his hope that the sick man would soon be much improved, he turned from this one person's illness to the illnesses afflicting humanity as a whole, particularly the diseases which Gorgas had done so much to curb. He mentioned especially the latter's work at Havana and in Panama, revealing a surprisingly extensive knowledge of it. This of course was extremely pleasing to Gorgas, who was eagerly drinking in every word. He was even more pleased when the King thanked him for what he had done to lift the health levels of the hundreds of millions of people living under the British flag.

The actual ceremony of presentation was no less informal and even more brief. His Majesty received from his Equerry the insigne of the Order of St. Michael and St. George and presented it forthwith to Gorgas.

"General Gorgas," he said to him, "it gives me very great pleasure to present you with the insigne of this Order; and, believe me, I very sincerely appreciate the great work which you have done for humanity—work in which I take the greatest interest."

Thus simply and briefly did the grandson of an Alabama governor and the son of an American military genius receive one of England's most coveted distinctions.

Solicitous lest his visit might have unduly excited the patient, the King sent a messenger to the hospital the following morning to inquire as to his condition. His Majesty was greatly amused by the reply the messenger brought—that Gorgas had suffered no ill-effects at all from the visit and was "ready for more."

The royal couple left a few days later for Scotland, but before their departure the King instructed his personal physician to call daily at the hospital and offer his services to those in charge of the case.

Although the others must have known as well as Gorgas did how serious his condition had been from the first and how extremely unlikely it was that he would ever be able to resume active work of any kind, it was not until June 15 that it was definitely decided to abandon the trip to West Africa, as far as he was concerned.

It was announced then that the other members of the
original group, headed by the devoted Dr. Noble, would
leave about a fortnight later and that Gorgas would return to the United States as soon as his health would
permit. But Gorgas was as much of a realist as ever. He
knew that he would never live to see his native land
again.

"Noble," he said earnestly to his friend, "send all
the party to Africa. You remain until a later boat, for
I think Marie may need you. The doctors are too
optimistic."

His condition grew steadily worse, and on Friday,
July 2, all hope was abandoned for his recovery. Those
who were with him then have told how deeply they were
moved by the simple, childlike faith which, always a
dominant characteristic of the man, appeared to reach
its finest expression in those hours when death seemed
ready momentarily to touch him and end his pain. At
eleven o'clock that night he received the last com-
munion, and at the end he looked up, smiled, and said:
"Most comforting. Most comforting." Later that night,
when he was alone with Mrs. Gorgas and General Noble,
it appeared several times as though he would not survive
the dawn.

There seemed to be a slight improvement in his
condition the next day. His mind was clear, and he
talked about any number of things. But he was not
fooled by this momentary change for the better.

"Well, if this is dying," he murmured about two
hours before midnight, "dying is very pleasant."

It *was* dying, as he well knew. About an hour later
he went to sleep and never awoke. Sometime during
the night—Dr. Noble said it was about an hour and a
half after midnight—he crossed over the unmarked
frontier between this life and the next. Those who
feared he would suffer great pain were relieved that he
went so quietly and painlessly. One who was with him

almost to the last said of his going: "It was as if 'the Lord
touched him and he fell asleep.' "

The first message of condolence to reach the grief-
stricken widow was from King George, and the next
few hours brought 150 cables. Three days later the suit-
case in which the messages were placed for safekeeping
until they could be acknowledged was full to overflow-
ing, and a small steamer trunk was pressed into service.

The King's message, sent to the War Office for de-
livery to Mrs. Gorgas, was as follows:

His Majesty is so sorry to read in this morning's paper of
the death of General Gorgas and wishes you to convey to his
wife the expression of the deep sympathy of the King and Queen
with her and her family in the great loss they have sustained.
Please also tell her how pleased His Majesty is to think that he
saw General Gorgas in the hospital and was able personally
to decorate him.

President Wilson's cable read:

Allow me to express my profound sympathy with you in the
loss of your distinguished husband, whose unselfish services to
mankind can never be forgotten.

The British Foreign Office sent the following message to the Gorgas family and to officials of the United
States Government:

His Majesty's Government has long regarded with admiration the work of this distinguished servant of the United States
Government, to whose zeal and energy is largely due the completion of the Panama Canal. His Majesty the King has commanded that, subject to Your Excellency's assent, Major General
Gorgas should be accorded the military funeral of a Major
General in the British Army, and it is proposed that the ceremony should be held at St. Paul's Cathedral on the 9th instant.

Other tributes inspired by his death showed how
firmly he had gripped the affections and admiration of
those who knew him and his work. Secretary Baker
called his career "an inspiration to doctors and soldiers
alike." Equally warm praise was conspicuous in the

expressions of high-ranking officials of many governments and the obituary editorials published in practically all the great newspapers and medical journals of the English-speaking world.

But all the tributes did not come from those in high places by any means. One of the warmest of them all was spoken in the simple words of an illiterate Alabama Negro. Said he when the news came that Gorgas was dead: "He led 'em down here and he's leadin' 'em up yonder."

The funeral procession to historic St. Paul's Cathedral was one of the longest and most impressive ever seen in London. At its head marched the uniformed band of the famous Coldstream Guards, playing Chopin's stately funeral march. Gorgas's favorite mount followed just behind, saddled but riderless, with its dead master's boots in reversed positions in the stirrups. Alongside the animal walked two of His Majesty's soldiers carrying the Gorgas medals and decorations that had been brought on this trip and those he had received since his arrival.

The King's and Queen's absence from England prevented them from attending the funeral services, but they sent their personal representatives. Others taking part in this friendly nation's final tribute included American Ambassador and Mrs. John W. Davis and the ambassadors and ministers of many other nations, as well as high-ranking officers of the Army and Navy, officials of many agencies of His Majesty's civil government, and as many persons of humbler station as could crowd into the large building. The funeral music was furnished by the Coldstream band, the Cathedral choir, and the great organ.

When the singing of "The Battle Hymn of the Republic" brought the brief but solemn ritual to an end, British soldiers, who had carried the flag-draped casket up the cathedral steps and to its position under the great dome, carried it back to the waiting caisson to begin the long voyage to its final resting place on a quiet Virginia hillside.

Among the letters, journals, and other material made available by members of the Gorgas family for use in the preparation of the present work, there was found a yellowed newspaper clipping which was either brought back by Mrs. Gorgas when she returned with her husband's body or sent to the family by a friend in England. Unlike most of the other material, it contained no penciled notation to indicate the publication from which it had been cut, and the article it contained was published anonymously. So it is impossible to give credit to its author or name the paper for which he was writing. But what he wrote pleased the surviving members of the family more perhaps than anything else that was written about that solemn procession through the streets of London.

A riderless horse walked up Ludgate Hill the other day behind its sleeping master, and, if a horse can feel and know what happens, its heart must have been breaking—unless there came to it new strength in the pride it felt in the sight of its master sleeping under the Stars and Stripes on his way to St. Paul's. For what was happening that day up Ludgate Hill was a rare and stirring thing. I looked down from the windows of the little House with Green Shutters in the very shadow of the dome, and I thought that here indeed was a public opinion of which our London, and our country, and all the entire world, might well be proud. For here was no great Englishman, no great Briton, going to his rest; here was a ragged, barefoot boy of Baltimore being carried to St. Paul's after his life's work was done.

He had done for the world one of the greatest things that an American brain has even done: he made the Panama Canal possible after thousands of people had died in the attempt.

Now think how he began his life. This is what he told us:

"I first came to Baltimore a ragged, barefoot little rebel, with empty pockets and an empty stomach. My father had gone south with Lee's army. At the fall and destruction of Richmond my mother's house with all that she had was burned, leaving her stranded with six small children. She came to Baltimore and was cared for by friends. These memories are vivid with me, and can never be effaced."

And the other day he rode up Ludgate Hill, sleeping his last sleep on earth, wrapped in the Stars and Stripes. There were thousands of men and women and children standing still, there were hundreds of men in khaki passing by, there were ambassadors and other great people, and the lonely woman who was on her way with her hero to conquer disease in Peru* when death took him from her. And there was the riderless horse.

All these came up Ludgate Hill, and as the sun poured down on this ancient way, our hearts and ears throbbing with the solemn music of the Dead March, we knew that we were looking on the passing of a man whose name would shine for ages in the history of our race.

It seemed good that death should find him here, for so there came our opportunity to do a great man honor. He passed through the great door through which the sun streams into the nave of St. Paul's, and there he lay with Nelson and Wellington and all that mighty host who came this way and passed into the universe.

They will take him to his own land, but in truth he belongs to us all. He was one of life's great helpers, for he cleaned up foul places and made them sweet, and now, as they said of Lincoln, "he belongs to the ages."

Eager to do honor to a man whom he had grown to admire greatly and at the same time to make a notable contribution to London's Museum of Medicine, Dr. Wellcome asked Mrs. Gorgas's co-operation in arranging a display showing in graphic style the dead sanitarian's most important activities in various parts of the world. Besides that, he wanted permission to hang a painting of Gorgas in the museum's portrait gallery of famous men of medicine.

"If you will hang a picture of his mother beside the one of him, you may," the widow replied. "One cannot think of him without thinking of his mother, and he

---

* The anonymous author was in error here of course, as Gorgas was not en route to Peru at the time of his death, and, as already pointed out, Mrs. Gorgas did not expect to accompany him farther than London.

would not want to have such an honor without her."

The body was returned to the United States on the army transport *Pocahontas,* accompanied by Mrs. Gorgas and the other members of the small group which set out from Quebec so happily just a few weeks before. The King's personal representative joined the party at South-hampton to express the royal good wishes on the eve of sailing; and, on this side of the Atlantic, ambassadors and ministers representing fifteen nations went aboard to pay their respects as soon as the ship docked at her Hoboken pier. A guard of honor stood on the dock, and there were also representatives of the Y. M. C. A., the Y. W. C. A., the American Red Cross, and numerous other organizations with which Gorgas had been identi-fied. As the party left the pier in the fifteen automobiles that had been placed at their disposal, the procession was joined by mounted policemen, who acted as an escort as far as the river. On the Manhatttan side horsemen of the New York Police Department escorted them to Pennsylvania Station, where the body was placed in a flag-draped room with another guard of honor to await its departure for Washington on a special train. Upon its arrival in the nation's capital, members of a cavalry regiment acted as an escort from the Union Station to the Church of the Epiphany. It lay in state in the church's Red Cross Room for four days, surrounded by flags and all but buried in flowers.

A second and final funeral service was held at the Church of the Epiphany on Monday, August 16, at-tended by cabinet members, members of the diplomatic corps, representatives of scientific societies in this coun-try and abroad, and officers of the Army and Navy. President Wilson, unable to attend, was represented by Rear Admiral Cary T. Grayson. The service, follow-ing the regular Episcopal ritual for the burial of the dead, was conducted by the rector.

The long funeral cortege that wended its way from

the heart of the city to Arlington National Cemetery was described by a newspaper writer as "the most impressive since the funeral of Admiral Dewey." As in London a few weeks before, Gorgas's horse, draped in somber black, followed close behind the gun carriage containing the flag-draped casket.

Colonel John T. Axton, chief of army chaplains, read the burial service. The honorary pallbearers were Secretary of War Newton D. Baker, General Peyton C. March, the justices of the Supreme Court, the chairmen of the House and Senate Military Affairs Committees, the Ambassador from Peru, the Minister of Ecuador, the chargé d'affaires of Panama, representatives of the Royal Institute of Public Hygiene, and vestrymen of the Church of the Epiphany, which Gorgas had served faithfully for many years as a member and officer.

The Smithsonian Institution borrowed from Mrs. Gorgas her husband's decorations and a number of articles associated with him and his work. These were placed on display in the museum's medical department. They included the decoration and star which he had received from King George that memorable day in London, the Grand Cross of the Order of the Crown of Italy, which had been conferred by King Victor Emanuel III, the Grand Cross of the Legion of Honor of France, the Distinguished Service Cross, awarded by his own government, diplomas attesting to the academic honors conferred upon him by numerous institutions of higher learning in his own and foreign countries, his dress uniform as a major general, the American flag which covered his casket during the funeral services in St. Paul's, the baptismal robe he used as an infant, and a pair of beaded moccasins he wore as a child.

In announcing the exhibit, Smithsonian Institution authorities called Gorgas "the most internationally honored American medical man who ever lived."

Rich though he was in honors and the symbols of a

world's affection, he died a comparatively poor man. When outstanding bills were collected and all obligations met, his estate amounted to only $20,500. Many a small-town merchant or country doctor entirely unknown to fame has done much better financially.

As he neared the end of his life and realized that his children would begin the grim struggle for success almost as inadequately protected against want as he himself had been at his father's death, he may have thought of what Josiah Gorgas had told him about the meager financial rewards to be expected by the army doctor, the long hours, the hard work, and never being able to have a settled place to live and bring up his family. But, if he remembered those things, they brought no regret. For, in spite of his comparative poverty, his never having been able to establish a home, and the other difficulties which his father had predicted and which he had come to know, he was glad to the hour of his death that he had decided to become a soldier. And millions of people the world over are happier and healthier because he did.

EPILOGUE

Coup de Grace

SCIENCE'S GRIM WAR against yellow fever did not end by any means when Reed, Gorgas, Finlay, and others turned to new tasks. Other and younger men have carried on the work they began so brilliantly. As a result of their labors, we now have powerful agencies for the protection of our people against this ancient and cruel scourge. In spite of the greater hazards brought by modern high-speed travel, a civilized community has no more reason to fear a yellow fever outbreak than it has to expect an epidemic of typhoid or smallpox. Thanks to the sanitation procedures introduced and used so successfully by Gorgas, yellow fever virtually disappeared from the North American continent. New Orleans, Mobile, Portsmouth, Savannah, and any number of other cities where for centuries it used to strike like a Providential visitation began seeing it only in relatively harmless forays, if at all. However, there was the uneasy realization that the powerful enemy was not dead but sleeping. The yellow fever areas in Africa to which Gorgas started but which he never reached were still breeding dangerous seeds of the disease. So were other known and unknown areas in South America and, no doubt, in other parts of the world. The Gorgas sanitation principles had erected a high, strong fence between them and the United States. But we could not be sure it was high enough or strong enough.

A carelessly fumigated airplane cabin, a lapse from alertness on the part of an immigration inspector or public health official—any number of things might happen to make that Maginot Line of health as deceptively ineffective in keeping out yellow fever as the real Maginot Line was in keeping out Nazi invaders. There remained an imperative need for subjugating yellow fever in the same way we have subjugated smallpox, typhoid, and diphtheria. Our successful battle would never become a victorious war until we had some means of making our people—and other people all over the world—immune to it.

The first significant step in that direction was taken in 1918, when, as wartime Surgeon General of the Army, Gorgas was carrying the extraordinarily heavy burden of safeguarding the health of the largest body of men ever to wear the American uniform up to that time. The person making that important initial move was Hideyo Noguchi. This crippled Japanese-born genius had been robbed by a childhood accident of the realization of his dream of becoming a physician. Already, however, he had made many contributions to medical knowledge. He had helped produce the first effective serum to protect victims of snakebite. He had studied ways to curb infection of wounds. He had done extensive research in syphilis, improving upon the well-known Wassermann test and perfecting another one of his own which still bears his name. He had delved importantly into the mysteries of Rocky Mountain spotted fever.

Gorgas had learned of these and other accomplishments and believed there was a great need for Noguchi in the continuing war against yellow fever. He was especially concerned over an outbreak in Ecuador. So he asked the crippled Japanese-American to go there and find out what he could about the disease.

Noguchi attacked the problem with his usual enthusiasm, working in a makeshift laboratory in the Guayaquil yellow fever hospital. After a few weeks his work seemed to be bearing fruit: he located what he believed to be the causative agent of yellow fever. It was not a

germ or a virus but a spirochete. It bore a striking re-
semblance to the spirochete of infectious jaundice, or
Weil's disease, and he could not be sure it was not that.
For Weil's disease was also widely prevalent in that part
of the world. Nevertheless, he felt he had a strong basis
for his belief that he had found the long-sought yellow
fever organism. For one thing, soon after he injected
his newly found spirochete into a guinea pig, it developed the clinical symptoms usually associated with yellow fever. For another, he had found that particular
organism in nearly a fourth of all the yellow fever cases
he had studied. And, finally, when he developed a vaccine from that spirochete and used it on Ecuadorean
troops just exposed to yellow fever for the first time, they
escaped the disease.

But Noguchi was not certain. His uncertainty was
increased by the frankly expressed doubts of a number
of medical scientists and bacteriologists who could not go
along with him on his spirochete theory. Back in New
York his doubts grew stronger. In Ecuador the blood
samples he had tested were brought to him by others.
He could not be sure about their source or handling.
Many other factors which might have affected the results
had also been beyond his control. Plainly, there was a
strong possibility that his conclusions had not been fully
justified. Nor were his doubts dissipated on another
trip to South America, this time to Peru. On the contrary, that trip intensified them.

For Noguchi, to have doubts was to resolve them, one
way or the other, as quickly as possible. He was not a
man to tolerate unsolved problems. But this time he had
to wait. There were other studies calling for his attention. He had begun research in other disease fields before answering Gorgas's call for help in the Ecuadorean
epidemic. His superiors at the Rockefeller Institute for
Medical Research asked him to get back to them.

But his withdrawal from the search did not mean

that nothing would be done about finding an answer to his riddle. Shortly after his return from Peru, the Rockefeller Institute for Medical Research sent a team of able investigators to the west coast of Africa, where there were many cases of yellow fever. Their instructions were to find spirochetes like those Noguchi had found in South America, if they could. If they couldn't, they were to carry on other research aimed at finding, in that wealth of yellow fever research material, the elusive causative agent of the disease.

In their first objective, these men failed completely. The spirochetes Noguchi had found so readily in South America did not show up in the blood samples they were examining with such painstaking care. And, as they studied case after case and conducted experiment after experiment, they were oppressed by a sense of handicap that had also borne down heavily upon others. Here were the yellow fever cases they needed for their studies. They were all around them in great abundance. But something else, also important for their success, was lacking. You couldn't do much experimenting, even with all the yellow fever cases in the world, without bodies to experiment upon. Experimenters in other fields were not troubled like this; there were monkeys, mice, and other laboratory animals—dumb, ignorant, unprotesting, and unlikely to cause a public outcry if one of them or a dozen or a hundred should die. But all attempts to give yellow fever to those lower animals had been unsuccessful. Thus far it had been a disease for humans only. Since man alone could get yellow fever, as far as they knew, man alone could be used to find ways to protect man against it. And researchers with only human volunteers to work with worked with their hands tied.

These Rockefeller researchers, like any number of others, fretted under this handicap. They devoutly wished they could do something about it, but so many others had tried and failed that it seemed fruitless to make the attempt. Still, it is a tradition of research to tackle tough problems and wrestle with them in the face of top-heavy odds. So, as dim as their prospects for success seemed, they decided they would make the effort.

Naturally, their first experiments were directed at monkeys. A number of them received injections of blood from yellow fever patients. Hopefully, the scientists watched for signs of illness. But none developed. Then other animals were brought in and received inoculations. But one after another—rabbits, guinea pigs, rats, dogs, kittens, goats—remained healthy. One more ambitious effort to breach that barrier between man and the lower animals had ended in failure.

But these were determined men. They grimly resolved to keep on. The monkeys they had been using were of the native African variety. Would it do any good to try a new species? It might. And it certainly wouldn't do any harm. Nine animals—known as crown or hooded monkeys, from Asia—were ordered from a Hamburg dealer. Two of them received inoculations like the others. And, to the delight of the experimenters, both developed yellow fever. The disease ran its fatal course in both, and post-mortem examinations completely confirmed the diagnosis.

As so often happens in organized research, this triumph was the work of a number of men. Major credit, however, has gone to Adrian Stokes. It was he who took the lead in the experiments. But he received particularly valuable assistance from J. H. Bauer and N. P. Hudson. Later, before he succumbed to the disease he was fighting so valiantly, Stokes made another notable contribution to yellow fever research. He succeeded in giving the disease to the cheaper and better known Rhesus monkeys.

The question logically arises: Why was Stokes able to transmit yellow fever organisms to Rhesus monkeys after the long succession of failures, starting with the

Reed Board and ending with himself? The answer, once understood, was simple: As careful as these people had been in other respects, they had overlooked an important factor—the possibility that their experimental monkeys had had yellow fever and therefore were immune.

Meanwhile, Noguchi had been growing more and more impatient to return to the yellow fever wars. He had been winning fresh success in other fields. But he still was without an answer to his challenging and troublesome question of several years before. His eagerness to get back into yellow fever research bounded upward when he learned what Stokes had accomplished. Nor did he lose any of his enthusiasm when news came that his friend and associate had died in the midst of the battle. He resolved to go to Africa. There he could study cases that were unquestionably yellow fever. There he would not be troubled by Weils disease. If he could find his spirochete in Africa, he would know— and he could make others agree—that it was due to yellow fever and nothing else. So Noguchi packed his bags and sailed for West Africa.

His work there was productive, as it almost always was. But its results were largely negative. The spirochete he had found so easily in South America, he decided reluctantly, was not the causative agent of yellow fever. An organism different from it was causing the yellow fever cases he was now studying. At last he was entirely willing to agree with those—some of them his close personal friends—who had been contending all along that his spirochete was the one responsible for Weil's disease. Noguchi had no reason to be embarrassed by his error. He was by no means the only eminent researcher to mistake the one for the other.

He also made a positive contribution to the battle against yellow fever. Unfortunately, humanity was unable to benefit from it. After failing to find his South American spirochete in African yellow fever cases, he plunged into other yellow fever research. Out of it came the isolation of another organism. This, he hoped, was the real yellow fever causative agent. But he was more cautious this time. He refused to express a positive opinion until he could carry on more studies. Many more tests were needed. But he did not have to make them in Africa. He had done the groundwork there. With the research material he had collected, he could finish the job in his well-equipped laboratories in New York. So he began studying steamship schedules.

But he never sailed. Somewhere in his work he had allowed himself to become infected. In bad health for a long time (some of his friends had strongly advised against his undertaking the African trip) he developed yellow fever before he could get away. Like Adrian Stokes, Clara Maass, and many another battler against Yellow Jack, he put up only weak opposition when it engaged him in a savage personal attack. In just a few days he was dead.

Meanwhile, in this country, others had also been hard at work trying to expose yellow fever's deadly secrets. Some of the results began to appear soon after Noguchi's death. As enthusiastically as Stokes's achievement had been greeted at the time, it soon became apparent that he had not entirely erased the marked disadvantage under which yellow fever researchers were working, as compared with those in other fields. Infinitely better than humans, Rhesus monkeys, nevertheless, are not ideal laboratory animals. They are comparatively scarce. They are expensive. They have to be imported, require considerable care, and take up a great deal of room. It costs a great deal to feed and house them. Mice are much better. They are cheap. They reproduce rapidly. Thousands can be kept in a small space at slight cost. They show quick reactions to scientific tests. They are quickly and easily disposed of when they have served their purpose.

Attempt after attempt was made to infect mice with the yellow fever virus. And attempt after attempt ended in failure. But at last an American scientist succeeded in penetrating that seemingly impenetrable wall of infection. Working in his Harvard University laboratory, Max Theiler tried a new mode of attack. Instead of injecting the virus into the body proper, he shot it into the mice's brains. And that proved to be as successful a procedure as he could have asked for. His mice developed the characteristic encephalitis associated with yellow fever and died. The experiment was repeated, and again it was successful. Later, still other experiments duplicated those earlier successes. At last yellow fever researchers had at their service a cheap, small, and easy-to-handle laboratory animal.

Theiler also made another important discovery: he could prevent his mice from developing yellow fever, in spite of those injections of virus, by injecting, along with the virus, a serum taken from laboratory animals which had had yellow fever and recovered.

Thanks to Theiler's double-barreled success, yellow fever minutemen were able to confirm what they had been suspecting for a long time: that extensive pools of yellow fever incidence were still in existence in many parts of the world. Noguchi and others working in South America had found many cases considerably distant from the coastal towns and cities where periodic epidemics had been raging for centuries. Post-mortem examinations had shown the characteristic physical changes produced by the disease. Especially impressive were those that had occurred in the livers of the victims, which have long been studied with particular care in autopsies. However, it had been virtually impossible theretofore to determine, by the slow process of post-mortem examinations, how extensive those inland yellow fever endemic areas were. Now Theiler had made it entirely possible, by means of what became known as the mouse protection test, to make mass studies of whole populations. At last health workers could search out those remote danger spots, mark them on the map, ascertain their extent, and take effective steps to prevent them from starting outbreaks elsewhere.

As already pointed out, the only mice which did not develop yellow fever after Theiler shot the yellow fever virus into their brains were those which had received, at the same time, a serum taken from animals which had recovered from yellow fever. From Theiler's and other men's experiments in this field—the others using larger animals before he showed that mice would do just as well—came an important conclusion: the immunity enjoyed by the recovered yellow fever victim is due to an antibody formed in the course of his body's fight against the invading yellow fever virus. Theiler and his fellow scientists had demonstrated that this immunity need not be acquired the hard way but could be transferred to others (who had not had yellow fever) by injecting some of the recovered victim's blood, or serum from it, into their veins. From this, it was easy to advance another step: if yellow fever virus should be injected into monkeys or mice, along with human blood samples or serum, the monkeys' or mice's reaction would show whether these people had ever had the disease. If an animal developed yellow fever and died, then the blood or serum had not contained antibodies. Therefore, the person who had supplied it had not had yellow fever. Conversely, if the animal showed no reaction to the virus, then obviously the blood or serum injected along with it had been furnished by someone who had had the disease (possibly in so mild a form as not to have known about it).

Here, then, was a quick, relatively cheap way of finding those widely scattered and dangerous yellow fever pools. With plenty of mice for the tests, it would be a simple thing to go into a community, take blood samples of the entire population, and find out how many had had yellow fever.

These mass tests brought some surprising revelations. Yellow fever endemic areas were found in many parts of Brazil. Others were found to exist in Colombia, Bolivia, and other South American countries. Even more surprising than the number of such areas was the fact that most of them were strangers to the *Aedes aegypti* mosquito, theretofore regarded as the sole link between old cases and new. Obviously, yellow fever, or at least jungle yellow fever, as the newly discovered cases began to be called, could be transmitted in other ways. Actually, no fewer than seventeen types of mosquitoes, in addition to the *Aedes aegypti,* were found to be capable of distributing the virus.

Similar in many respects to the long-familiar coastal type, jungle yellow fever, nevertheless, is also different. It is usually much milder than the urban type. Instead of spreading rapidly from person to person (with the aid of the *Aedes aegypti*), it spreads slowly. The insects normally carrying it have a greater fondness for the out-of-doors. They usually bite people while they are at work or walking in the woods or near-by clearings. Occasionally the gap between human cases is so great that the case-to-case chain would seem to be broken. But eventually another person develops the disease. When that happens, animal links are substituted for human links in that chain of infection. It goes without saying that, as sources of human infection, those animal cases are as dangerous as any human case.

If jungle yellow fever could be kept in the jungles, it would never have been a serious problem elsewhere. But, obviously, it has not been kept in the jungles. Otherwise, there would not have been those wildfire-like epidemics along the southeastern coast of the United States and in other countries. For—there is no doubt about it—those jungle pools of endemic yellow fever

were the source of those urban outbreaks. This is easy
to understand when we consider that any person or animal coming within mosquito-flight distance of an urban
center while suffering from even a mild case of jungle
yellow fever has the same epidemic-starting potentialities
as someone with a classic case of urban yellow fever. All
that is necessary is for such a person or animal to be
bitten by an *Aedes aegypti* mosquito and for the mosquito, at the proper time, to bite someone in the coastal
community. Then the fire has been lighted. How fast
and how far it spreads and how many deaths it causes
are dependent upon the usual factors controlling
epidemics.

Obviously, it is impossible to prevent people and
animals in jungle areas from being bitten by *Aedes
aegypti* mosquitoes. A disease as widespread as jungle
yellow fever (which has been found along a wide belt on
both sides of the equator in both eastern and western
hemispheres) cannot be wiped out by any sanitation
measures developed by Gorgas or anyone else. The only
way the people of coastal cities can be effectively and permanently protected against that constant threat is to
provide artificial immunity.

This newly exposed facet of the yellow fever problem
set new goals for the generals commanding the armies
of extermination fighting this ancient enemy. They
must find a safe and effective vaccine against Yellow
Jack. An excellent start had already been made of
course. But the major task still lay ahead.

Soon after Stokes succeeded in giving monkeys yellow fever, efforts were made to afford immunity by weakening the virus sufficiently to make it harmless. But
none of these attempts was successful. When, however,
it was learned that mice could also get the disease, the
effort was renewed with mouse experiments. Experimenters discovered that the desired weakening could
be accomplished by taking the virus from one mouse,

injecting it into another, and then repeating the process over and over. Using monkeys to determine the effectiveness of this weakening process, research workers found it to be entirely satisfactory. After the vaccine thus developed had proved not only harmless but also sufficiently protective against yellow fever in a large number of trials, the jump was made to humans.

In those early human trials, however, this mouse vaccine was not used alone. It was mixed with serum obtained from former yellow fever patients. And this posed a serious problem for those thinking of wholesale immunization campaigns: because of the large quantities of human serum required for such a mixture, it became evident that other immunizing methods would be needed if yellow fever immunization was to be carried out on a large scale. The situation called for a vaccine that could be used without convalescent serum.

Experimental work continued under the impetus of that need. The weakening of the virus became more and more successful. But there were still a few reactions that caused concern to those in charge of the tests. As long as they occurred, it was considered inadvisable to undertake large-scale immunizations with the mouse virus alone. After a while, however, as one improvement after another was made, these reactions were greatly reduced. Finally they were ended. Credit for that final achievement goes to staff members of the Rockefeller Foundation's International Health Division. They accomplished it by culturing the yellow fever virus in chicken embryos, from some of which the spinal cords and brains had been removed. It was found even more satisfactory to use very young chick embryos in which the brain and spinal cord presumably had not had time to develop. The vaccine obtained in this way was found to be entirely satisfactory from the point of view of effectiveness, as well as safety.

So, at long last, yellow fever was added to the list

of diseases to which man can obtain immunity without having the disease itself.

This country's entry into World War II provided the first big-scale test for the new vaccine. As soon as it became certain that American troops would see service in South America, Africa, and other war theaters that were still plagued with yellow fever, they began receiving yellow fever "shots" routinely, along with their injections against smallpox, tetanus, and typhoid. Thanks to the protection those "shots" afforded, yellow fever was no more of a problem than those other diseases. *Aedes aegypti,* loaded with the deadly virus, could and did bite them in droves, with no more effect than if they had been licked by a friendly dog.

How happy Gorgas would have been to see this *coup de grace* administered to the ruthless enemy against which he had struggled so valiantly and, in his own way, so successfully!

Bibliography

Books and Pamphlets

ALABAMA STATE DEPARTMENT OF HEALTH. *Annual Report, 1888.*

ANDERSON, GAYLORD (WITH MARGARET ARNSTEIN). *Communicable Disease Control.* New York, 1946.

ASHBURN, P. M. *A History of the Medical Department of the United States Army.* Boston and New York, 1929.

AUGUSTIN, GEORGE. *History of Yellow Fever.* New Orleans, 1909.

BISHOP, JOSEPH BUCKLIN. *Theodore Roosevelt and His Time.* New York, 1920.

BRADLEY, G. H. (WITH W. V. KING AND T. E. McNEEL). *The Mosquitoes of the Southeastern United States* (Miscellaneous Publications No. 336, U. S. Department of Agriculture). Washington, June, 1939.

BULLARD, ARTHUR. *Panama, the Canal, the Country, and the People.* New York, 1914.

CARTER, HENRY ROSE. *The Early History of Yellow Fever.* Baltimore, 1931.

DAVIS, JEFFERSON. *Rise and Fall of the Confederate Government.* New York, 1881.

GOETHALS, GEORGE WASHINGTON. *Government of the Canal Zone.* Princeton, 1915.

GORGAS, MARIE D. (WITH BURTON J. HENDRICK). *William Crawford Gorgas, His Life and Work.* Garden City, 1924.

GORGAS, WILLIAM CRAWFORD. *Sanitation in Panama.* New York, 1918.

HACKETT, L. W. *Malaria in Europe.* New York, 1937.

HALLOCK, GRACE T. (WITH C. E. TURNER). *Health Heroes (Edward Jenner).* New York, 1926.

IRELAND, SURGEON GENERAL MERRITTE W. (WITH COL. CHARLES LYNCH, LT. COL. FRANK W. WEED, AND LEY McAFEE). *The Surgeon General's Office* (Vol. I of *The Medical Department of the United States Army in the World War.*) Washington, 1923.

IRVING, WASHINGTON. *Life and Voyages of Christopher Columbus.* New York, 1872.

KEAN, JEFFERSON RANDOLPH. *The Scientific Work and Discoveries of the Late Major Walter Reed.* Washington, 1903.

KELLY, HOWARD A. *Walter Reed and Yellow Fever.* New York, 1906.

KOMP, W. H. W. *A Guide to the Identification of the Common Mosquitoes of the Southeastern United States.* Washington, 1923 (revised 1938).

LAMPSON, ROBIN. *Death Loses a Pair of Wings.* New York, 1939.

LEE, ROGET I. *Health and Disease, Their Determining Factors.* Boston, 1921.

MARTIN, FRANKLIN H. *Fifty Years of Medicine and Surgery.* Chicago, 1934.

————. *Major General William Crawford Gorgas.* Chicago, 1924.

————. *Digest of Proceedings of the Council of National Defense during the World War.* Washington, 1934.

MEARS, JAMES EWING. *Triumph of American Medicine in the Construction of the Panama Canal.* Philadelphia, 1911.

Memorial Services Held in Honor of Major General William Crawford Gorgas by the Southern Society of Washington, D. C. Senate Document No. 390. Washington, 1921.

OSLER, WILLIAM. *Modern Medicine, Its Theory and Practice.* Philadelphia, 1907.

PADELFORD, NORMAN J. *The Panama Canal in Peace and War.* New York, 1942.

PANAMA CANAL HEALTH DEPARTMENT. *Annual Report for 1938* (including morbidity and mortality tables for previous years). Mount Hope (C. Z.), 1939.

PARSONS, ROBERT P. *Trail to Light: A Biography of Joseph Goldberger.* Indianapolis, 1944.

PEPPERMAN, W. LEON. *Who Built the Panama Canal?* New York, 1915.

RAVENEL, MAZYCK P. *A Half Century of Public Health.* New York, 1921.

REED, WALTER. *Recent Researches Concerning the Etiology, Propagation and Prevention of Yellow Fever by the U. S. Army Commission* (in U. S. Senate Documents, Vol. 9). Washington, 1903.

RICHARDSON, JAMES D. *Messages and Papers of the Presidents.* Washington, 1910.

ROSENAU, MILTON J. *Preventive Medicine and Hygiene.* New York, 1935.

RUSH, BENJAMIN. *An Account of the Bilious Remitting Yellow*

Fever, as It Appeared in the City of Philadelphia in the Year 1793. Philadelphia, 1794.

SCOTT, H. HAROLD. *A History of Tropical Medicine.* Baltimore, 1939.

SEELYE, E. E. *Story of Columbus.* New York, 1907.

SEIFFERT, GUSTAV. *Virus Diseases in Man, Animal and Plant.* New York, 1944.

SIMMONS, JAMES STEVENS. *Malaria in Panama.* Baltimore, 1939.

SMITH, GEDDES. *Plague on Us.* New York, 1941.

STRODE, HUDSON. *Pageant of Cuba.* New York, 1934.

SURGEON GENERAL, U. S. ARMY. *Annual Report to Secretary of War, July 1, 1913—June 30, 1914.* Washington, 1914.

———. *Annual Report to Secretary of War, July 1, 1914—June 30, 1915.* Washington, 1915.

———. *Annual Report to Secretary of War, July 1, 1915—June 30, 1916.* Washington, 1916.

———. *Annual Report to Secretary of War, July 1, 1916—June 30, 1917.* Washington, 1917.

———. *Annual Report to Secretary of War, July 1, 1917—June 30, 1918.* Washington, 1918.

———. *Annual Report to Secretary of War, July 1, 1918—June 30, 1919.* Washington, 1919.

TOBEY, JAMES A. *The National Government and Public Health.* Baltimore, 1926.

VAUGHAN, VICTOR C. *Epidemiology and Public Health.* St. Louis, 1923.

———. *A Doctor's Memories.* Indianapolis and New York, 1926.

WILSON, CHARLES MORROW. *Ambassadors in White: The Story of American Tropical Medicine.* New York, 1942.

WOOD, L. N. *Walter Reed: Doctor in Uniform.* New York, 1943.

Magazine and Newspaper Articles

"A Bearer of the White Man's Burden." *Munsey's Magazine,* LVI, 413-415 (December, 1915).

"Accuses General Gorgas." New York *Times,* July 2, 1918, p. 8.

"A Great American, London's Homage to General Gorgas." London *Morning Post,* July 10, 1920.

"American Army Healthiest of All." New York *Times,* November 26, 1914, p. 14.

"A Notable Form of Recognition." New York *Times,* July 10, 1920, p. 6.

"Antitoxin Found for War Gangrene." New York *Times,* July, 1917, sec. I, p. 15.

"Approves Health Promises." New York *Times,* May 12, 1918, sec. I, p. 6.

"Army Orthopedic Board." New York *Times,* August 21, 1917, p. 8.

"Army's Excellent Health." New York *Times,* December 7, 1918, p. 10.

"Army Wants Free Doctors." New York *Times,* August 5, 1917, sec. I, p. 4.

"A Soldier of Humanity." New York *Times,* July 5, 1920, p. 8.

"A Victory Not Yet Completed." New York *Times,* April 30, 1914, p. 10.

"Baker and Gorgas at Camp Gordon." New York *Times,* February 17, 1918, sec. I, p. 12.

"Baker Eulogizes Gorgas." New York *Times,* July 5, 1920, p. 8.

"Baker in France on New Mission." New York *Times,* September 9, 1918, p. 1.

"Baker Tribute to Gorgas." New York *Times,* October 27, 1918, sec. I, p. 4.

"Big Army Hospital for Staten Island." New York *Times,* November 28, 1917, p. 8.

"Body of Gen. Gorgas Saluted from Fort." New York *Times,* August 13, 1920, p. 9.

"Camp Pneumonia Spreads." New York *Times,* November 30, 1917, p. 7.

"Canal Defenses Adequate." New York *Times,* January 21, 1913, p. 9.

"Carter, Reed, Gorgas." Richmond *News-Leader,* November 10, 1914.

"City Boards Ready for Actual Draft." New York *Times,* July 20, 1917, p. 4.

"Clara Maass, R. N., Forgotten Martyr to Science and Humanity." *R. N.,* Vol. XII, No. 3 (December, 1948).

"Col. Gorgas at Johannesburg." *Engineering and Mining* (undated clipping).

"Col. Gorgas Boosted for Secretary of War." Birmingham *News,* February 5, 1913.

"Col. Gorgas Called to Africa to Fight Grippe Plague." New York *Times,* October 26, 1914, sec. V, p. 9.

"Col. Gorgas Takes Hold." New York *Evening Sun,* March 3, 1902.

"Columbia Is Ready to Start Hospital." New York *Times,* April 26, 1917, p. 11.

"Confirm Gorgas as Surgeon General." New York *Times,* January 31, 1914, p. 8.

"Death of General Gorgas." *Bulletin of the Pan-American Union*, LI, 278-283 (September, 1920).

"Disease Spreading all over Serbia." New York *Times*, April 17, 1915, p. 3.

"Dr. Carrell Coming for War Work Here." New York *Times*, March 29, 1917, p. 3.

"Dr. Gorgas Gets Medal." New York *Times*, April 29, 1914, p. 10.

"Dr. Gorgas's Criticism." New York *Times*, May 4, 1915, p. 14.

"English Surgeons Praise Our War Aid." New York *Times*, June 1, 1918, p. 6.

"For Medical Preparedness." New York *Times*, February 8, 1916, p. 6.

"Found Wounded Cheerful." New York *Times*, September 12, 1918, p. 3.

"14 Hospitals Chosen for War's Disabled." New York *Times*, April 1, 1918, p. 7.

"Gave Up Hope for Gorgas." New York *Times*, June 18, 1920, p. 17.

"Gen. Gorgas Buried with Great Pomp." New York *Times*, August 17, 1920, p. 13.

"Gen. W. C. Gorgas Dies in London." New York *Times*, July 4, 1920, sec. I, p. 21.

"General Gorgas Home from South Africa." New York *Times*, April 2, 1914, p. 7.

"General Gorgas Honored." New York *Times*, January 9, 1916, sec. II, p. 14.

"General Gorgas to Weed Out Medical Incompetents." New York *Times*, December 22, 1917, p. 1.

"General Gorgas Unheeded." New York *Times*, January 27, 1918, sec. II, p. 4.

"General Josiah Gorgas." Tuscaloosa (Alabama) *News*, January 18, 19, 1938.

"General William C. Gorgas, Wholesale Saver of Human Lives." *Literary Digest*, LXVI, 50-52 (July 24, 1920).

"Greatest Sanitarian of World, General Gorgas." *El Siglo Medico* (Madrid), LXVII, 797 (October 23, 1920).

"Gorgas and the Scientists." New York *Times*, August 14, 1920, p. 6.

"Gorgas Appeals Direct to Congress." New York *Times*, March 16, 1918, p. 8.

"Gorgas Ascribes Deaths to Haste." New York *Times*, January 26, 1918, p. 1.

"Gorgas as Surgeon General." New York *Times,* January 17, 1914, p. 1.

"Gorgas, A World Benefactor." Atlanta *Journal,* July 10, 1920.

"Gorgas Fighting Fever." New York *Times,* September 25, 1919, p. 7.

"Gorgas Funeral Friday." New York *Times,* July 6, 1920, p. 15.

"Gorgas Funeral Plans." New York *Times,* August 7, 1920, p. 5.

"Gorgas Funeral Today." New York *Times,* July 9, 1920, p. 13.

"Gorgas Gets Italian Decoration." New York *Times,* November 6, 1918, p. 7.

"Gorgas Has Dropped 1,000 Medical Men." New York *Times,* February 27, 1918, p. 4.

"Gorgas Honored in London." New York *Times,* March 24, 1914, p. 3.

"Gorgas, in London Hospital, Is Made Knight by King George." New York *Times,* June 9, 1920, p. 17.

"Gorgas Is Called to Save Serbia." New York *Times,* April 11, 1915, sec. II, p. 1.

"Gorgas Is Near Death." New York *Times,* July 3, 1920, p. 24.

"Gorgas Leaves Guayaquil." New York *Times,* September 29, 1919, p. 15.

"Gorgas May Run as Single Taxer." New York *Times,* February 25, 1920, p. 11.

"Gorgas Near Retirement." New York *Times,* September 28, 1918, p. 4.

"Gorgas Needs Women Scientists." New York *Times,* April 2, 1918, p. 11.

"Gorgas Party Reaches Panama." New York *Times,* June 1, 1919, sec. II, p. 2.

"Gorgas Reports Troops at Camps Crowded, Ill-Clad." New York *Times,* December 19, 1917, p. 1.

"Gorgas Returns to Panama." New York *Times,* October 6, 1919, p. 16.

"Gorgas's Body in State." New York *Times,* August 14, 1920, p. 7.

"Gorgas's Condition Improves." New York *Times,* July 1, 1920, p. 18.

"Gorgas's Condition Improving." New York *Times,* June 22, 1920, p. 25.

"Gorgas's Condition Still Critical." New York *Times,* June 30, 1920, p. 17.

"Gorgas, Seriously Ill, Abandons African Trip." New York *Times,* June 16, 1920, p. 1.

"Gorgas Tells How Armies Beat Disease." New York *Times*, May 27, 1917, sec. VI, p. 7.

"Gorgas to Rest in Arlington." New York *Times*, July 25, 1920, sec. I, p. 4.

"Gorgas Would Put Soldiers in Huts." New York *Times*, December 7, 1918, p. 10.

"Health during Washington's Period." *Illinois Health Messenger*, IV, 1 (March 15, 1932).

"Health of Troops in Competent Hands." New York *Times*, July 29, 1917, sec. I, p. 8.

"High Honors Given for War Service." New York *Times*, February 14, 1919, p. 12.

"Holds Up Removal of Camp Greene Force." New York *Times*, February 14, 1918, p. 22.

"Honors for Gen. Gorgas." New York *Times*, July 8, 1920, p. 11.

"Honors U. S. Officers." New York *Times*, January 10, 1919, p. 7.

"Housing under Way for 4675 Families." New York *Times*, June 30, 1919, p. 15.

"How Civilization Was Brought to the Isthmus." New York *Times*, March 11, 1914, p. 10.

"Howe Urges Single Chamber at Albany." New York *Times*, January 31, 1915, sec. II, p. 13.

"How Gorgas Cleaned Up the Isthmus." New York *Times*, May 10, 1915, p. 14.

"How Typhus Can Be Conquered." New York *Times*, April 15, 1915, p. 12.

"Human Guinea Pig Tells of Yellow Fever Terror in Cuba." *Eufala* (Alabama) *Tribune*, July 20, 1935.

"Hygiene at Panama." *Medical Times*, April, 1908.

"Influenza Epidemic Hits Camp Devens." New York *Times*, September 15, 1918, sec. I, p. 14.

"In Justice to General Gorgas." *New Republic*, II, 295 (April 24, 1915).

"In Memory of Gorgas." *Tuscaloosa* (Alabama) *News*, May 27, 1940.

"Insubordinate, but with Good Reason." New York *Times*, March 16, 1918, p. 12.

"Italy Honors Americans." New York *Times*, October 6, 1918, sec. I, p. 8.

"Job for Col. Gorgas." New York *Times*, April 1, 1913, p. 10.

"King Condoles Mrs. Gorgas." New York *Times*, July 7, 1920, p. 11.

"Leprosy Increases: Needs U. S. Control." New York *Times,* June 24, 1914, p. 22.

"Maj. Gen. Gorgas Returns." New York *Times,* April 17, 1920, p. 14.

"Major Gen. Goethals Now." New York *Times,* March 5, 1915, p. 4.

"Major William C. Gorgas Leaves Today." Havana *Post* (undated clipping).

"Many Promotions in Army and Navy." New York *Times,* October 4, 1918, p. 8.

"Mayor Gets Medal as Orphan's Friend." New York *Times,* January 20, 1917, p. 10.

"Need More Artillerymen." New York *Times,* December 6, 1914, sec. II, p. 18.

"Need of Army Dentists." New York *Times,* August 7, 1918, p. 2.

"New Plan in Rand Urged by Gorgas." New York *Times,* March 18, 1914, p. 4.

"Osteopaths and the Medical Corps." New York *Times,* July 3, 1918, p. 12.

"Our Army Healthiest." New York *Times,* April 28, 1918, p. 4.

"Our Healthy Army." New York *Times,* November 27, 1914, p. 10.

"Permanent Post for Col. Gorgas." New York *Times,* April 12, 1915, p. 3.

"Peru Engages General Gorgas." New York *Times,* April 3, 1920, p. 6.

"Physicians Gather for War Discussion." New York *Times,* June 11, 1918, p. 7.

"Plan Gorgas Memorial." New York *Times,* August 23, 1920, p. 10.

"Plans His Typhus Fight." New York *Times,* May 13, 1915, p. 11.

"Princeton Confers Degrees upon 232." New York *Times,* June 17, 1914, p. 7.

"Promotion Earned Obliquely." New York *Times,* January 2, 1914, p. 8.

"Red Cross Anxious to Fight Typhus." New York *Times,* December 25, 1915, p. 3.

"Red Cross Calls for 15,000 Nurses." New York *Times,* May 30, 1918, p. 9.

"Renews Fight on Plague." New York *Times,* December 14, 1918, p. 24.

"Retain General Gorgas." New York *Times,* May 31, 1918, p. 12.

"Revealing Canal Dissensions." New York *Times*, May 3, 1915, p. 10.

"Ronald Ross and the Prevention of Malarial Fever." *Scientific Monthly*, III, 132-150 (August, 1916).

"Six Generals to Get D. S. C." New York *Times*, December 29, 1918, sec. I, p. 9.

"Spanish American Clean-Up." New York *Times*, August 15, 1913, p. 4.

"Studied Tropical Diseases." New York *Times*, December 12, 1916, p. 11.

"Surgeon General Gorgas Appeals to Christians to Help Increase Wages." *Current Opinion*, LXI, 337 (November, 1916).

"Taft Speaks for U. S. Quarantine." New York *Times*, April 21, 1915, p. 22.

"The Clean-Up of Panama." New York *Times*, July 28, 1914, p. 6.

"The Heroism of Gorgas." New York *Times*, April 16, 1915, p. 12.

"The Mayor and the Police." New York *Times*, April 3, 1914, p. 10.

"To Entertain Col. Gorgas." New York *Times*, February 27, 1914, p. 4.

"To Improve Soldiers' Food." New York *Times*, September 25, 1917, p. 9.

"Traces Army Epidemics." New York *Times*, December 17, 1917, p. 13.

"Transport to Bring Gorgas's Body." New York *Times*, July 21, 1920, p. 17.

"25,000 War Nurses Needed This Year." New York *Times*, May 12, 1918, sec. II, p. 13.

"Typhus Discovery Described in Paper." New York *Times*, May 17, 1914, sec. II, p. 13.

[Untitled editorial]. London *Lancet*, 1920 (quoted in Birmingham *Age-Herald*, May 29, 1930).

"Urges Collection of Data on Cancer." New York *Times*, September 10, 1915, p. 12.

"Want Gorgas Retained in Office." New York *Times*, May 30, 1918, p. 20.

"Wants New Canal to Start." New York *Times*, March 18, 1916, p. 6.

"Warning from Daniels." New York *Times*, October 23, 1917, p. 2.

"Whitman Welcomes Health Convention." New York *Times*, September 8, 1915, p. 4.

"William Crawford Gorgas." *Medical Journal and Record*, CXXI, 772-774 (June 17, 1925).

"Winter Clothing Is Now at Camps." New York *Times*, December 20, 1918, p. 1.

"Women to Teach Invalid Soldiers." New York *Times*, September 15, 1918, sec. III, p. 7.

"Wood Criticises Continental Army." New York *Times*, January 27, 1916, p. 4.

"World's Surgeons in Session Here." New York *Times*, April 14, 1914, p. 5.

"Yellow Fever." *Canal Record*, February 2, 1910.

See also New York *Times* for March 3, 1914, p. 4; March 25, 1914, p. 4; March 3, 1915, p. 5; April 14, 1915, p. 3; April 16, 1915, p. 5; May 1, 1915, p. 1; June 27, 1915, sec. IV, p. 5; July 7, 1915, p. 12; June 15, 1916, p. 22; July 24, 1916, p. 7. And see the London *Times*, March 24, 1914; and the *Rhodesian Herald*, January 24, 1914.

ANDERSON, JOHN H. "Gorgas and the Ending of Yellow Fever." New York Evening *Post* (reprinted May 27, 1920).

BAKER, J. N. "Jerome Cochran, Founder of Alabama's Health System." Radio talk, delivered May 4, 1939, Station WSFA, Montgomery, Ala.

———. "William Crawford Gorgas, His Contribution to Civilization." *Journal of the Medical Association of the State of Alabama*, VI, 192-97 (December, 1936).

———. "Public Health in Alabama Fifty Years Ago." Radio talk, delivered June 23, 1937, Station WSFA, Montgomery, Ala.

———. "Sanitary Achievements of General Gorgas." Radio talk, delivered November 26, 1937, Station WSFA, Montgomery, Ala.

———. "Outstanding Alabamians in the Field of Public Health." Radio talk, delivered February 22, 1940, Station WSFA, Montgomery, Ala.

BAUER, JOHANNES H. (with ADRIAN STOKES and N. PAUL HUDSON) "Experimental Transmission of Yellow Fever to Laboratory Animals." *American Journal of Tropical Medicine*, VIII, 103-64 (March, 1928).

BISHOP, JOSEPH BUCKLIN. "The Personality of Colonel Goethals." *Scribner's Magazine*, LVII, 129-52 (February, 1915).

CALHOUN, C. H. "Canal Open!" *New York Times Magazine*, August 13, 1939, pp. 9, 18.

COLLINS, JOHN O. "Southern Men in Sanitation in the Canal Zone." *Manufacturers Record* (undated clipping).

CRAWFORD, WILLIAM H. "Men Who Are Winning the War." *Leslie's Weekly*, November 24, 1917.

DALYRYMPLE, DOLLY. "Amelia Gorgas—A Portrait of a Lady." *Birmingham News-Age Herald Magazine*, November 28, 1937.

DENISON, LINDSAY. "Making Good at Panama." *Everybody's Magazine*, XIV, 579-80 (May, 1906).

DOWLING, OSCAR. "William Crawford Gorgas—An Appreciation." *Pan American Magazine*, XXXIX, 129-33 (September, 1926).

DUFFUS, R. L. "The Spark That Set the Nation Ablaze." *New York Times Magazine*, April 12, 1936, pp. 10, 11, 24.

EDWARDS, ALBERT. "How We Pulled the Teeth of the Tropics." *Outlook*, XCVIII, 961-69 (August 26, 1911).

FISKE, ANNETTE. "Titans of the Tropics." *Hygeia*, XVI, 45-47 (January, 1938).

FRANK, GLENN. "Gorgas, Chevalier of Health." *Century*, C, 656-67 (September, 1920).

GAINES, MARION TOULMIN. "Crumbling Mass of Masonry in Wild Shrubbery All Remaining of Birthplace of Gen. Gorgas." *Montgomery Advertiser*, July 18, 1920, p. 8.

GIBSON, JOHN M. "The Miracle Man of the Confederacy." *South Atlantic Quarterly*, XLIII, 52-62 (January, 1944).

GOETHALS, GEORGE WASHINGTON. "The Building of the Panama Canal." *Scribner's Magazine*, LVII, 265-82, 395-415, 531-48, 720-34 (March, April, May, June, 1915).

GOODMAN, HERMAN. "Attitude toward Venereal Diseases and Their Prevention." *Medical Life* (Gorgas Number), November, 1924.

GORGAS, WILLIAM CRAWFORD. "A Short Account of the Results of Mosquito Work in Havana, Cuba." *Journal of the Association of Military Surgeons of the United States*, 1903.

———. "Health Conditions on the Isthmus of Panama." *Scientific American*, LVII, 238-56 (July 16, 1904).

———. "Disappearance of Yellow Fever from Havana." *Medical News*, January 3, 1903.

———. "Anti-Mosquito Work at Panama." (Lecture before Royal Society of Medicine). London *Times,* March 23, 1914.

———. "Economic Causes of Disease." (Address delivered at Business Men's Club of Cincinnati, September 28, 1915). Reprint.

———. "Solving the Health Problems at Panama." *American Review of Reviews,* XXX, 52-56 (July, 1904).

———. "Sanitation in the Tropics." (Address) *Transactions of the Medical Association of the State of Alabama,* 1915, pp. 336-47.

———. "The Credit Side of Our War Ledger." *Collier's Weekly,* June 8, 1918.

HEISER, VICTOR G. "Yellow Jack Breaks Jail." *Saturday Evening Post,* CCX, 12, 13 (May 21, 1938).

HILL, LISTER. "William Crawford Gorgas." (Speech). *Congressional Record,* March 28, 1928.

HUBER, JOHN B. "Colonel Gorgas, Panama and the World's Sanitation, A Twentieth Century Epic." *American Review of Reviews,* XLIX, 308-16 (March, 1914).

KEIFER, J. WARREN. "William Crawford Gorgas." (Speech). *Congressional Record,* January 23, 1908.

KROCK, ARTHUR. "Our Twelve Great Scientists." *Technical World Magazine,* XXI, 816-21 (August, 1914).

LePRINCE, JOSEPH A. "The Achievements of William Crawford Gorgas." *Health Officer* (United States Public Health Service), March, 1938.

LITTLE, S. W. "General Gorgas and Dr. Finlay." *Outlook,* CXXVI, 71 (September 8, 1920).

MOORE, JOHN BASSETT. "Gorgas, Redeemer of the Tropics." *American Review of Reviews,* LXV, 188-94 (February, 1922).

NOBLE, ROBERT E. "William Crawford Gorgas." *American Journal of Public Health,* XI, 250-56 (March, 1921).

REED, CHARLES A. L. "Isthmian Sanitation." *Journal of the American Medical Association,* XLIV, 812-18 (March 11, 1905).

ROBERTS, S. R. "William Crawford Gorgas." *Southern Medical Journal,* XVIII, 859-64 (December, 1925).

SAVAGE, CLARA. "Health to Our Boys." *Good Housekeeping,* LXV, 43-44 (December, 1917).

SHOCKLEY, M. A. W. "William Crawford Gorgas." *Southwestern Medical Journal,* VIII, 534-46 (November, 1924).

STEPHENS, FRANK A. "A Momentous Hour at Panama." *Science*, n.s., LXXI, 550-52 (May 30, 1930).

THATCHER, MAURICE H. "The Panama Canal—Its History and Significance" (Speech). *Congressional Record*, May 29, 1930. (Reprinted, 1930).

TILLER, THEODORE. "Gorgas, Commander of a Great Army of Doctors." New York *Tribune* (reprinted in *Kansas City Times*, July 2, 1918).

TOWNLEY, SUSAN. "The Panama Canal." *Living Age*, CCL, 387-403 (August 18, 1906).

WILSON, OWEN. "The Conquest of the Tropics." *World's Work*, XVI, 10432-45 (July, 1908).

Index

Greensboro, 31-32, at New Orleans, 32-33, at University of the South, 34; and New Orleans epidemic, 34; graduation from University of the South, 37; attempts to get into West Point, 39-40; in Bellevue Medical College, 40; and Memphis epidemic, 43; graduation from Bellevue Medical College, 44; Army, 45; Siboney yellow fever camp, 54; Havana sanitary officer, 56; Havana clean-up campaign, 58; Havana anti-mosquito campaign, 82; success of Havana yellow fever campaign, 88; and malaria in Havana, 89-90; admiration for Reed, 91; and father's Confederate cross, 93; on defeat of Confederacy, 93; and membership in Isthmian Canal Commission, 100; Havana people and press on, 101; representative of U. S. Army at Egyptian Medical Congress, 102; chief sanitary officer in Panama, 102; and Admiral Walker, 103; red tape, delays, and confusion in Panama, 117-124; on Reed report, 137-138; removal sought by Shonts, 141; threatened with dismissal by Taft's weakness, 142; staunch support of Drs. Lambert and Welch, 143-145; promise of President's support, 145; Shonts as supporter of, 145; praised in letter to Boston *Transcript*, 146; health-protection campaign in Panama, 147-150; virtual elimination of mosquitoes in Panama, 150-151; rebuke from Roosevelt, 155; member of reorganized Canal Commission, 160; Goethals's unco-operative and hostile attitude, 161; president of American Medical Association, 165; replies to charges of excessive costs, 166-171; on death and immortality, 175; refusal of presidency of University of Alabama, 176-177, and University of the South, 176-177; on Goethals and incomplete malaria success in Panama, 182-184; address at Sewanee, 191-192; on disease-free tropics, 196; South African assignment, 202; Major Noble and Dr.

Darling sent to Ishambane, 205; Surgeon General of Army, 208; report on South African pneumonia study, 208; honorary degree from Oxford University, 209; and the fight against typhus in Serbia, 215, 217; National Defense Act of 1916, 223; member of Medical Committee of Council of National Defense, 224; member of General Medical Board's Executive Committee, 227; high sanitary standards for camps, 232; Division of Military Orthopedic Surgery, 233; epidemics in military camps, 236-237; health conditions at Camp Sevier, 237-238; testimony on soldiers' health before Senate Military Affairs Committee, 238-242; attempts to gain higher military rank for medical officers, 245; lobbying charge, 246; support of Owen-Dyer Bill before Senate Military Affairs Committee, 248-249; succeeded as Surgeon General by General Ireland, 252; letter of commendation from Secretary Baker, 252-253; grand officer of Crown of Italy, 253; report on health of American troops in war, 254; acceptance of Rockefeller Foundation's offer to resume fight against yellow fever, 258-259; and yellow fever campaigns in Ecuador and Peru, 261-262; and Single Tax Party, 263-264; acceptance of future position with Peruvian government, 266; given order of Star of Belgium and Harbin medal, 268; illness in London, 270; order of St. Michael and St. George conferred by King George V, 271-273; death, 274; funeral services in London and Washington, 276-277, 279; honors, 280
Grant, U. S., rejection of Willie Gorgas's application for West Point, 39-40
Grayson, Rear Admiral Cary T., member of General Medical Board's Executive Committee, 227
Grunsky, Carl E.: member of Canal Commission, 103; strong criticism of in Reed report, 129-137